Confound and Destroy

100 Group and The Bomber Support Campaign

Confound and Destroy

100 Group and
The Bomber Support Campaign

Martin Streetly

MACDONALD AND JANE'S · LONDON

Copyright © Martin Streetly, 1978
First Published in 1978 by
Macdonald and Jane's Publishers Ltd.
Paulton House, 8 Shepherdess Walk
London N1 7LW

Printed in Great Britain by
Redwood Burn Limited

ISBN 0354 01180 4

CONTENTS

INTRODUCTION

In the thirty-three years since the end of the Second World War, a massive volume of literature has appeared on the activities, personalities and equipment of the Royal Air Force during that conflict. Much of this corpus concerns Bomber Command and its predominantly night offensive against Germany. So much has appeared in print that the interested reader can acquaint himself with almost every facet of the bomber offensive from the type of rivet used in the construction of a Lancaster to the highest policy decision. What he will not find, however, is the story of the Command's most fascinating formation, 100 Group.

Covered by a mantle of secrecy both during its wartime service and for much of the time since 1945, 100 Group remains one of the RAF's least well documented units. This book sets out to rectify this and to present the reader with as full an account of the electronic warfare and fighter campaigns the Group waged in support of the bombers as possible.

Confound and Destroy (100 Group's motto) was born out of family connections with the Group and that most perverse of human desires, to know what others do not want to be known; the fact that the records detailing the bomber support campaign were covered by the 'thirty year rule' and therefore unavailable to the public only serving to spur the author on to greater efforts to find out.

A half-way stage was reached with the production of a degree thesis in 1974 which forms the basis of the work. At the time, many crucial questions remained unanswered because of the aforementioned classification of source material. The opening of official archive material which has taken place in the last few years has gone much of the way towards filling these gaps and has allowed the original manuscript to be completely revised and enlarged into its present form.

The work is divided into two parts, the first of which deals with the course of bomber support operations in narrative and chronological form ending with an appraisal of the effectiveness of the campaign in Chapter Seven. This is followed by a number of appendices in which the reader will find details of the equipment, units and aircraft used as well as a brief view of electronic warfare outside the European theatre with the RAF and with the other Allied Air Forces. It will be noticed also that much space in this section has been devoted to the Luftwaffe's night fighter organisation, it being felt that a clear understanding of this campaign of move and counter move is only possible by the inclusion of such material. The decision to divide narrative and raw data was arrived at in order not to burden the reader with an unwieldy 'read' punctuated with an overwhelming weight of footnotes. The appendices themselves have been prepared as entities in their own right and are fully cross-referenced with the main text.

The work is rounded off with notes on source material and a selective bibliography. It should be noted that the maximum use has been made of original documentation, most of which has never been published before, and that where there is doubt over a particular point or conflicting evidence about it, this is clearly indicated.

The photographic illustrations used emphasise the electronic equipment rather than any other facet. This is because the devices themselves have never been properly depicted, ninety per cent of the photographs used having only recently been discovered or were specially commissioned for this work. The half-tones are complemented by line and tone drawings, maps and diagrams. All the drawings of the aircraft involved are based on photographic or eye witness evidence and it is hoped that they will clarify points not readily evident in the none-too-clear prints available and that they will be of use to modelling enthusiasts.

Finally, the reader's attention is drawn to the details of individual claims by 100 Group's fighter squadrons which appear in Chapters Two, Three and Five. These relate only to aircraft destroyed, claims for damage or probable destruction being ignored.

The bomber support campaign is a fascinating subject representing as it does a fundamentally intellectual conflict between the scientific communities on both sides. Many questions about it unfortunately must even now remain unanswered, the relevant documents having been lost with the passage of time or being still unavailable for security reasons. The author claims no definitive status for this work and will be most happy to hear from anyone who can provide information to clarify or supplement the existing text.

Martin Streetly
Stanmore, 1978

ACKNOWLEDGEMENTS

In the preparation of this manuscript, I have received enormous help and encouragement from many sources. I am particularly indebted to Air Vice-Marshal Addison and Sir Robert Cockburn for graciously granting me interviews and to my good friend Jerry Scutts who has supplied both photographs and rare documentation relating to the 8th Air Force's RCM operations. Mr R A Freeman has provided information on the RAF use of the B-17 and photographs of same, while the Reverend J D R Rawlings and Mr E J Creek have generously supplied illustrations of British and German aircraft. Mr D Wood, UK editor of the journal *Interavia*, has provided much information relating to the German radar system and the bomber support campaign in general.

In the course of my research, many official institutions were visited and I would like to thank Mr F F Lambert (late of 515 Squadron) at the Public Records Office, the staff of the photographic library at the Imperial War Museum, those of the library at the RAF Museum and the Ministry of Defence Air Historical Branch. A special 'thank you' must go to Messrs Geddes, Liffen and Voller of the Science Museum, who went to enormous trouble to arrange the photographing of that institution's collection of radar and jamming gear and to Mr I C Graham of the Royal Signals and Radar Establishment who allowed me access to their collection of glass plate negatives which form the bulk of the photographs in the book. At all these places I was met with the utmost courtesy and helpfulness.

At Macdonald and Jane's I would like to recognise the work of Messrs Minns and Chevannes and Mrs J Harris who respectively designed the book, designed the jacket and oversaw the whole project from galley stage to bound copy. Paul Ellis edited the manuscript and expertly guided me through the reefs and currents of a 'first' book.

The maps were produced by Mr A Spark and Ms I Smythe-Wood typed the manuscript with the greatest precision and constant cheerfulness. Mr A Vanags gave generously of his time translating German material and of his fund of knowledge of the wartime Luftwaffe. I would also like to thank my studio manager for her understanding which has made the conflict between authorship and full-time work a little more bearable. And lastly my wife Susie; not only has she taken on the whole of the household responsibilities during the production of the manuscript, but has also read and corrected it in its entirety. More importantly, she has been a constant source of encouragement when things were at their blackest. Without her, *Confound and Destroy* would never have been written.

Chapter 1

The Beginning:
1942 to November 1943

During the 1930s, as Europe prepared itself for a seemingly inevitable war, Britain and Germany began the practice of 'seeing' with radio energy. Radar, as this branch of electronics would later be known, was not new; the principle had been laid out by a German, Christian Hülsmeyer, in a patent of April 1904 The deteriorating international situation caused the RAF to cast around for means of improving its home defence system during the mid-1930s. Among the many ideas looked at was radio direction finding, as set out by Robert Watson-Watt (the superintendent of the Radio Department of the National Physical Department) in a memorandum to the Air Ministry dated 12 February 1935. This document set out the principles of radar, how a radar chain could be set up and a projection of its performance, how to translate the information gained into a form usable by Fighter Command and, most significantly, the ways in which an enemy could interfere with such a system.

With commendable speed, the Air Ministry set up a trial and on 26 February a Heyford bomber was detected by Watson-Watt and his team at a range of eight miles (13 km). For the experiment, the BBC short-wave transmitter at Daventry was used along with an extremely crude receiver. The success of this

A photographic record of one of the early radar test flights made on 24 July 1936. The test took place between 11.26 and 12.15 am and was an attempt to keep a formation of Wallace aircraft under continuous observation. The trace for the Wallaces is marked 'W'. (Crown Copyright)

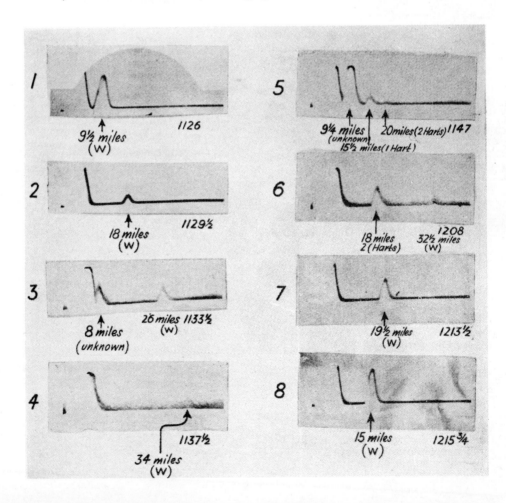

trial led to the setting up of the Air Ministry Research Establishment at Badsey to handle the development of radar.* The first Chain Home station was erected at that place and by the end of 1936 was detecting aircraft up to 100 miles (161 km) away. Two years later, the system was well on the way to completion and the Badsey team was able to turn its attention to building anti-jamming circuitry, E C Williams having proved radar's vulnerability when he operated a modified hospital diathermy machine from the prototype Sunderland flying boat off Felixstowe during the early part of 1938.

On the other side of Europe, Dr Rudolph Kuhnold, head of the German Navy's signals research department, was overseeing the development of a radar during late 1933/early 1934. This device, built by the GEMA company, was first tested at Kiel on 20 March 1934, detecting the *Hessen* at a range of 500 yards (457 m). By the end of 1936, this set had been fully developed into the operational *Freya* device with a range of 50 miles (80 km) which was ordered by both the Navy and the Air Force.

During the following year, GEMA went on to produce the *Seetakt* radar for naval gun ranging. This device, with a range of nine miles (14.5 km) entered service during 1938. In the same year, Telefunken began the production of the *Würzburg* gun laying radar which had a range of 25 miles (40 km).

Thus, by the outbreak of war, both the major protagonists were well equipped with radar. Alongside the development of this technology, both powers were putting a great deal of effort into the development of electronic aids for their respective air forces. In Germany, Dr Hans Plendl was putting the finishing touches to the world's first blind bombing device, the *X-Gerät*, while the RAF was introducing VHF radio into its fighter aircraft for effective direction from the ground. In addition, work was being done on an identification system tied in with the radar chain which was to become IFF and, more importantly, RDF 2 was being developed which was to appear as the first AI (Airborne Interception) radar.

For the first two years of the war, Britain was predominantly on the defensive and her first use of electronic counter-measures was in this vein. During 1939, the Air Ministry Directorate of Intelligence first became aware of the existence of German blind bombing devices (*X-Gerät* now being joined by the *Knickebein* system). By 21 June 1940, a complete picture of the *Knickebein* system had been drawn up and Air Commodore Lywood (Directorate of Signals) was charged with the establishment of a unit to counter the device.

To command the new organisation, now known as 80 Wing, Lywood chose Wing Commander E B Addison. The two men were known to each other through mutual service in Egypt before the war and Lywood had arranged for Addison to be posted to the Directorate of Signals from Palestine in February 1940. Addison jumped at the chance to escape from the Air Ministry and set about the organisation of radio counter-measures (RCM), his own term, with a will. No 80 Wing set up a headquarters at Garston while Addison strove to become operational in the shortest possible time. Personnel were a problem in that electronic warfare was a totally new field and needed first class minds to make it work. Fortunately, the Wing's work was considered so important that it

---

*The term radar came into general use in January 1944. Previously, the technique had been known as radio direction finding or radiolocation.

was given *carte blanche* in its search for men and materials.

Away in Swanage, a team under Dr Robert Cockburn began the development of a suitable jamming device. He worked for the recently established Telecommunications Research Establishment (TRE). This organisation was simply an enlarged and re-named Air Ministry Research Establishment. The TRE's jammer would take time to develop and Addison initially had to make do with modified diathermy machines, similar to that used back in 1938, by Williams, transmitting a mush of noise over the *Knickebein's* frequencies.

From these small beginnings 80 Wing mushroomed. It soon outgrew its HQ at Garston and moved to Radlett where it was to remain for the rest of its operational life. Between June 1940 and the winter of 1941, the Wing successfully countered *Knickebein*, the *X-Gerät* and finally the newly introduced *Y-Gerät*. By the latter date, however, its usefulness was diminishing as the Luftwaffe's bomber force turned its attention towards Russia.

With the decline of defensive requirements, Cockburn's jamming team at the TRE began to look for other means of employment. In late 1941, a joint services committee was set up to study the future application of RCM and the TRE tentatively suggested that such measures could be usefully employed in support of the RAF's offensive operations.

From the outbreak of war, Bomber Command had striven to carry the war to the enemy's homeland, indeed until 1942 it was Britain's only viable offensive force. The idea of RCM in support of the bombers was totally rejected on the grounds that the Command had to retain radio silence, if it was to operate successfully in the face of the enemy's rapidly growing defences. Fighter Command on the other hand had no such reservations and welcomed measures designed to support its Circus operations.

Before the TRE could produce suitable jammers, it had to know exactly what it was to jam. From 1939 work had been going on to discover whether or not the Germans had radar. The first real indication came in December of that year when Mr L Bainbridge Bell, a radar expert, examined the *Seetakt* aerial on the still burning hulk of the partly sunk *Graf Spee* in the River Plate. In July of the following year references to something called *Freya* began to appear in intelligence reports. By the end of the month, it was obvious that *Freya* was also a radar set. *Freya* continued to be somewhat elusive until February 1941 when almost simultaneously its operating frequency was identified and photographs of its aerial array were obtained by a reconnaissance Spitfire. The identification of *Freya's* operating frequency was of the greatest importance in that it allowed the plotting of such sets and by October 1941, 27 locations had been identified in an area stretching from Norway to Bordeaux. During the period, a second radar had been identified but proved to be even more difficult to pinpoint than *Freya*. In November 1941, the mystery was solved when aerial photographs were brought back of the *Würzburg* set situated at Bruneval. These photographs not only proved the existence of *Würzburg* but also provided the germ of a most audacious idea. If the radar station at Bruneval was so near to the coast would it not be possible to land a small party near to the post to examine the radar?

This idea was brought to fruition on the night of 27/28 February 1942 when operation *Biting* was executed. Twelve Whitley aircraft of 51 Squadron dropped 119 men by parachute near Bruneval. When this force was picked up in the pre-dawn hours of the 28th, it had achieved its object admirably. At a cost of 15 casualties the force returned to Britain with one of the operators, the set's

Two views of the Telecommunications Research Establishment after its move to Malvern. In the second photograph, work is being carried out on wave guides. (IWM/Crown Copyright)

receiver, the receiver amplifier, the modulator, the transmitter and the aerial dipole. An interesting by-product of the raid was that the Germans, fearful of a repeat performance, surrounded all their radar stations along the European coast line with barbed wire entanglements. This only served to enhance their visibility to the searching camera lenses of the RAF reconnaissance aircraft.

It will be seen, therefore, that by February 1942 a fairly complete picture of German radar operations had been gained. Of even greater importance as far as RCM was concerned, the major objection to offensive measures was removed. The differences between Fighter and Bomber Command over the employment of such measures palled beside the fact that if the German radar could be tampered with so could the British chain, and no one was prepared to start a campaign in which the enemy's capabilities were totally unknown.

The evening of 11 February 1942 settled the problem most dramatically. At 10 o'clock the battle cruisers *Scharnhorst* and *Gneisenau* weighed anchor in Brest and headed out into the Channel to make the dangerous journey home to German waters. That they succeeded in sailing up the Channel in broad day-light at times not more than 20 miles (33 km) from the English coast was a grave blow to British morale; what was more important to this story is that their success was due in no small part to the effective jamming of the British radar chain. This fact removed any doubts as to Germany's ability to jam radar and left the British with no reason to delay the opening of their own offensive RCM campaign. Within days of the so-called Channel Dash, Cockburn was given the go-ahead to produce a whole range of such measures.

As 1942 progressed, Bomber Command's attitude towards RCM began to change. The rising losses over Germany could be directly attributed to the introduction of radar and radio aids into that country's defensive system. It was obvious that if the Command was to continue its operations, some means of countering the enemy's electronic aids would have to be found. Equally, the problems in navigation being experienced by the bomber crews would have to be solved before the offensive would become really effective. The introduction of navigational aids would inevitably lead to the cherished radio silence being broken, if not by actual transmissions from the aircraft then at least by transmission to them. Faced with these difficult truths in combination with the knowledge that the enemy had a jamming organisation and was prepared to use it, Bomber Command slowly felt its way towards sanctioning offensive RCM on its behalf.

This, however, was some way in the future and it was to be Fighter Command which employed the TRE's first offensive jammer, *Moonshine*, operationally. *Moonshine* (see page 160) came directly from the technology developed during the Battle of the Beams. One of the measures used by 80 Wing was beacon masking or *Meacon*. Developed by GPO engineers in the early part of 1940 *Meacon* picked up the enemy signals and re-transmitted them exactly in phase. In this way, the German navigation beam could be distorted, thereby lowering the aircrew's faith in the device. *Moonshine*, developed by a former employee of EMI named Hardwick, operated in much the same way as *Meacon*, only against the *Freya* set. The blip produced by the re-transmitted signal had the appearance of an extremely large target or of a compact forma-tion of several aircraft. Thus an aeroplane carrying *Moonshine* could appear to the radar operator as several and a group of *Moonshiners* could take on the appearance of a sizeable raid.

During April 1942, a unit was set up within 12 Group to operate the device. Known as the Defiant Flight, the organisation was based at Northolt and was equipped with specially modified Defiant II aircraft (see page 240). The working-up period needed to bring the new measure to operations was some-what protracted and it was not until 6 August 1942 that *Moonshine* was tried against the enemy. On this date, eight Defiants began transmitting from a holding pattern south of Portland. On the other side of the Channel, 30 interceptors were scrambled to meet the incoming 'raid'. Eleven days later *Moonshine* was used in earnest for the first time, giving support to an 8th Air Force raid on Rouen. The measure remained operational until October 1942, by which time it had been used on a total of 30 occasions.

While Fighter Command had been pushing ahead with *Moonshine*, Bomber Command had begun to take steps to start its own counter-measures. On the night of 30 May, Harris (C-in-C Bomber Command from 20 February 1942) launched the first 'thousand bomber' raid against Cologne. Apart from the unprecedented number of bombers employed (actually 1,046), the night was unusual in that it was the first time the Command had used the 'stream'. Pre-viously, the bombers had attacked a target singly over an extended period. Accordingly, the Luftwaffe had arranged its defences to deal with one bomber at a time, (the *Himmelbett* system, see page 215). Now the bombers were con-centrated together so that they would all cross the enemy coast in one place thereby swamping that part of the defensive chain penetrated. This grouping was to be maintained over the target (the bombing of Cologne lasting 90 minutes) and on the return trip.

The use of the stream tactic paid off handsomely. A total of 34 bombers was lost due to enemy action giving a percentage of 3.9 of the total involved. This was in fact slightly lower than the norm against such a target in the prevailing weather conditions (moonlight and no cloud which favoured the interceptors) but was absolutely phenomenal considering the number of aircraft involved. From this time on until the end of the war, the stream was to be an integral part of the Command's operations.

While Bomber Command was still officially against active RCM, a number of crews had begun to use their IFF equipment against the suspected radar control of enemy searchlights. From early 1942, the use of the IFF set in this way gained wide currency amongst the crews. Unfortunately, there was not the slightest evidence to suggest that as a counter-measure IFF had any effect. By July of that year the practice was so widespread that the Command officially recognised it by having all IFF Mk II equipments modified to allow them to transmit continuously when the 'J' or jamming switch was operated. This move was most unfortunate for the crews in that the unmodified IFF *did not* transmit when switched on *unless* it was triggered by a suitable interrogator, a most unlikely situation over occupied Europe. Whereas use of IFF as a 'counter-measure' had previously been a relatively harmless morale booster, the introduction of the 'J' switch made it positively lethal. The crews took the official recognition to mean that the measure worked and were only too ready to use it as much as possible. The ensuing stream of transmissions were soon being tracked by the Luftwaffe's signals service with dire results for the bombers, as they provided the enemy with a most accurate means of plotting their track.

The 'J' switch was soon replaced by *Shiver* (see page 160). This was a modifica-tion of the IFF set to allow it to act as a true jammer as well as in its normal capacity. *Shiver* became operational on 7 October 1942 but like its predecessor proved to be ineffective and its use was discontinued some three months later, on 29 January 1943*. By this time, however, the damage had been done. The Command had lost its valued radio silence (the main reason for its opposition to RCM in the first place) for nothing and the crews were so wedded to the idea of IFF as a counter-measure that its use, although by now totally prohibited, continued until the end of the European war. The introduction of *Shiver* coincided with the decision that Bomber Command should adopt supportive RCM. At the beginning of October a meeting was convened at the Command's head-quarters which recommended the immediate use of IFF for jamming *Würzburg*, the development of a more effective anti-*Würzburg* measure and the introduction of ground and airborne equipment to deal with the *Freya*. This advice was accepted and speedily acted upon and it can be said that this meeting marked the beginning of the RCM campaign in support of the Command.

Whilst the debate had been going on, the TRE had been working on its first true offensive jammer, *Mandrel* (see page 160). This device was aimed at *Freya* and was eagerly taken up by both Fighter and Bomber Command. *Mandrel* was developed in ground and airborne forms, both entering service in the early part of December 1942 (airborne *Mandrel I* becoming operational on the night of 5/6th). Fighter Command's Defiant Flight, known as 515 Squadron from 1 October 1942, also received the device. No 515 Squadron continued operations until July 1943, by which time it was flying Beaufighters (replacing its Defiants from May of that year) but it is not at all clear which jamming equipment it was now using (see page 36). At one time or another the squadron received or was earmarked to receive *Carpet, Mandrel* and *Moonshine* sets.** In any event, the squadron completed 202 plus jamming sorties during the period being reviewed for the loss of one aircraft. After July 1943, the squadron became virtually non-operational until its transfer to 100 Group on 16 December 1943.

With the growth of RCM there was an increasing need for air intelligence, that is, aircraft fitted with the necessary receiving equipment to pick up and record signals which could not be heard from monitoring stations on the ground. The RAF's first electronic intelligence, or ELINT as it is now known, formation was the Wireless Intelligence Development Unit. Under the command of Wing Commander Blucke, this unit was most probably formed in mid-June 1940, and with a strength of three Anson aircraft was charged with the plotting of the enemy's blind-bombing beams from its base at Wyton. On 10 December 1940 the unit was redesignated 109 Squadron. The scope of its operations was now widened to include development work in the electronics field, notably on the *Oboe* bombing aid. The new squadron was equipped with both Anson and Wellington aircraft and was based at Wyton until July 1943. By this time, the squadron was mainly involved with the development of *Oboe* and a month later, on 6 August, it became part of 8 Group as a target marking

---

* It was later resurrected for use in 199(SD) Squadron's *Mandrel* aircraft.

** There is evidence to suggest that this unit's Defiants carried *Moonshine* and *Mandrel* whilst its Beaufighters carried only *Mandrel*, being earmarked only for *Carpet* and *Moonshine*.

squadron. Its ELINT duties were continued on a very limited scale until the following November.

On joining 8 Group, the squadron's 'B' Flight was detached and became 1474 Flight to carry on the squadron's previous ELINT role. It was equipped with Wellington IC aircraft and was mainly employed on the detection of enemy AI frequencies over Occupied Europe. Nearer home, another ELINT Flight, No 1473, had been formed and operated five Anson aircraft from Finmere on flights over the UK during 1943.

On 4 January 1943, 1474 Flight was redesignated 192 Squadron. The new squadron was most probably based at Gransden Lodge and at its formation had a strength of eight Wellington Xs, one Halifax II and three Mosquito IV aircraft. The squadron's ELINT work was regarded as most important and in consequence it expanded rapidly, gaining six more Wellingtons (four Xs and two ICs) and another Halifax by the beginning of February. The squadron's aircraft were fitted out with special receiving gear which were fed by one or a combination of the following aerial arrays:

A quarter-wave vertically-polarised general search dipole.
A half-wave horizontally-polarised general search dipole.
Half-wave vertically- and horizontally-polarised dipoles on the port and starboard sides of the airframe respectively.
A quarter-wave cone covering the 1 to 5000 MHz band for general search purposes.
A special wide-band capped cone covering the 200 to 1000 MHz band.*

The aircrew operating the special equipment were trained by the TRE.

For the first six months or so of its life, 192 Squadron's main operational area was the Western Mediterranean, where it plotted and identified the enemy radars. At the end of this operation, the unit turned its attention to Western Europe where it concentrated its efforts to the time it joined 100 Group in November 1943.

With the introduction of *Mandrel*, the RCM campaign gained rapid momentum. The next measure introduced was *Tinsel* (see page 161). This device was something of a departure in that it was aimed at the enemy's ground-to-air HF R/T links whereas all previous measures had been directed against radars. *Tinsel*, which entered service on 3 December 1942, was operated by a German-speaking crew member who on detecting the correct enemy transmission blotted it out with engine noise.

The early part of 1943 was dominated by one single measure, *Window* (see page 161). Simple in the extreme, *Window* was to have the most devastating effect of any RCM device introduced by the RAF during the Second World War. As early as 1938, Professor Lindemann (Churchill's scientific adviser) had outlined the principle of dropping 'oscillators' to produce spurious responses on a watching radar. The idea was resurrected by Lindemann in 1940 as a means of diverting the enemy's bombing beams but this was quickly proved to be impractical. In the September of the following year, 148 Squadron was making a series of wireless investigation flights in North Africa. The specially equipped Wellington used surprisingly found itself singled out for heavy fire from the enemy's Flak defences. It occurred to someone that perhaps the aerial array

---

* The aerial types remained constant throughout the squadron's operational life.

carried by the aircraft was causing an enlarged radar echo. Accordingly, the bombing elements of the squadron were issued with 18×1 in (45.7×2.5 cm) (the size of the aerial) aluminium strips which they dropped during an attack on Benghazi, with no noticeable effect. A second dropping produced similarly disappointing results and the idea was not pursued.

At the end of 1941, the idea was once again taken up this time by the TRE. By March 1942, Mrs Curran, the only female scientist in that establishment, had established that the concept was both effective and practical for use against radar with a frequency of 200 MHz or over. Her initial work was carried out with foils shaped like propaganda leaflets (the idea being that the operational version would be sandwiched between such material in order to disguise its true purpose) but it soon became clear that the best results were obtained with a simple oblong shape made out of the tin foil used in the manufacture of radio condensers. By 4 April, the Air Ministry had sanctioned *Window's* use by Bomber Command. Preparations for its use were well in hand when the decision was reversed on 5 May. The C-in-C of Fighter Command, Sholto Douglas, on becoming aware of *Window's* potential against his own radar chain, had asked the Chief of the Air Staff, Portal, to delay its introduction until such time as trials had been carried out to gauge its true effect against British defensive radars. Douglas' arguments prevailed and another series of tests was carried out. The results were striking, the latest AI radar, Mk VIII, was severely affected by the measure. The major fear now was whether or not the enemy had discovered the concept and if not, whether the use of *Window* would reveal it to him and allow him to severely cripple Britain's night defences.

The argument raged back and forth with a strong lobby promoting its use as the only really effective measure against the important *Würzburg* set, the cornerstone of a defensive system which was costing Bomber Command increasingly heavy losses. The pro-*Window* faction received a lift when it was reported in November that the imminent arrival of new GCI and AI radars would counter *Window's* effect on the British system by mid-1943. Their hopes were promptly dashed by Air Vice Marshal Saunby who expressed great reluctance to use the device in order not to exhaust the RAF's RCM hand too quickly. This argument won the day and Portal ruled that trials should continue and that the whole matter should be reviewed again in six months' time. The review took place on 2 April 1943. By this time the RAF's defensive system was regarded as effective in the face of the measure, if not toally unaffected. Harris argued most forcefully for its introduction, claiming that it could 'save one third of our losses over German targets' and this consideration clinched the matter. *Window* was finally sanctioned for use by Bomber Command as from 1 May.

Its operational baptism came on the night of 24/25 July 1943 and it achieved all that had been hoped for. The German defensive system was totally paralysed and although it made a speedy recovery, *Window* remained a most potent measure for the rest of the war.

Whilst the *Window* controversy had been raging, work on other jammers had continued unabated. The widespread use of the FuG 202/212 series of AI radars (identified in December 1942) by the enemy was viewed with growing alarm by Bomber Command. The first measure to counter these radars was *Ground Grocer* (see page 158), which became operational on the night of 26/27 April 1943. Being ground based, this device was only a partial solution in that it had a limited range and was only effective when the interceptor was within the bounds of the transmitted beam. Fortuitously, *Window* proved to be as potent against FuG 202/212 as it was against *Würzburg*, its intended target. With the operational use of the former measure, *Ground Grocer* quickly passed out of service.

The introduction of *Tinsel* had led the Luftwaffe to increase the spread of frequencies used for GCI purposes. This in turn led to the introduction of new counter-measures by the RAF. The first of these was *Ground Cigar* (see page 158), which became operational on 30/31 July 1943. This measure was aimed at the VHF transmissions now being used by the enemy. The change-over from the *Himmelbett* to the *Wilde*/*Zahme Sau* techniques with their greater reliance on the broadcast running commentary (see page 218) led to an increase in the emphasis placed on R/T and W/T jammers. Within a month of the introduction of *Ground Cigar*, *Tinsel* was modified to make it more effective. Now known as *Special Tinsel* (see page 161) it was the same basic equipment but with the operators being instructed from Britain which frequencies to jam. This had the effect of concentrating the jamming rather than the previous situation where each operator was pursuing his own course with the consequential dilution of effort.

Neither of these measures provided a complete answer to the problem. The introduction of the airborne version of *Cigar*, *ABC* (see page 153) on the night of 7/8 October 1943 helped the situation but again could not be regarded as a permanent solution. *ABC* was initially carried by the aircraft of 101 Squadron based at Ludford Magna. The special equipment was installed in standard Lancaster bombers (see page 235), the squadron's jamming aircraft continuing to carry a normal bomb load on operations. An additional crew member who could speak German was added to the normal complement to operate the new equipment. These Special Operators (SO) were trained on the squadron under conditions of great secrecy and other aircrew were strictly forbidden to question them about their work. It seems likely that such personnel were trained for verbal jamming, that is, the issuing of contradictory instructions purporting to come from a German fighter controller, as well as pure electronic jamming.* The use of this technique was extremely limited for fear that the true target might be inadvertently revealed. There is also some evidence to suggest that 101 Squadron's SOs were also used to monitor and record the general effectiveness of the various counter-measures employed during a particular operation from the responses of the various Luftwaffe controllers.

Between October 1943 and the squadron's last offensive operation on 25 April 1945 (a raid on Berchtesgaden), 101 Squadron despatched a total of 2,477 *ABC* sorties. From the early months of 1944, *Windowing* was also added to the unit's duties. Strangely, 101 Squadron never came under the control of 100 Group and remained part of 1 Group for the whole of its wartime service. The squadron was also unusual in that a number of its aircraft were fitted with non-standard tail turrets. These, manufactured by the firm of Rose-Rice at Gainsborough, carried twin 0.5 in Browning machine guns in place of the standard quadruple 0.303s. The use of the Rose-Rice turret was restricted to 1 Group squadrons and in fact of these only Nos 101 and 166 seem to have been so fitted.

---

*Training in verbal jamming was definitely given to the special operators of 214 Squadron who also operated *ABC* for a short period. This squadron's SOs were trained at Stradishall.

In the autumn 1944 the tail armament of 101 Squadron's aircraft was further modified by the installation of the AGL(T) or *Village Inn* radar-controlled turret. This device consisted of an installation armed with four 0.303 in machine guns below which was mounted a small parabolic radar scanner. The gunner was provided with a CRT on which he could track an interceptor closing on his aircraft. The use of radar enabled him to open fire on an attacker without necessarily seeing it. AGL(T) [Automatic Gun Laying Turret] had a protracted development and in the event only saw service with 49, 101, 156 and 635 Squadrons. Considerable work on testing the device was carried out by the TRE's flying unit, the TFU, based at Defford. During 1944, this unit was operating the following Lancaster aircraft in connection with AGL(T):*

The AGL(T) turret fitted to an operational Lancaster bomber. The aerial above the turret is for the Boozer *device. (Crown Copyright)*

* Apart from the aircraft mentioned, the TFU was also operating the following Lancasters during 1944:

ED350 – H2S Mk III trials	JB544 – H2S Mk VII trials
JA845 – H2S Mk IV trials	JB558 – H2S Mk IIIF scanner trials
ND823 – H2S Mk VI trials	PA976 – X-band ASV trials
PA976 – H2S Mk VI trials	EE187 – General RCM trials
PB151 – Computerised bombing and navigation trials	

In addition, two unidentified Lancasters were used for H2S Mk V and H2S Mk VI prototype trials.

ND712 – Development work on automatic turrets in combination with *Monica*.
JB705 and LL737 – AGL(T) Mk III trials.
KB805 – American AGL(T) trials.

In service, *Village Inn* proved to be difficult to use and to be prone to mechanical failure; consequently it was never employed at the intended general squadron level. Development was continued throughout the war and in September 1945, major proving trials were conducted by 115 Squadron, (using 49 Squadron's aircraft), but again no general service use was forthcoming.

The concept of verbal jamming was brought to its logical conclusion with the operational debut of *Corona* (see page 157) on the night of 22/23 October 1943. *Corona* was aimed at R/T transmissions in the 2.5 to 6 MHz band, which were monitored for the purposes of this measure from stations in the UK. When a communication channel had been identified, a special operator would begin to feed in to it misleading or contradictory information. He or she, (WAAF SOs being brought in when the Luftwaffe began to use female controllers to beat the *Corona* interference) would not attempt to divert enemy fighters to the wrong target but would transmit such things as false fog warnings or landing instructions. Initially *Corona* caused great confusion and not a little grim humour as the

A close up of the scanner dish and its associated drive mechanism used in the AGL(T) installation. (Crown Copyright)

exchanges between the ghost and the real controllers as to whose orders were to be followed, reached explosive levels. Gradually the Germans overcame the worst effects of the measure by increasing the frequency spread used and making rapid changes of frequency during operations. This made life harder for the Luftwaffe's wireless operators but did mean that at some point clear instructions could be received.

With the introduction of *Corona*, all the pre-100 Group radio countermeasures were in service. It is interesting to note that most of the ground-based measures were operated by the original RCM organisation, 80 Wing. On 11 November 1943 it too came under the auspices of 100 Group and for the remainder of the war undertook work with the following measures in support of Bomber Command:

(1)   *Fidget* (see page 158), *Meacon* and *Mimic* jamming of the enemy's running commentary transmissions.
(2)   *Corona* operations from the station at Canterbury. (Latterly, *Corona* transmissions took the form of recordings of superimposed German-speaking voices rather than false orders.)
(3)   *Ground Mandrel* transmissions.
(4)   *Special Mandrel* jamming of 30 MHz signals during August 1944.
(5)   *Cigar* jamming of the 38 to 42 MHz band from the station at Sizewell in the autumn of 1944.
(6)   Monitoring of the frequencies used by SN-2 and *Bernhardine* (see pages 180 and 195 respectively).
(7)   *Ground Grocer* jamming from stations at Dunwich, Walmer and Sizewell.
(8)   *Rayon* (see page 160) jamming of signals in the 31.2 to 32.1 MHz band from the station at Mundesley.

In addition to these operations, 80 Wing continually monitored and recorded all forms of enemy signals traffic and was to have taken over the *Dartboard* (see page 157) measure late in the war, presumably from 26 Signals Group.

Before passing on to the development of fighter support operations for Bomber Command, consideration should be given to two other electronic devices introduced into service with the bombers during the period, namely *Boozer* and *Monica* (see pages 164 and 166 respectively).

The proliferation of enemy radars and especially the appearance of AI devices led Bomber Command to seriously consider providing some form of electronic warning system for its aircraft. Both the Royal Aircraft Establishment (RAE) and the TRE developed warning sets to this end, the RAE producing *Monica* and the TRE *Boozer*. The latter device first entered service in the spring of 1943. *Boozer* was a passive device which gave a visual indication of both FuG 202 and *Würzburg* transmissions. *Monica*, on the other hand, was an active device designed to give warning of the approach of an interceptor from astern. Development of the device began in 1942 and it became operational on the night of 19/20 June 1943.

In service, both devices proved to be something of a mixed blessing. *Boozer* was not at all well received as it tended to operate continuously over enemy territory because of the vast numbers of transmissions of the right frequency received. Obviously, all such signals were not directed at a particular aircraft and confusion amongst the crews as to which warnings to respond to and which to ignore tended to cancel out the device's usefulness. Much the same was true for *Monica*. The device was unable to differentiate between friendly or hostile contacts, responding solely to the presence of another aircraft. When flying in a stream, a bomber pilot was in receipt of a constant stream of aural warnings (the device producing a clicking sound in the pilot's headphones which increased in number as a contact drew closer). This led crews to ignore its warnings when they knew that they were in the vicinity of friendly aircraft and to lower generally confidence in the measure. Both types were continued with, however, and *Monica* went on to play an important part in the fighter support operations mounted for and by Bomber Command, as will be discussed later.

As the night Blitz built up during the winter of 1940, Fighter Command began to attack the Luftwaffe's night bombers at their bases during take-off and landing. These operations were named intruder patrols, and it was not long before the idea occurred that these sorties could be employed in support of bombing raids.

The first major bomber support operation undertaken by the Command came on the night of the first 'thousand bomber' raid on Cologne in May 1942. On that night a total of 38 Boston, Havoc and Hurricane aircraft drawn from 1 (Hurricane IIC), 3 (Hurricane IIC), 23 (Havoc/Boston) and 418 (Boston) Squadrons were despatched against the airfields at Venlo, St Trond, Eindhoven, Leeuwarden, Gilzerijen, Schipol, Deelen and Soesterburg. In addition, 50 Blenheims drawn from 2 Group and Army Co-operation Command attacked the airfields at Bonn, Vechta, Osnabruck, Twente, Venlo, Juvincourt and St Trond. This force achieved very little, only one Hurricane pilot, Warrant Officer Scott, actually fired on an enemy night fighter, a Ju88, near St Trond, claiming it as a probable. The bombs dropped on the various airfields did no significant damage either. One of the major problems for the fighters was the lack of AI radar; at this stage the authorities refused to allow the use of such equipment over enemy territory for fear that a crash might compromise it. The radar problem was further compounded by the lack of adequate navigational aids.

The introduction of the Mosquito night fighter with its remarkable performance and range promised a much more effective bomber support vehicle than anything previously seen. With this in mind, Harris suggested to Sholto Douglas in October 1942 that 'some Mosquito fighters might profitably be mixed in the bomber stream.' It was not until June of the following year, however, that Fighter Command began systematic bomber support operations. In that month, radar-equipped aircraft were at last released for operations over enemy territory. The squadron chosen for such operations was No 141 based at Wittering and equipped with AI Mk IV carrying Beaufighter VIf aircraft (see page 240). More importantly, their aircraft were also equipped with the *Serrate* and *Gee* devices (see pages 167 and 197 respectively).

The *Serrate* homer was developed by the TRE and was aimed at the enemy's FuG 202/212 family of AI radars. After a brief period of training, the squadron took the device into action on the night of 14/15 June 1943 when five Beaufighters made patrols of Deelen, Gilzerijen and Eindhoven. *Serrate* operations were continued until the following September, when the squadron began converting to the Mosquito. During the period, 233 sorties were despatched of which 179 completed a patrol. Some 20 combats were recorded which resulted in the destruction or damaging of 18 enemy aircraft. A full statistical break-down on these operations reads as follows:

The Beaufighter VIf of the type used by 141 Squadron for Serrate operations in 1943. Clearly visible are the wing-mounted receiver aerials and the nose-mounted transmission aerial of the AI Mk IV radar. (via J Scutts)

Period covered:	14/15 June to 6/7 September 1943
Sorties despatched:	233
Sorties completing patrols:	179
Casualties:	3 aircraft lost and 3 damaged
Serrate contacts:	Approximately 1,180
Too brief or distant to follow:	Approximately 520
Held and followed:	Approximately 490
Converted to AI:	108
Resulting visuals:	33
Resulting combats:	20
Claims:	13 destroyed, 1 probable and 4 damaged
Remarks:	54 contacts were obtained by AI without *Serrate*. None of these resulted in combats and 10 were on friendly aircraft. Four visual sightings were reported which resulted in one enemy aircraft being damaged.

The principal lesson learnt from these initial *Serrate* operations was that the Beaufighter was not suitable for bomber support duties. The failure of many potential interceptions was simply due to the Beaufighter being outrun or out-manoeuvred by the German night fighters. The Operational Research Section of Fighter Command suggested that the projected Mosquito XIV would be most suitable for future *Serrate* operations. In fact, 141 Squadron was re-equipped with the Mosquito II aircraft for such duties with 100 Group, which organisation it joined on 3 December 1943.

Parallel with *Serrate* operations, Fighter Command introduced *Flower* patrols. These were attacks on enemy night fighter airfields whilst the bombers were passing through the coastal radar chain. The first *Flower* patrol was flown on the night of 11/12 June 1943 by Mosquito IIs of 605 Squadron, based at Castle Camps. Again, the aircraft involved carried no radar. On 26/27th of the following month 605 was joined by 25 Squadron, (Church Fenton). On this date the latter squadron despatched its first such sortie, again using non-radar Mosquito IIs.

In the middle of August *Mahmoud* patrols were begun. These sorties were flown by AI Mk IV-equipped aircraft against the so far identified enemy night fighter assembly points (22 in number) in the hope of intercepting his aircraft. *Mahmouds* were flown by single aircraft and arose from experience gained during the *Serrate* operations. During these it had been found that single British night fighters seemed to make attractive targets for the enemy interceptors. The technique evolved was for the RAF aircraft to fly a steady course until a contact appeared on the tail warning *Monica* set.* The unidentified aircraft was allowed

Two of 605 Squadron's Mosquito II aircraft on a daylight training flight. This squadron began Flower *operations in June 1943. (IWM)*

---

*The use of *Monica* in this manner was developed by the Fighter Interception Unit (FIU) based at Ford, under the code name *Whiting*. This organisation was responsible for the evaluation under operational conditions of all new RAF night fighting aids and aircraft. During 1943 it was heavily involved in the development of bomber support tactics and equipment, a role which it was to continue until the setting up of the BSDU (see page 208). The FIU was commanded by Wing commander Chisholm who later went to 100 Group to oversee their fighter operations. The type of *Monica* used for *Mahmouds* was most probably the visual Mk III (see page 166).

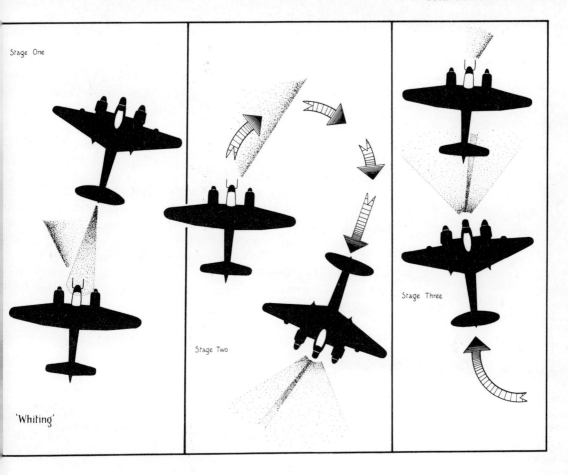

Stage One

'Whiting'

Stage Two

Stage Three

The Whiting manoeuvre. *Stage one – A 'bogey' was picked up on the rearward looking* Monica *device and allowed to approach to within 5 to 6000 ft. Stage two – At this distance, the fighter swung round through 360° in an attempt to close with the 'bogey' from astern. Stage three – An attempt was made to pick up the target on the forward AI and after a visual identification had been made, an attack would be instigated.*

to approach to a range of 5,000 to 6,000 ft (1,524 to 1,829 m) at which point the *Mahmoud* fighter would execute a 360° turn to position itself behind the enemy aircraft. From this point a normal stern AI interception would be pursued. *Mahmouds* were flown well clear of the bomber streams because of the problem of identification, a problem which was to bedevil similar 100 Group activities until well into 1944 (see page 199). On 9 August 1943, 25 Squadron's A Flight was issued with six Mosquito VIs fitted with AI Mk IV and *Monica* for such operations. These it continued until the following December, by which time it had achieved one success, a Ju88 destroyed by DD759 near Kassal.

At the same time as 25 Squadron was starting *Mahmoud* operation, 605 Squadron extended its patrols to include loose escort of the bomber streams, the first squadron aircraft reaching Berlin on 31 August. The general *Mahmoud* effort was reinforced by FIU aircraft which carried out such patrols and additional *Flowers* until at least October 1944. No 605 Squadron continued its escort and *Flower* patrols until it joined the defensive effort over the Normandy beach head in June 1944.

The *Flower* force was further increased during August by elements of 410

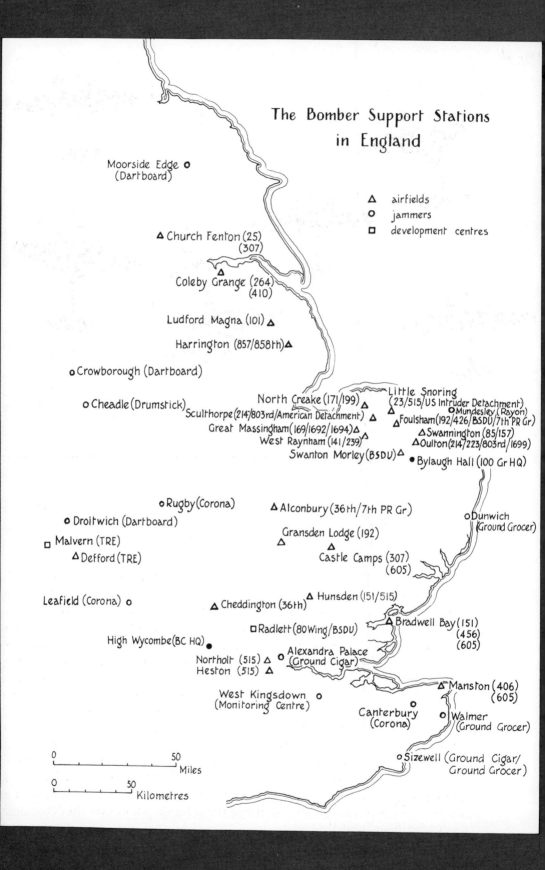

The Bomber Support Stations in England

Moorside Edge ○
(Dartboard)

△ airfields
○ jammers
◻ development centres

△ Church Fenton (25)
(307)

△ Coleby Grange (264)
(410)

Ludford Magna (101) △

Harrington (857/858th) ▲

○ Crowborough (Dartboard)

○ Cheadle (Drumstick)

North Creake (171/199) △   Little Snoring
(23/515/US Intruder Detachment)
Sculthorpe (214/803rd/American Detachment) △   ○ Mundesley (Rayon)
Great Massingham (169/1692/1694) △   △ Foulsham (192/426/BSDU/7th PR Gr)
West Raynham (141/239) △   △ Swannington (85/157)
Swanton Morley (BSDU) △   △ Oulton (214/223/803rd/1699)
● Bylaugh Hall (100 Gr HQ)

○ Rugby (Corona)   △ Alconbury (36th/7th PR Gr)
○ Droitwich (Dartboard)   Gransden Lodge (192)   ○ Dunwich
◻ Malvern (TRE)   △   △   (Ground Grocer)
△ Defford (TRE)   Castle Camps (307)
(605)

Leafield (Corona) ○   △ Cheddington (36th)   △ Hunsden (151/515)

◻ Radlett (80 Wing/BSDU)   △ Bradwell Bay (151)
(456)
(605)

High Wycombe (BC HQ) ●
Northolt (515) △   ○ Alexandra Palace
Heston (515) △   (Ground Cigar)

West Kingsdown ○   △ Manston (406)
(Monitoring Centre)   (605)
Canterbury   ○
(Corona)   ○ Walmer
(Ground Grocer)

○ Sizewell (Ground Cigar/
Ground Grocer)

0 ———————— 50
Miles

0 ———————— 50
Kilometres

Squadron (based at Coleby Grange flying Mosquito II and VI aircraft). During the following month it also began to participate in *Mahmouds* but its bomber support duties were quickly terminated, all such sorties ceasing in mid-September. Its place was taken by 264 Squadron (based at Firwood Common and Coleby Grange flying Mosquito VI aircraft) who began *Flower* sorties in September. These were changed to *Mahmouds* during the following month and the squadron continued spasmodic bomber support patrols until December, when it joined the Second Tactical Air Force. During this month, 25 Squadron also ceased its bomber support role.

Thus, by December 1943, Fighter Command's first phase of bomber support was over (squadrons of the Command were to operate in this role again late in 1944, which will be discussed in later chapters). The three types of operations undertaken, escort, *Flowers* and *Mahmouds*, were not particularly successful in terms of damage done to the enemy, but they did provide valuable lessons for the future operations of 100 Group's fighter element.

By mid-1943 it was becoming obvious to the officers at Bomber Command headquarters that the RCM, so far introduced on the Command's behalf,* was becoming large and unwieldy. It was also realised that to remain successful they would become even more complex. In addition, the spoof tactics, diversionary raids, false target marking and deceptive routing being forced on the Command by the enemy's use of the *Zahme Sau* technique were diverting more and more bombers away from their real task of dropping bombs. Thus, the Command's thinking swung towards the creation of a specialised organisation to handle both RCM and spoof operations.

This proposal was accepted by the Air Ministry and the Directorate of Signals was instructed to find a Commanding Officer for the new unit. (This was because it was felt that RCM would be the force's main task; much of the spoofing, by its very nature, having to remain in Main Force hands.) Lywood approached the most obvious man, Addison, with his 80 Wing background. The latter accepted the post on the proviso that the new formation would be large enough to handle its brief (see page 35). In the way, Number 100 (Special Duties) Group, Bomber Command was formed in November 1943.

Lest anyone doubt the importance attached to 100 Group let the last word on the subject of its formation rest with Harris himself. In a letter to the Air Ministry dated 7 December 1943, he stated that 'overriding priority should be given to the formation and equipment' of the Group and that 'priority in labour and materials over all conflicting claims' should be given to the necessary electronic equipment.

---

*After the October 1942 meeting at Bomber Command, all offensive RCM came under the auspices of that organisation.

Chapter 2

The First
Seven Months:
November 1943 to May 1944

On 23 November 1943, 100(SD) Group was officially established within Bomber Command to pursue and develop the bomber support campaign. The new Group's role was defined in an Establishment Directive issued on 8 November as follows:

(1) To give direct support to night bombing or other operations by attacks on enemy night-fighter aircraft in the air or by attacks on ground installations.
(2) To employ airborne and ground radio counter-measures equipment to deceive or jam enemy radio navigational aids, enemy radar systems and certain wireless signals.
(3) To examine all intelligence on the offensive and defensive radar, radio navigation and signalling systems of the enemy, with a view to future action within the scope of 1 and 2.
(4) To provide immediate information, additional to normal intelligence information, as to the movements and employment of enemy fighter aircraft to enable the tactics of the bomber force to be modified to meet any changes.

For the first week of its existence, the Group consisted of little more than a nucleus staff based at 80 Wing's HQ at Radlett. With a rapid build-up, and armed with the highest priority, the formation received its first operational squadron, No 141, on 3 December. This unit, the original *Serrate* squadron, came from 12 Group and was now based at West Raynham (having previously been stationed at Wittering). Their new airfield, and that at Great Massingham, came under 100 Group's control on the same day. Now that the formation controlled stations of its own, its headquarters moved from Radlett, taking up residence at West Raynham at the same time as 141 Squadron. Later in December, the Group's headquarters found a permanent home at Bylaugh Hall. This Victorian country house situated in its own grounds outside Swanton Moreley was to serve the Group for the rest of its operational life.

Expansion continued, and on 7 December, the airfields at Foulsham, Little Snoring, Oulton, North Creake and Swannington came under the Group's control. Two ELINT units, 192(SD) Squadron (from 3 Group) and 1473(SD) Flight joined the formation on the same day, (taking up residence at Foulsham and Little Snoring respectively), as did 169(SD) Squadron, the Group's second fighter unit. Originally a fighter-reconnaissance unit flying Mustangs with 13 Group, 169 Squadron had been re-formed as a night-fighter unit at Ayr in October 1943. Now based at Little Snoring, the Squadron was ear-marked for *Serrate* duties. Two days later, the Group's third such unit, 239 Squadron, moved from Ayr and 13 Group to Little Snoring from where 1473 Flight moved on 12 December. The Flight was now stationed alongside 192 Squadron at Foulsham.

On 10 December, 1692(SD) Flight was transferred from 13 Group and Drem to Little Snoring whilst a third fighter squadron joined the Group on the 16th, when 515(SD) Squadron established itself at Little Snoring. This unit was previously based at Hunsdon as part of 11 Group.

Thus, by mid-December, the Group had the following establishment:

141(SD) Squadron, equipped with Beaufighter VIf and Mosquito II aircraft.
169(SD) Squadron, equipped with Mosquito II aircraft.

192(SD) Squadron, equipped with Wellington, Halifax and Mosquito aircraft.
239(SD) Squadron, re-equipping with Mosquito II aircraft.
515(SD) Squadron, equipped with Beaufighter II and Defiant II aircraft.
1473(SD) Flight, equipped with Anson aircraft.
1692(SD) Flight, equipped with Beaufighter and Defiant aircraft.

The number of units available belied the operational potential of the Group. The two ELINT units, 192 Squadron and 1473 Flight, were fully operational, although 1473 Flight could only operate over the British Isles by virtue of the limited range and defensive inadequacies of its aircraft. Of the four fighter units, 141, 169, 239 and 515 Squadrons, only 141 Squadron could be considered operational. Even then it was in the throes of converting to the Mosquito with a consequential drop in strength. The two ex-13 Group Squadrons, Nos 169 and 239, had both undergone intensive training in *Serrate* at Drem which was by no means complete by the time they joined 100 Group. Also, 239 Squadron was still awaiting its operational aircraft and in consequence neither squadron was to become operational until January 1944.

The fourth fighter squadron, No 515, was in an even sorrier state. It had been non-operational since July 1943. Originally a jamming organisation (see Chapter One), the squadron's role within 100 Group was not finalised until February 1944. On 6 February, headquarters 100 Group sent a signal to Bomber Command concerning this squadron, the gist of which was as follows:

> On taking over the squadron's aircraft from Fighter Command on 15 December 1943, the training of the aircrew was found to be woefully inadequate. The squadron's aircraft had been standing in the open for two years and the state of serviceability was grave. The installation of *Carpet*, *Mandrel* and *Moonshine* jamming equipment in these aircraft had been an extremely protracted affair. During the period of installation, it had been decided not to continue the use of *Moonshine* and that the *Mandrel* cover which could be provided by the squadron would be totally inadequate.
>
> A proposal had been brought forward to use the squadron in the *Jostle* role to supplement 214 Squadron's B-17s. The squadron's Beaufighter II aircraft were regarded as totally unsuitable for this role by the Group. The Group, therefore, was of the opinion that 515 Squadron should become a standard fighter squadron equipped with Mosquito VI aircraft.

This, the penultimate signal in a protracted correspondence, led to the decision to drop the unit's jamming role (taken on 14 February) and to use it in the role described previously. In consequence, 515 Squadron did not become operational until March 1944. The remaining unit, 1692 Flight, was a *Serrate* training unit. This situation was further complicated by the necessity of fitting out the Mosquito aircraft for the *Serrate* Squadrons with the necessary electronic equipment. This comprised *Monica* tail warning sets, *Gee* navaids, AI Mk IV and *Serrate* homers. This, of course, took time.

Despite these difficulties, the Group became operational remarkably quickly. The first *Serrate* sortie was despatched on the night of 16/17 December when 141 Squadron sent two Beaufighters and two Mosquitos in support of a raid on Berlin. Squadron Leader Lambert and Flying Officer Dear, flying Mosquito HJ659, claimed damage to a Bf110 50 miles west of Berlin. Three nights later two of the squadron's Beaufighters accompanied the bombers to Frankfurt. On the night of 23/24th, three Beaufighters went on patrol to Berlin

Flight Lieutenant Kelsey and Pilot Officer Smith destroyed at Ju88 near Duren while Flying Officer Funnill and Flight Sergeant Hansen failed to return, the Group's first loss. The squadron rounded off the month by despatching two more Beaufighters to Berlin on the night of 29/30th.

The two ELINT units were also active during the month: 1473 Flight was operational on 15 nights monitoring the enemy's VHF transmissions which could be received over the UK, while 192 Squadron was out on 12 occasions investigating German signals in an area from the Baltic to the Bay of Biscay and along the routes taken by main force raids. These operations involved 192 Squadron in the despatch of 52 individual aircraft sorties of which eight returned early. The successful sorties were made by Wellingtons on four nights, Mosquitos on six and Halifaxes on two.

The Group's first heavy jamming squadron, No 214, joined the Group on 17 January 1944, having previously been a Stirling bomber unit in 3 Group. The squadron was now based at Sculthorpe and was in the process of converting to the B-17 with the aid of a small 8th Air Force detachment (see page 77). The use of the B-17 as an electronic warfare platform forms a most complicated story with a number of obscure facets to it, not least of which is why the B-17 was used at all. Various reasons have been cited in the past including the aircraft's altitude performance which enabled the jammer to escape interception. The author has been unable to confirm or deny this explanation. All that can be said with certainty is that the type was used for a number of reasons including the type's availability and spacious radio operator's compartment which provided a suitable environment for a jamming operator to work efficiently. That considerable thought went into the use of the B-17 as a jamming aircraft is shown by the following extract from the minutes of a meeting held at High Wycombe on 12 January 1944 about the employment of the type for radio counter-measures purposes:

(1) Bomber Command has requested the supply of 14 B-17 aircraft from the US 8th Air Force, plus replacements. These aircraft are to be replaced in American service by an equal number of B-17G aircraft off-set from future British Lend-Lease contracts.

(2) The following standards were laid down for B-17 RCM aircraft serving in Bomber Command:

(a) *Electronic equipment*
Each aircraft must carry H2S, *Gee* or *Loran*, API and AMU, a DR compass, *Monica IIIA*, MF and HF communications gear, HF and VHF R/T, *Jostle IV* and four *Airborne Grocers*. The installation of *Jostle* and *Airborne Grocer* would be acceptable.

(b) *Armament*
Each aircraft should carry a rear, mid-upper and ventral turret.

(c) *Performance*
The following estimates have been arrived at:

(i) For an aircraft with the full electronic fit and armament as described and having an overall weight of 60,500 lb (27,442 kg). A range of 1,150 mls (1,851 km) at 235 mph (378 km/h) at an operational height of 30,000 ft (9,144 m).
A range of 1,400 mls (2,253 km) at 215 mph (346 km/h) at an operational height of 25,000 ft (7,620 m).

(ii)   For an aircraft without H2S or the ventral turret and having an overall
        weight of 59,000 lb (26,762 kg).
        A range of 1,220 mls (1,963 km) at 230 mph (370 km/h) at an operational
        height of 30,000 ft (9,144 m).
        A range of 1,500 mls (2,414 km) at 212 mph (341 km/h) at an operational
        height of 25,000 ft (7,620 m).

(d)   *Crew*
        The crew will comprise a pilot, navigator, flight engineer, wireless
        operator, special operator, airbomber (to act as second navigator and air
        gunner) and two air gunners.

Some two weeks later, a schedule for the conversion of such aircraft was
issued, the gist of which was as follows:

Aircraft 1	To Sculthorpe for conversion training. Later to be fitted with the interim jamming gear at that location.
Aircraft 2	To Sculthorpe for conversion training. Later to Scottish Aviation for the main RCM installation.
Aircraft 3	As aircraft 2.
Aircraft 4	To the TRE to act as a prototype for the interim RCM fit. Later to Sculthorpe as pattern aircraft for numbers 1, 6, 8, 9 and 10.
Aircraft 5	To Scottish Aviation for prototype main RCM fit. Later to Sculthorpe.
Aircraft 6	To the RAE for fitment of *Monica IIIA* and navigational gear. Later to Sculthorpe for interim RCM fit.
Aircraft 7	To Scottish Aviation for trial installation of main navigational gear. Later to TRE for prototype main RCM fit and then to Sculthorpe.
Aircraft 8	To Sculthorpe. On the return of numbers 4 and 6, to be given an interim RCM fit at that location.
Aircraft 9	As number 8.
Aircraft 10	As number 8.
Aircraft 11	To Sculthorpe. Later to Scottish Aviation, as required, for main RCM fit.
Aircraft 12	As number 11.
Aircraft 13	As number 11.
Aircraft 14	As number 11.
Interim programme	Aircraft numbers 1, 4, 6, 8, 9 and 10.
Main programme	Aircraft numbers 2, 3, 5, 7, 11, 12, 13 and 14.

The first B-17F, 41-24577, arrived on 20 January, six more (B-17G, 42-31031
and B-17Fs 42-31027, 42-30970, 42-30812, 42-30639 and 42-30241) following
on the next day. The eighth aircraft, B-17F 42-30809, was delivered on the 24th
and two more arrived before the end of the month. These were B-17F 42-3177,
on the 25th and B-17F 42-30014 on the 30th.

The non-availability of *Airborne Grocer* (until May 1944) and *Jostle* led to a
revision of the proposed schedule. Prototype fits were undertaken and six aircraft were earmarked for an *ABC* installation as a temporary measure. This
ABC fit was different from the 101 Squadron installation in that each B-17
carried six Type T1624A/Type 20G receiver/indicator units. (101 Squadron

Two views of B-17s undergoing modifications for the RCM role. The first shows a rear view of a Fortress at the Telecommunications Flying Unit at Defford and displays the aerials associated with ABC (the fuselage mast), Airborne Grocer (flanking the tail guns) and Monica (below the guns). The nature of the aerials either side of the fin are unknown. The head on view depicts a B-17 after modification by Scottish Aviation at Prestwick and clearly shows the H2S radome under the nose and the flame dampers over the exhausts. Both aircraft are finished in Smooth Night overall. (Crown Copyright/via J Scutts)

carrying one such combination per aircraft) and more than the standard three T1260B transmitters. Work on these *ABC* fits was started at the end of January.

The fighter elements of the Group were operational on eight nights of the month (2/3rd, 5/6th, 14/15th, 20/21st, 21/22nd, 27/28th, 28/29th and 30/31st). The night of 20/21st marked the debut of 169 and 239(SD) Squadrons, when three aircraft from these units patrolled the Friesian Islands.

One of the B-17s field transferred from the 8th Air Force. Clearly visable are the recently painted out American markings, the triangle on the fin indicating that the aircraft had originally belonged to a squadron of the First Air Division. (via R Freeman)

Forty-seven plus individual sorties were despatched over the eight nights and four enemy aircraft were claimed as destroyed. These were a Bf109 and three Bf110s. The Bf109 was shot down by Flying Officer White (flying HJ941) of 141 Squadron near Berlin on the night of 28/29th whilst the Bf110s went to Flying Officer Munro of 141 Squadron on 28/29th (flying HJ644 near Berlin), Flight Lieutenant Rice, also of 141 Squadron, on 30/31st (near Hamburg) and Squadron Leader Cooper of 169 Squadron on the same night (flying HJ711 west of Berlin). On 28/29th Flight Lieutenant Brachi and Flying Officer MacLeod of 239 Squadron failed to return.

The efforts of the *Serrate* squadrons were continued in February during which a total of 104 individual aircraft sorties were despatched by the three squadrons. A total of 51 of these completed a patrol, 17 from 141 Squadron, 18 from 169 Squadron and 16 from 239 Squadron. Four victories were claimed: a Bf110 by Pilot Officer Miller of 169 Squadron on 5/6th (flying HJ707), a He117 by Flying Officer White of 141 Squadron on 15/16th (flying DZ 726 near Berlin), another Bf110 by Flying Officer Knight of 239 Squadron on 20/21st (flying DZ 270 near Stuttgart) and a third such aircraft by Flight Lieutenant Woodman of 239 Squadron on 25/26th.

Against this, three aircraft were lost during the month. Pilot Officer Snape (141 Squadron) failed to return on 24/25th as did Flying Officer Knight (239 Squadron) on the following night. During the same operation, Flying Officer Munro crashed his aircraft whilst landing at West Raynham. The alarming rise in losses suffered by the *Serrate* squadrons was due to the state of their aircraft rather than to enemy action. The Mosquito IIs supplied to the Group were old airframes with many flying hours logged. More seriously, the engines were proving unreliable, being prone to cutting-out particularly under the strain of take-off. This problem shows up clearly in the 53 aborted sorties recorded during the month. This figure was made up of 17 instances of engine failure, 20 of radar failure (a problem not connected with the state of the aircraft but grave enough in itself), 3 of oxygen failure and 13 of 'other causes'. Consequently, towards the end of the month, it was decided to reduce the level of operations and give each *Serrate* aircraft a major overhaul including a change of engines (Merlin XXIIs now being installed). By the end of March this programme had been completed, improved serviceability allowing 175 *Serrate* sorties to be despatched during April as against the January figure of 41.

The decision to utilise 515 Squadron in the intruder role during February was quickly followed through when, on the 29th, the unit received its first Mosquito aircraft. These were, however, MkIIs which were to be used for training pending the arrival of its intended MkVIs.

The Group's sole jamming squadron, No 214, was still not operational during February. By the end of the month, the unit had received a total of 21 B-17 aircraft. This number was divided into 14 F-models and 7 Gs. Ten of the Fs were despatched to the various locations cited in the schedule drawn up by Bomber Command (see page 38) for the installation of the necessary electronic equipment. The other four plus the seven G-models (which were on loan from the 8th Air Force) were used for crew training and were retained at Sculthorpe. This training fleet was augmented by another B-17 which had had a most varied career. This machine, AN520, was one of the original Fortress I aircraft supplied to 90 Squadron during 1941. After the ill-fated attempts at high-altitude daylight bombing undertaken by this unit, the aircraft passed to 220 Squadron, Coastal Command, in February 1942. In February 1944 it arrived at Sculthorpe still wearing its white camouflage, to provide crew training for 214 Squadron. In this role it ended its career, being reduced to scrap in September 1944.

The Group's two ELINT units, 192 Squadron and 1473 Flight were amalgamated on 1 February. The new unit, known as 192 Squadron, now had the following aircraft to hand: six Wellington Xs, eight Halifax Vs, six Mosquito IVs (including DZ375, DZ376 and DZ410) one Anson, and one Tiger Moth. The Halifax Vs were replaced by Mk IIIs on 20th. During the month, the squadron was mainly involved in plotting and identifying the enemy's radar coverage along the western seaboard of France, Belgium, Holland, Denmark and Norway in preparation for the Allied invasion of Europe. Work of this nature was to take up most of the unit's time until June.

Despite the overhaul and re-engining programme, the *Serrate* squadrons despatched a total of 143 individual sorties on 17 nights during March. A total of 95 of these sorties completed a patrol (141 Squadron despatching 27, 169 Squadron despatching 45 and 239 Squadron despatching 23), resulting in the destruction of five enemy aircraft as follows:

18/19th – Aircraft HJ710 'T' of 141 Squadron destroyed a Ju88 near Frankfurt.
18/19th – Aircraft DZ761 'c' of 141 Squadron destroyed a Ju88 near Frankfurt.
24/25th – Aircraft DD717 'M' of 141 Squadron destroyed a Fw190 near Berlin.
30/31st – Aircraft DZ661 of 239 Squadron destroyed a Ju88 over the Ruhr.
    ?   – An Aircraft of 239 Squadron destroyed a Bf110.

In addition, 141 Squadron claimed a Ju88 damaged on 26/27 near Essen.

Forty-eight sorties returned early, 19 of which were due to radar failures and

12 to engine failures. Out of the aircraft completing a patrol, eight were lost, known details of which are as follows:

1/2nd   – Flight Lieutenant Foster of 169 Squadron during a patrol to Stuttgart.
15/16th – An aircraft crashed on take-off.
23/24th – Flight Lieutenants Armstrong and Butler of 239 Squadron during patrols to the Low Countries and Berlin.
25/26th – Flying Officer Vanderplasshe of 141 Squadron during a patrol to Maubeuge.

The group's intruder element became operational during the month when Wing Commander Lambert and Flight Lieutenant Morgan flew a borrowed 605 Squadron aircraft on a patrol to Melun and Bretigny. During this sortie, an He177 was claimed as destroyed. No 515 Squadron was training with 605 Squadron Fighter Command at this time and, being deficient in squadron's aircraft, this was undertaken when and as it could. Although the Group had other intruder squadrons earmarked for its establishment, none had yet materialised. As a consequence, the 8th Air Force offered the use of some of its escort fighter force to 100 Group for this purpose. This led to the formation of an American Intruder Detachment at Little Snoring during March for trial purposes. The experiment was not a success and the unit was disbanded in April (see Chapter Four).

During March, 192 Squadron continued its investigation of the enemy radar chain while 214 Squadron proceeded with its conversion to the B-17 and awaited the arrival of its first fully equipped aircraft.

The *Serrate* squadrons continued to increase the number of sorties despatched during April. The total number of individual aircraft despatched during the month was 208 of which 29 were cancelled and 35 returned early. Of the 144 successfully completed sorties, 141 Squadron contributed 53, 169 contributed 53 and 239 contributed 38. Out of the 35 which returned early there were 14 instances of engine failure, 13 of radar failure, two of oxygen failure and two of ASI failure.

Claims were made for the destruction of 11 enemy aircraft as follows:

Flight Lieutenant Rice (141)	One FW190 while flying HJ712 'R' in the Baltic area on 23/24th.
Flying Officer White (141)	One Do217 while flying DD732 on 20/21st.
Flight Lieutenant Cremer (169)	One Bf110.
Pilot Officer Johnson (169)	One Bf110 while flying DD799 near Compiegne on 18/19th.
Pilot Officer Miller (169)	One unidentified enemy aircraft while flying W4085 near Cologne on 23/24th.
Flight Lieutenant Woodman (169)	One Bf110 while flying W4076 south east of the Ruhr on 22/23rd and a second Bf110 while flying the same aircraft on 27/28th.
Flying Officer Breithaupt (239)	One Bf110.

Flying Officer Dopper (239)   One Bf110.

Squadron Leader Reeves (239)   One Do217 while flying DZ262 on
                                  11/12th and a Bf110 at a later date.

[239 Squadron's records show that Bf110s were credited to aircraft W4078
(27/28th), DD622 (28/29th) and DZ309 (28/29th) but it has not proved
possible to ascribe these aircraft to a particular pilot. Some sources quote
DZ309's victory as being a Ju88.]

No 141 Squadron lost two of its flight commanders, Squadron Leader
Forshaw and Squadron Leader Lovel, during this period, while 239 Squadron
lost Squadron Leader Kinchin, its commanding officer.

April saw 515 Squadron getting into its operational stride, the Squadron
despatching 75 individual aircraft sorties during the period. Some 57 patrols
were completed, during which 12 enemy airfields were attacked. Warrant
Officer Ecclestone claimed two aircraft destroyed while Squadron Leader
Martin claimed another and one damaged. Two crews failed to return and
there were two instances of engine failure reported.

The month also saw 214(SD) Squadron finally become operational. By the
last day in March, the unit had received six B-17s fitted out with the *ABC*
device. Some thought was given to the way in which these aircraft should be
used and it was finally decided that they should be stationed at 20 ml (32 km)
intervals within the bomber stream to supplement the work of the similarly
equipped Lancasters of 101 Squadron. The first operational sortie was
despatched on the night of 20/21st. For the rest of the month, the squadron
could muster five serviceable aircraft per night. No 214 Squadron now shared
its airfield with the 803rd Squadron of 8th Air Force which had been formed
from the American Detachment on 28 March. This unit was designated as a
Mandrel/Carpet jamming squadron and was to serve as part of 100 Group in all
but name until November 1944 (see Chapter Four).

The ELINT unit, 192 Squadron, received a welcome boost to its strength
when four Mosquito IV aircraft were delivered during April. Operationally, the
survey of the enemy's radar chain begun in previous months was continued.
April also saw the formation of a new unit within the Group, the Bomber
Support Development Unit (BSDU).

This formation, based at Foulsham, was created to handle the development
and trials of new equipment and tactics pertinent to the Group's operations.
Previously, all the testing and evaluation of equipment and the development of
suitable tactics for the bomber support fighter units had been handled by the
Fighter Interception Unit (FIU) at Ford. Similarly, the development and
evaluation of new jamming and ELINT gear had been undertaken by the TRE
and its Development Flight at Defford. This was held to be rather a clumsy
arrangement and the creation of the BSDU was designed to streamline it. The
FIU now handed over all bomber support development to the new unit, for
which the BSDU had a flight of nine Mosquito fighter aircraft. The TRE continued to develop equipment but the majority of tests on it were now
undertaken within the Group. The BSDU's usefulness was further enhanced by
the transfer to it of 80 Wing's workshop facilities at Radlett. This meant that
100 Group could build new or modify existing electronic equipment without
being reliant on external sources.

A much modified Mosquito II, nicknamed Eleanora, *belonging to the Fighter Interception Unit at Ford. This aircraft clearly shows the blunt nose associated with the carriage of centimetric radar (in this case AI Mk X) and the black undersurface camouflage carried by many bomber support Mosquito fighters. (via J Scutts)*

May saw no let up in the activities of the *Serrate* units, 212 individual aircraft sorties being despatched during the period, of which 196 were completed. Two aircraft and crews (one from 169 Squadron and one from 239 Squadron) were lost and 18 enemy aircraft were claimed to have been destroyed. Details of these victories, where known, are as follows:

11/12th W4078 of 239 claimed a Bf110 near Courtrai.
13/14th W4078 of 239 claimed another Bf110.
13/14th W4092 of 239 claimed a Ju88.
15/16th DZ478 of 169 claimed a Bf110 and two Ju88s near Kiel.
23/24th DZ309 of 239 claimed a Bf110.
25/26th DZ265 of 239 claimed a Bf110.
25/26th DZ297 of 239 claimed a Ju88.
27/28th HJ941 of 141 claimed a Bf109 near Aachen.
28/29th DD622 of 239 claimed a Bf110 near Leeuwarden.
30/31st DZ297 of 239 claimed a Bf110 near Trappes.

In addition to these figures, 141 Squadron claimed a further two destroyed, 169 Squadron a further two and 239 Squadron a further two plus one damaged.

During the month, the Group began to record statistics on the performance of *Serrate*, the first set of figures being as follows:

Sorties completing a patrol	196
Serrate contacts reported	approx 220
Serrate contacts converted to AI	25
Combats resulting	12
AI contacts without *Serrate*	approx 55
Combats resulting	6

The Group's intruder element, 515 Squadron, despatched 120 individual aircraft sorties during May, from which six crews failed to return. Towards the end of the month, the unit began to receive Mosquito VI aircraft. The ELINT squadron, No 192, despatched 81 patrols during the same period from which two aircraft failed to return. Again, its main concern was the mapping of the enemy's radar chain in connection with the forthcoming invasion.

On 1 May, a second jamming unit, 199(SD) Squadron, was drafted into the Group. Previously a Stirling bomber unit within 3 Group, the Squadron was now based at North Creake in the *Mandrel* role. For the first week of its existence, 199 Squadron had no aircraft, receiving its first Stirling III fitted with *Mandrel*, *Shiver* and *Gee* on the 10th. Over the next 14 days a further 12 such aircraft arrived on the squadron. During the same period, three more of the unit's Stirlings were being fitted out at Defford (TRE) and another four were undergoing a similar operation at Foulsham (BSDU). For the rest of the month, the squadron underwent intensive training for its new role.

The Group's only operational jamming squadron had a busy month. Between 27 April and 10 May, the unit despatched 35 *ABC* sorties with an average of five aircraft per operation. Three combats were reported during this period which resulted in a Bf109 being claimed as damaged. On the 16th, Sculthorpe was closed and 214 Squadron, along with the 803rd, moved into Oulton. Between 10 and 24 May, a further 60 *ABC* sorties were despatched with an average of four aircraft available per night. Four combats were reported and claims were made for two Bf110s being damaged. Further work was being carried out on the electronic fit in the squadron's aircraft and by the middle of May all available B-17s had been fitted with the *Monica III* tail warning device which was generally regarded as being 'most helpful'. At about the same time, the first *Jostle* jammer arrived at Oulton. No trials with the device were held in order not to make a premature disclosure of its potential to the enemy. By the end of the month, 214 Squadron had 22 crews fully trained on the B-17.

Although the jamming element of the Group was small, considerable work on such devices was carried out during the period November 1943 to May 1944. During this time, the following devices had made their appearance:

Dartboard	First used operationally on 6/7 December 1943. This was a ground measure designed to disrupt enemy GCI control channels.
Modified ABC	Two modified forms of *ABC* became operational during this period; namely one tuned to jam 31.2 MHz VHF R/T and W/T transmissions which was first used operationally on 14/15 January 1944, and one to jam the *Benite* navaid which became operational on 27/28 January. Presumably both these types were used by 101 Squadron.
Drumstick	First used operationally on 21/22 January 1944. This was a ground measure designed to disrupt enemy HF W/T transmissions in the 3–6 MHz band.
Carpet II	First used operationally on 24/25 March 1944. This was a device designed to jam GCI/GL radar in the 500 to 580 MHz band. The users were most probably 8 Group.
Fidget	First used operationally on 27/28 April 1944. This was a ground measure designed to jam enemy MF R/T and W/T transmissions.

May 1944 also saw the arrival of two more fighter squadrons within the Group. Both units, 85 and 157(SD) Squadrons, were transferred as a direct result of the disastrous raid on Nuremburg on 30/31 March. Both squadrons had previously served with 11 Group and were now based at Swannington No 85 Squadron arrived first, becoming part of 100 Group on 30 April, 157 Squadron following on 7 May. Perhaps more important than their presence, these two squadrons brought centimetric AI to the Group with all its attendant

The introduction of centimetric AI radar proved to be of the greatest value to the bomber support campaign, giving the squadron's a set which was resistant to Window and better able to follow the smallest movement of a target. The particular radar depicted is the AI Mk IX, a British development which was abandoned when the superior American SCR 720 unit became available. (Crown Copyright)

advantages over the equipment already in use. No 85 Squadron was equipped with a mixture of Mosquito XII (AI Mk VII) and XVII (AI Mk X) aircraft whilst 157 Squadron was flying Mosquito XIX (AI Mk X) from 21 May. Although centimetric radar had been cleared for use over enemy territory in April* these two squadrons did not become operational until June, being held in readiness for the invasion.

Thus ended 100 Group's first seven months of operations. During the period under review, Bomber Command was involved in two distinct series of operations, the Battle of Berlin and during the late spring of 1944, the general attack

---

*Previously such flights had been banned for fear that the Magnetron valve, the core of centimetric radar, might fall into enemy hands. This was a very real possibility as the standard RAF demolition charge fitted to all sensitive equipment proved incapable of even damaging the Magnetron let alone destroying it!

on transport targets in France. With the Battle of Hamburg behind him, Harris felt that with the bomber force now under his command, a series of similar raids against the German capital could cost the enemy the war. So confident of this was he that at the beginning of the battle he stated that:

> 'If the Americans will come in with us [meaning the 8th Air Force making daylight attacks in conjunction with Bomber Command's night raids] we can wreck Berlin from end to end. It will cost us 500 aircraft, but will cost Germany the war!'

Unfortunately, the Americans did not 'come in' and by 31 March, when the battle ended, Berlin was heavily damaged but by no means 'wrecked from end to end'. More to the point, Bomber Command had lost 1,047 aircraft (more shockingly, this figure meant the loss of more than 7,000 aircrew) and a further 1,682 damaged out of a total 20,224 individual sorties despatched. Far from ending the war, the battle nearly destroyed Bomber Command. The one thing which was clear was that the Command could not sustain such casualties and continue the bombing of Germany. During the course of the battle, 16 attacks were directed at Berlin and a further 19 against Ludwigshafen, Leverkusen, Frankfurt, Stuttgart, Leipzig, Stettin, Brunswick, Magdeburg, Schweinfurt, Augsburg, Essen and Nuremburg. The climax of the series of operations was the raid on Nuremburg on the night of 30/31 March, when no less than 95 bombers were shot down (out of a total of 795). A further ten aircraft out of this force were destroyed in crash landings and another 59 were variously damaged. Never before had Bomber Command suffered such a defeat and the whole concept of the area offensive was called into question. It was clear that the tactical and scientific innovations so far produced to aid the bomber force and the growing strength of that force could not prevail against the enemy's defences. The prospects for 1944 seemed bleak indeed and for the first time doubts about continuing the offensive were evident in Harris himself.

Against this grim backdrop, 100 Group began its operational career. As will have become clear, the first seven months of its existence was mostly taken up with fighter operations, no jamming squadron being available until April 1944. Two distinct sides to such operations were envisaged, namely attacks on enemy night fighter airfields and roving patrols to intercept such aircraft while they were searching for the bombers. The airfield attacks did not begin until March/April when 515 Squadron became operational, and then only on a limited scale due to a lack of aircraft.

The main burden of operational flying therefore devolved on the three *Serrate* squadrons, Nos 141, 169 and 239. In November 1943, 141 Squadron was the only operational one of the three, 169 and 239 Squadrons not making their presence felt until late January 1944. Although the *Serrate* homer itself proved to be an effective device, the three squadrons were faced with a number of problems which drastically reduced their effectiveness until at least the end of March 1944. No 141 Squadron was the only fully operational unit of the three, 169 and 239 Squadron's crews still being in the throes of *Serrate* training when they joined the Group. All three Squadrons were also involved in re-equipping with the Mosquito II aircraft with the obvious loss in operational strength which this entailed. Further, the Mosquito aircraft themselves were far from ideal. All were old and their engines were in a very poor state, a factor amply confirmed by the statistics for engine failures previously quoted in this chapter. It is most probable that the majority of losses suffered by these three squadrons during

the period were due to engines ceasing to function at critical moments rather
than to any action on the part of the enemy.

So serious had this problem become by February 1944 that the decision was
reluctantly taken to reduce the level of operational flying so that all the *Serrate*
aircraft could be overhauled and re-engined. This decision must have been all
the more difficult in view of what was happening in the winter nights over
Northern Germany and the certain knowledge that the bomber crews needed
every scrap of help they could get. The sense of urgency must have been
transmitted to the squadron engineering sections for the figures for sorties
despatched did not drop dramatically and the Group's records show that the
whole programme had been completed by early April.

Apart from problems with the airframes, the squadrons' difficulties were
further compounded by low AI serviceability, the figures show that this was the
cause of a large proportion of the early returns during the period. The
particular type of radar, AI Mk IV, also proved to be inadequate for the
demands being made on it. When used near the bomber streams it was completely swamped by unwanted returns, the more so when *Window* was being
used. Even when used away from the bombers, the flood-light quality of its
transmissions made it difficult to follow a target amongst ground returns and
other superfluous clutter. Because of these failings, it proved very difficult to
switch from *Serrate* to AI for the final interception, the target being frequently
lost during the changeover.

Again, tactically the *Serrate* squadrons were at an initial disadvantage. In
November/December 1943, there was little information on the enemy's tactics.
Changeover to the *Zahme Sau* system did not help as the Group's intelligence
branch proved incapable at first in keeping abreast of new developments. Three
types of patrol were tried out during this early period, namely sorties over the
target during and after raids, patrols of known enemy night fighter assembly
points and the loose escort of the streams themselves. Of these, the target area
patrols proved to be most successful but none were helped by the appalling
weather conditions encountered over Germany during the winter of 1943 and
the early spring of 1944 and the lack of long-range navigation experience
amongst the crews.

The problem of accurate intelligence was gradually overcome as 1944
progressed. The main contribution came from 192 Squadron's systematic
survey of the enemy's radar chain in Europe. This had the dual purpose of
finding out what the bombers were up against as well as plotting those parts of
the chain which would have to be neutralised for the invasion. Other sources of
information were the various monitoring stations set up in England, chief
among which was Kingsdown. Here, the enemy's GCI transmissions were
recorded providing an eventual picture of his operations. It is interesting to note
that the TRE, when it was not satisfied with the data supplied by the RAF
pertaining to a particular problem, set up its own ad hoc monitoring posts on a
number of occasions during the war.

The final link in the intelligence chain was the Air Ministry's Directorate of
Intelligence, the scientific branch of which (dealing with radar etc) was headed
by Dr R V Jones. This organisation provided the Group with regular reports
which Addison has described as 'first class' and 'most accurate'. Here again
can be found the *eminence gris* of Enigma, the decoding apparatus which allowed
the Allies to evesdrop on Germany's military traffic throughout the war.

The Kingsdown monitoring station. In this view, RAF SOs operate American equipment to evasdrop on German signals traffic. The set on the left is an HRO while the other two are AR.88s. (IWM)

Although its use was unknown even to Addison at the time, it has since become clear that Enigma was responsible for the remarkably accurate details of the dispositions and strengths of fighter units etc, that the Group was in receipt of.

At the end of March 1944, Bomber Command turned its attention towards transport targets in France in preparation for the invasion. Initially, enemy night fighter reaction over that country was limited, but by April, opposition was growing as units were moved in from Germany and Holland. By May, losses of up to 4% were being experienced by the bombers over the more important targets in this area. To combat this, the *Serrate* squadrons provided route escort for the bombers, the Mosquitos flying parallel to and criss-crossing the track of the stream. Such operations proved to be successful and this can be attributed to the increasing skill of the *Serrate* operators, better weather conditions and shorter sorties reducing crew fatigue.

During the period in question, 100 Group could only muster three jamming squadrons, Nos 199, 214 and the 803rd on loan from the 8th Air Force. One other squadron, No 101, was operational in this role but never came under the Group's control. Of the first three squadrons mentioned only 214 Squadron became operational, making its first sortie in April; 199 and 803 Squadrons did not start operations until June. No 214's gestation was somewhat protracted

due to a lengthy installation programme for the necessary electronics and slow
crew conversion. Nos 199 and 803 were held in readiness for the invasion, the
Air Ministry wishing to retain the maximum effect of the *Mandrel* screen, which
these squadrons were to operate for this operation, by not disclosing it pre
maturely to the enemy. More subtly, the equipment of the Group's heavy
squadrons was held up by the fact that the TRE, the main suppliers of jamming
gear, was totally involved in producing measures to support the invasion. Not
only did this hinder the Group's progress but probably emphasised the need for
self-sufficiency and was in this way instrumental in the setting up of the BSDU.

Chapter 3

Invasion and Divers:
June to November 1944

At 0630 hours on 5 June 1944, the first Allied troops were wading through the morning tide towards a 56-mile stretch of the Normandy coastline between Valognes and Cabourg. Eight days later, Mr Wraight and Mr Woodland were manning their Observer Corps post in the Martello tower at Dymchurch. At 0408 hours on 13 June they saw a most extraordinary sight coming towards them from the coast of France. When the object was some five miles from them, both observers were quite sure of what they were seeing. Without hesitation, Woodland reported to the Maidstone centre 'Mike Two – *Diver* – *Diver*, one four, north west, one at one.' These two events, the invasion of Europe and the appearance of the V-1 flying bomb, dominated Allied military thinking and operations for the remaining summer and autumn months of 1944. No 100 Group was as heavily involved in these operations as any other RAF formation.

For the landings in Normandy, the Group contributed both jamming and fighter support. Indeed, as has been recounted, its three jamming squadrons, Nos 199, 214 and the American 803rd, had been held in reserve for this event. Now, on the night of 4/5 June they were unleashed. No 199 and the 803rd set up their first *Mandrel* screen in a line from Littlehampton to Portland Bill to give cover to the advancing invasion fleet. No 199 contributed 16 aircraft to this operation while the 803rd supplied four, the 20 aircraft being divided between ten jamming centres. No 214 Squadron despatched five B-17 aircraft (flown by the squadron commander McGlinn, the two Flight Commanders, D Murray Peden and one other) to join 24 aircraft of 101 Squadron in an *ABC/Window* barrage along the line of the Somme estuary. This force, with its total of 82 *ABC*s, was designed to distract enemy night fighter attention from some 1,000 Allied transport aircraft on their way to drop paratroops on the Cherbourg peninsula and to the east of Caen.

The 214 Squadron aircraft were airborne for 6½ hours, patrolling back and forth along 90-mile (145 km) beats at an operational altitude of 27,000 ft (831 m). McGlinn's aircraft was attacked by a Me410 which was destroyed in an exchange of fire with the B-17's rear gunner, and a Lancaster of 101 Squadron was shot down. This operation was completely successful, being described in the official report on the action as follows:

'. . . The night fighter force was sent into the *ABC* area [which was presumed to be] the main bomber stream of a major attack. On their arrival in the area, the fighters found that they were being subject to serious jamming on the R/T communications channel. They returned toward their control points, but appear to have received instructions to go on hunting in the bomber stream as there was sporadic fighter activity in that area between 0105 and 0355 hrs.'

The airborne jamming was backed up by ground stations in the UK and the *Mandrel* screen, *Ground Mandrel* and *Window* were all aimed at the early warning radars in the 90 to 200 MHz band. The *Window* employed was type MB (see page 162) which was used for the first time during this operation and was the first of the family to be aimed at the *Freya* device.

The *Mandrel* screen used what was known as the Racecourse Pattern. This was evolved by the navigation section at North Creake. The idea was to fly circuits up and down the *Gee* lines most nearly perpendicular to the enemy coast. The first circuit was 10 miles (16 km) long, rate-one turns being made between the straight legs and each successive circuit was adjusted to take account of the prevailing wind conditions so that it took exactly 10 minutes.

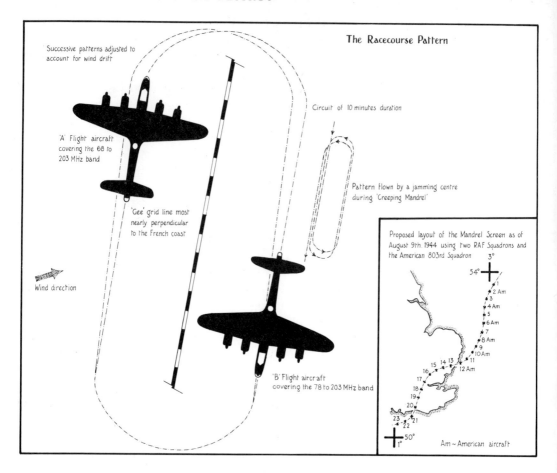

The aircraft of each pair (two aircraft forming a jamming centre) started at opposite ends of the circuit, thus maintaining a strong average intensity of jamming. This technique was maintained for the rest of the war only being changed slightly for *Creeping Mandrel* when an aircraft would slightly shorten its down leg and make the following up leg correspondingly longer thereby shifting the position of the circuit forwards each time. Flying of this nature obviously required a very high standard of piloting and navigation. No 199 Squadron's Stirlings were stretched to their fullest by this regime, having to fly at their maximum altitude (the screen was initially operated at 15,000 ft (4,615 m) and then at 19,000 ft (5,846 m) from the night of 27/28 June) often in adverse weather conditions. The *Gee* transmissions were badly affected by the *Mandrel* jamming so the navigator had to rely on dead reckoning to account for wind drift once the screen was in operation.

The fighter elements of the Group were equally active on the night of the invasion, despatching the following aircraft between 10pm on the 5th and 10pm on the 6th:

Serrate Squadrons:
141 – six sorties to the Paris area
169 – ten sorties
239 – five sorties to Northern France

Intruder Squadrons:
85 – twelve sorties over the beach-head
157 – four sorties to Dutch airfields
515 – ten sorties to Belgian and Dutch airfields

From this effort, two of 515 Squadron's aircraft failed to return and DD789 and DZ256 of 239 Squadron claimed a Ju88 and a Bf110 respectively as destroyed.

Once the invasion had begun, 100 Group turned its full attention towards bomber support duties. During the whole of June the three *Serrate* squadrons despatched a total of 330 sorties of which 287 completed a patrol. Two aircraft failed to return and 17 enemy aircraft were claimed as destroyed, one probably destroyed and one damaged. Statistically, this effort broke down as follows:

Sorties completing a patrol	287
Serrate contacts reported	Approximately 70
Serrate contacts converted in AI	4
Successful combats	2
AI contacts without *Serrate*	Approximately 150
Successful combats	17

The details of 15 of these victories are as follows:

1/2nd – Aircraft DZ265 of 239 Squadron, one Bf110
5/6th – Aircraft DD789 of 239 Squadron, one Ju88
6/7th – Aircraft DZ256 of 239 Squadron, one Bf110 near Aachen
9/10th – Aircraft DD241 of 169 Squadron, one Do217
12/13th – Aircraft DZ256 of 239 Squadron, one Bf110 near Paris
13/14th – Aircraft DZ254 of 169 Squadron, one Ju88 near Paris
14/15th – Aircraft DZ240 'H' of 141 Squadron, one unidentified enemy aircraft
17/18th – Aircraft W4076 of 169 Squadron, one Ju88 near Paris
17/18th – Aircraft W4092 of 239 Squadron, one Ju88 near Eindhoven
22/23rd – Aircraft DZ290 of 239 Squadron, one He177
25/26th – Aircraft DD759 of 239 Squadron, one Ju88 near Paris
27/28th – Aircraft DZ240 'H' of 141 Squadron, one Ju88
27/28th – Aircraft HJ911 'A' of 141 Squadron, one Ju88
28/29th – Aircraft DD759 of 239 Squadron, one Me410 near Paris
28/29th – Aircraft DD749 of 239 Squadron, one Ju88 near Brussels
28/29th – Aircraft NT150 of 169 Squadron, one Bf110

The intruder units were equally busy during the month despatching between them a total of 317 sorties from which two aircraft failed to return. Fifteen enemy aircraft were claimed as destroyed with a further five damaged, known details of these claims being as follows:

13/14th – Aircraft MM630 'E' of 157 Squadron, one Ju188 near Compiegne
15/16th – Aircraft MM671 'C' of 157 Squadron, one Ju88 near Juvincourt
15/16th – Aircraft 'Z' of 85 Squadron, one Ju88
16/17th – Aircraft MM671 'C' of 157 Squadron, one Ju88 near Creil
17/18th – Aircraft 'C' of 85 Squadron, one Bf110
21st – Aircraft ? of 515 Squadron, one Bf110 on a *Day Ranger*
30th – Aircraft PZ203 of 515 Squadron, one He111 and one Ju34
30th – Aircraft PZ188 of 515 Squadron, one He111

The two AI Mk X squadrons, Nos 85 and 157, were initially used for low-level intruder work because their AI sets had no tail-warning capacity, a prerequisite in the Group's eyes for high-level patrols. Therefore the two squadrons were used at low level to get them into operations as soon as possible while the BSDU worked up a modified *Monica I* for use in this role with AI Mk X. This was seen as only a temporary measure and although completed in July 1944, further work was undertaken which resulted in *Monica IV* which could give both a range and azimuth reading. This device was approved for use in September 1944.

The four heavy squadrons of the Group, Nos 192, 199, 214 and the 803rd, despatched a total of 266 individual sorties during the month. No 192 Squadron despatched a total of 134 ELINT sorties (79 of these taking place between the 7th and the 21st) concentrating on Western Europe. The two *Mandrel* squadrons, No 199 and the 803rd, contributed 107 sorties to the general total, 199 Squadron despatching 30, from which one Stirling failed to return, and the 803rd despatching 11 between the 7th and the 21st. On 16/17 June, the *Mandrel* screen was modified to cover the 70 to 200 MHz band, and after it had been discovered that the *Mandrel* jamming badly affected the Army's and the Navy's radio communications in the beach-head area when used over the Channel, the screen was deployed over the North Sea, usually some 80 miles (129 km) off the enemy coast.

No 214 Squadron contributed the remaining 25 sorties to the total, all taking the form of *ABC* patrols, 16 taking place between the 7th and the 21st. One Me410 was claimed on the 4/5th and aircraft 'F' was written off in a crash landing at Woodbridge on the night of the 21/22nd.

Early in June the squadron embarked on the second of the frequent equipment changes which were to become a regular feature of its existence. Two of the unit's B-17s were involved in trials at Number 12 Bomber Development Unit to determine whether the ventral turret was of value in the night defence of the aircraft. After a number of mock attacks by a Beaufighter, it was determined that visability from the turret was almost non-existent in conditions of darkness. On the basis of these trials, the squadron began to remove such turrets from its B-17s.

In the middle of the month, 214 Squadron received its first three Fortresses fitted with *Jostle* and *Airborne Grocer* (see pages 158 and 154 respectively). Neither of these measures was used operationally, *Grocer* in fact being removed from the aircraft at the end of the month because of its vulnerability to being homed on to.* Air testing was, however, carried out with *Jostle* and the crews discovered something of this communications jammer's power when high altitude tests with the device were conducted over the Atlantic, half way to Iceland, so that its 2,500 watt output would not interfere with Allied transmissions. This impression was enhanced when instructions were issued that any functional tests with the device over England should be carried out below 500 ft (154 m) in order not to blank out even the BBC's transmissions over a substantial area!

June also saw the Group begin daylight operations. No 214 Squadron despatched its first such sortie on the 1st. No 515 also began *Day Rangers* during the month. In total, the Group despatched 17 daylight sorties before the 30th. On the 25th of the month, 85 Squadron ceased bomber support and joined in the anti-*Diver* (or V-1) campaign, making its first claim in this role the following night. On the 27th, 157 Squadron was likewise allocated to the new role, the

---

*Although *Airborne Grocer* was removed from 214's aircraft at the end of June 1944, the four Yagi aerials associated with the device remained on the B-17s; there is a possibility that they were later used in an interim *Piperack/Dina* installation (see page 98).

decision being taken on the same day to employ the two squadrons fulltime on this for the duration of the emergency. To this end both the squadrons were transferred to West Malling, the move being completed by 14 July.

The loss of its only AI Mk X squadrons was regarded with the utmost gravity by 100 Group, AI X being considered as the best radar available for the fighter elements of the bomber support campaign and vital to its success. Consequently, the BSDU was put to work to find a substitute for it; presumably on the basis that if the Group had to lose some of its fighter strength in this way better not the AI Mk X squadrons. The solution arrived at was a modified *Monica III E* mounted for forward range-finding. This device was tested during July but in the event was not taken up. However, as has already been described, the two squadrons were fitted out with *Monica* tail warners during the month in preparation for their return to bomber support duties.

On 8 July, 85 and 157 Squadron's Mosquitos began to be converted to increase their maximum speed. This involved the fitting of stub exhausts and adjustment of the engine boost pressure to allow the use of 150 octane fuel. These modifications increased the forward speed to 360 mph (579 km/hr) and were completed by the 16th. In addition, after 157 Squadron's MM630 had suffered a failure of the nose structure on the 27/28 June, both units put in hand the strengthening of this area on all their aircraft. When the units returned to bomber support duties, flame damping exhausts were certainly re-fitted but it is unclear whether a return was made to the engines' normal octane-rated fuel.

Anti-*Diver* patrols were continued until 29 August when the units returned to Swannington. During the early part of the month, 85 Squadron had begun patrols of the Dutch coast watching for launches from that area, the first such sortie being flown on the night of the 3/4th. It should be noted that although 85 and 157 Squadrons were supposed to be on fulltime anti-V-1 work from 27 June, bomber support patrols were continued until the move to West Malling was completed. Between the nights of 1/2 and 19/20 July, 85 Squadron despatched 15 airfield intruder sorties (resulting in one AI contact) 11 high level patrols (four AI contacts) and two *Night Rangers* (to Denmark), while 157 despatched 22 intruder sorties (resulting in two AI contacts and two victory claims) and 11 high-level patrols (two AI contacts). No complete figures for the numbers of V-1s destroyed by the two Squadrons between 27 June and 29 August are available, but it is known that between 1/2 and 19/20 July, 85 Squadron despatched 67 *Diver* sorties and claimed 12 V-1s destroyed while 157 Squadron despatched 72 and claimed 20. In addition, 85 Squadron is known to have destroyed another five before the end of July and 13 in August.

Despite the loss of the two AI X squadrons, the Group's fighter element kept up the pace of operations during July. The three *Serrate* squadrons despatched a total of 338 sorties during the month, 311 of which completed a patrol. Two aircraft from these units failed to return and claims were made for 21 enemy aircraft destroyed and a further five damaged in 25 combats. Details of the destroyed claims are as follows:

1/2nd – Aircraft DZ265 of 239 Squadron, one Ju88
4/5th – Aircraft NT121 of 169 Squadron, one Bf110
4/5th – Aircraft DD725 'G' of 141 Squadron, one Me410 near Orleans
5/6th – Aircraft DZ298 of 239 Squadron, one Bf110 near Paris
5/6th – Aircraft NT121 of 169 Squadron, one Ju88

7/8th – Aircraft HJ911 'A' of 141 Squadron, one Bf110
8/9th – Aircraft DD789 of 239 Squadron, one Fw190
8/9th – Aircraft W4097 of 239 Squadron, two Bf110s
8/9th – Aircraft DZ298 of 239 Squadron, one Bf110 near Charleroi
14/15th – Aircraft NT112 of 169 Squadron, one Bf110
18/19th – Aircraft HJ659 'B' of 141 Squadron, one Bf110
20/21st – Aircraft DZ267 'Y' of 141 Squadron, one Bf110
21/22nd – Aircraft NT113 of 169 Squadron, one Bf110, near Courtrai. This
sortie, flown by Wing Commander Bromley provided the Group with its 100th
victory.
21/22nd – Aircraft NT121 of 169 Squadron, one Bf110 near Courtrai
23/24th – Aircraft HJ710 'J' of 141 Squadron, one Ju88
23/24th – Aircraft NS997 of 169 Squadron, one Bf110 near Kiel
25/26th – Aircraft DZ661 of 239 Squadron, one Bf110
28/29th – Aircraft HJ712 'R' of 141 Squadron, two Ju88s
28/29th – Aircraft HJ741 'Y' of 141 Squadron, one Ju88 near Stuttgart

These victories were gained under increasingly difficult circumstances.
Firstly, 169 Squadron was in the throes of converting to the Mosquito VI, flying
its last Mosquito II sortie on the night of 17/18th. All three *Serrate* squadrons
were earmarked for re-equipment with this former type but the conversion was
somewhat protracted, 141 Squadron using the type from August 1944 and 239
Squadron from September.

More importantly, during June and July, the number of *Serrate* contacts
dropped dramatically to the point where, in July, an average of one such
contact was being reported for every ten sorties despatched. Though it was not
known at the time, this was due to the phasing in of the SN-2 AI set by the
Luftwaffe. At the same time the number of direct AI contacts increased,
especially during patrols of known night fighter beacons. Even this, however,
was to be short lived as, towards the end of July, the enemy began the serious
jamming* of AI Mk IV. This phenomena was particularly marked over the
Ruhr and the coastal radar chain. By the end of July, the *Serrate* units had all
but lost their hard-fought-for effectiveness.

The Group's intruder element received welcome reinforcement when 23
Squadron moved into Little Snoring at the end of June. This unit had previously been stationed in Malta and became operational in the bomber support
role on the night of 5/6 July. The two intruder squadrons, Nos 23 and 515
despatched between them 244 sorties during the month. No 23 Squadron
despatched 122 sorties towards this total on 16 nights from which two Mosquitos failed to return. (The unit was operational on the Mk VI variant, as was
515, which began conversion to the type in March 1944.) Two enemy aircraft
were claimed as destroyed and the airfields at Schipol, Beauvais, Bonn, Cam-
brai/Epinoy, Chievres, Clastres, Coulommiers, Creil, Deelen, Eindhoven,
Florennes, Gilze Rijen, Laon/Couvron, Le Culot, Melun, Roye Amy, St
Dizier, St Trond, Soesterberg, Twenthe, Vechta, Venlo and Volkel were
attacked. In addition, the squadron despatched seven *Day Rangers* from which
one aircraft failed to return.

---

*Although there is evidence to suggest that the Germans were jamming AI Mk IV during this
period, there is the possibility that frequency changes in his ground radar brought about by the
intensity of the RAF measures, were responsible for the interference on the aforementioned set.

The effect of intruder operations. Two Bf110G-4 aircraft of 2/NJG 5 lie wrecked on the airfield at Laon Athies in the late summer of 1944. The aircraft in the foreground illustrates several interesting points of camouflage, namely the low visibility national markings on the fuselage and the rudder and the 'splinter' scheme on the wings. (IWM)

No 515 despatched an equal number of sorties during the month, but spread over 17 nights. One Mosquito failed to return and two enemy aircraft were claimed as destroyed. Airfield attacks were carried out against Chateaudon, Chievres, Coulommiers, Dole/Tavaux, Florennes, Juvincourt, Laon/Athies, Laon/Couvron, Le Culot, Melun, Metz, Mondidier, St Trond, St Dizier Soesterberg, Venlo and Volkel. The squadron also despatched eight *Night Rangers* and 34 *Day Rangers* (on 12 days) during which three victories were claimed. Known details of victory claims are as follows:

5/6th – Aircraft PZ163 of 155 Squadron, one Ju88 near Coulommiers
10th – Aircraft of 515 Squadron claimed a Ju88 and a Ju188 during a *Day Ranger*.
14th – An aircraft of 515 Squadron claimed a Ju34 during a *Day Ranger*.

The two *Mandrel* squadrons, Nos 199 and the 803rd, were operational on 17 nights during July, 12 in support of Main Force attacks and five spoof operations. Between the 4th and the 18th, the two squadrons despatched 110 sorties between them, 199 Squadron despatching a further 117 sorties between 18 July and 2 August. It should be noted that not all 199 Squadron's sorties were *Mandrel* operations, the creation of the *Special Window Force* (see below) causing it to become involved in *Windowing*. Details of the spoof operations are as follows:

14/15th – A fake bomber stream approached the Dutch islands and was intercepted by the two Gruppen of enemy night fighters.
17/18th – This operation combined a *Mandrel* screen, *Bullseye* aircraft, (code-

name for night flying exercises carried out by Operational Training Unit [OTUs]), *Window* droppers (Types MB and N) and *Serrate* aircraft.

19/20th – During this operation nine *Windowers* and a force of *Bullseye* aircraf were variously described as '100 to 200 aircraft', 'a very large force' and '10(aircraft' by the enemy fighter controllers.

21/22nd – During this operation, a small number of *Windowers* supported b· intruder aircraft were described as '70 to 80 aircraft'.

23/24th – No less than five Gruppen of night fighters were vectored on to a forc· of *Window* and *Bullseye* aircraft during this operation.

The *Special Window Force* (SWF) became operational on the night of 14/1 July and was made up from available aircraft from the ggroup's heav· squadrons, initially Nos 192, 199 and 214. Its purpose was to divert the enemy· interceptors away from Main Force during its attacks by creating a fak bomber stream or to provoke a reaction when Main Force was not operating The force grew out of the realisation of the potential of combining *Mandrel* an· *Window* to produce a 'bomber stream' for the enemy's radar operators. I should be stressed that the SWF was never intended to reproduce exactly bombing force but rather to simulate the radar, radio and jamming transmis sions from such a force. Its main weapon in this field was *Window*, for with thi measure, given the right dropping rate and individual aircraft locations, ten air craft could be made to appear as 100 or more. Obviously a high standard c navigation and very precise timing were essential to the success of such opera tions. The SWF adopted the very high rate of *Window* dropping of ten packet per minute. This was in direct contrast with the rates for Main Force crews wh· usually dropped one bundle every two minutes. A look at the table of *Windov* types (see page 162) will give some idea of the difficulties of *Window* dropping a the SWF rate. Manually it must have been an exhausting task and the Grou; devoted much effort towards the development of automatic dispensers (se page 199) which were to see service late in the war.

By the very nature of the campaign it was waging, the SWF had to constantl· change tactics to remain convincing. Additionally, the overall effect of eact spoof had to be constantly enlarged as the enemy's experience of such tactic: grew. The force was always short of aircraft and was never large enough to b· 100% convincing even at the end of the war. The permutation of tactic: indulged in by the Force were endless but one of the most interesting an· durable was 'conditioning'. This involved the production of a false strean (perhaps involving a deliberate gap in the *Mandrel* screen to allow the stream t· be seen for a brief period before being swallowed up again in the clutter o jamming, emerging with even greater clarity due to the 'breakdown' to displa· the full spectrum of transmissions associated with a major raid) over a giver route and following the same route on the same or next night for an actual raid

The German controller having once been fooled would be wary of doing th· same again and experience proved that operations conducted in this way wer· often discounted as yet another spoof. Despite all shortfalls in numbers an· technical difficulties, the SWF was to remain one of the Group's most poten measures for the remainder of the war.

No 192 Squadron continued its ELINT activities during July, despatching 49 sorties between 21 June and 4 July. One Halifax failed to return from thi· serial, which was mainly concerned with the investigation of SN-2 AI an·

various tail warning radars. From the 4th to the 18th, a further 58 patrols were despatched, divided between investigating SN-2, *Freya* and *Würzburg* transmissions and monitoring R/T traffic in Northern Denmark. The month was completed (18 July to 2 August) by another 86 sorties investigating VHF R/T traffic along the west coast of Denmark; the relative densities of FuG 202/212 and SN-2 transmissions, *Würzburg*, centimetric and tail-warning radars and signals in the 30 to 40 MHz band.

The Group's remaining heavy squadron, No 214, was also busy during the month. Between 21 June and 4 July, the unit despatched 10 sorties, from which one B-17 failed to return and another was written off in a crash landing at Woodbridge (see page 56). On the night of the 21/22nd, a Ju88 was claimed as destroyed and a Fw190 as damaged. On the last night of this period, *Jostle IV* made its operational debut, spot jamming the 3 to 6 MHz band. Another 37 *ABC/Jostle* sorties were despatched between the 4th and the 18th with the squadron making its first contribution to the SWF on the night of the 12/13th. The remainder of the month (18 July to 2 August) saw a further 74 *Jostle* sorties completed and the steady removal of the *ABC* equipment from the squadron's aircraft. Again during late July, six of the unit's B-17s were fitted out with *Mandrel III* (six per aircraft) and quickly began operations as a supplement to the *Mandrel* screen.

July also saw the BSDU begin to function properly. The unit was heavily involved throughout the month with trials of a modified *Monica IIIE* used as a forward range-finder in connection with anti-*Diver* patrols. These tests were carried out in conjunction with 515 Squadron and the FIU. By the 4th of the month, the BSDU had fitted 12 of 85 and 157 Squadrons' aircraft with *Monica* tail warners. Between 18 July and 2 August, the unit was involved in camouflage trials with a 4 Group Halifax which had had its undersurfaces sprayed with a high gloss black paint, and with trials with *Airborne Grocer II* to see whether it was vulnerable to being homed on to. *Grocer II* was a modified version of the original device (see page 158) most probably aimed at the enemy SN-2 set and these tests proved that it would be difficult to home on to, unlike its forebear.

Three new counter-measures were introduced during the month: *Jostle IV* (as had already been described) on the 4/5th; *Tuba* (aimed at the 70 to 200 MHz band) on the 16/17th; and *MB Window* against the 60 to 200 MHz band on the 23/24th.

Just as it seemed as though the Group had seen the last of the enemy's V-1 pilotless bomb, August produced a new and altogether more frightening spectre in the form of the V-2 ballistic missile. Back in June, the inhabitants of Gräsdals Gärd in eastern Sweden had been shaken by a mid-air explosion in the late afternoon of the 13th. Inspection of the ensuing wreckage showed the culprit to be a V-2 rocket (W.Nr.4089) launched from the experimental station at Peenemünde on the other side of the Baltic. Under an agreement between the British and Swedish governments in which the latter country received a quantity of gun laying radars, the wreckage was transported to Britain in mid-July. Investigation of these remains at Farnborough gave reality to a previously rather ethereal intelligence picture of the device. Of the greatest interest to the British researchers was the rocket's radio guidance system, a previously unknown facet of the weapon. Equally unknown was the fact that what they were looking at had nothing to do with the V-2, for W.Nr.4089 was a test round used in the development programme of the *Wasserfall* anti-aircraft missile. The guidance system lying on the Farnborough work benches actually belonged to the latter weapon and not the V-2. As all this was to remain unknown until the war's end, urgent steps were taken to institute counter-measures against the 'radio controlled' V-2s under the code-name *Big Ben* in which 100 Group was to be heavily involved.

Back in the bomber support theatre, the Group's *Serrate* Squadrons were as busy as ever during August despatching 331 sorties, 302 of which were completed, during the month. *Serrate* contacts dropped to an all time low of seven and only ten claims (three Ju88s, one Bf110, two Bf109s and two Fw190s destroyed and two Bf109s damaged) could be set against the entire month's effort. The virtual drying up of *Serrate* contacts and the ever increasing interference being suffered by AI Mk IV meant that these squadrons had become virtually impotent by the end of the month. The only bright spot was 141 Squadron's operational debut with the Mosquito VI on the night of the 16/17th when HR213 claimed the destruction of a Ju88 and the damaging of a Bf109 near Ringkjobing in Denmark. The squadron flew its last Mosquito I sortie on 29/30 August. Known details of these claims are as follows:

8/9th – Aircraft W4092 of 239 Squadron, one Bf110
9/10th – Aircraft DZ298 of 239 Squadron, one Bf109
9/10th – Aircraft DZ256 of 239 Squadron, one Fw190
9/10th – Aircraft NT156 of 169 Squadron, one Fw190 near Abbeville
10/11th – Aircraft NT176 of 169 Squadron, one Bf109
16/17th – Aircraft HR213 'G' of 141 Squadron, one Ju88
26/27th – Aircraft NT146 of 169 Squadron, one Ju88 near Bremen
30/31st – Aircraft W4097 of 239 Squadron, one Ju88 near Stettin

Intruder activities during the month presented a somewhat brighter picture 23 and 515 Squadrons despatching a total of 222 such sorties during August. A total of 131 of these were contributed by 23 Squadron over a period of 16 nights. Claims were made for the damaging of four enemy aircraft and the airfields at Aine, Cerfon, Florennes, Gilze Rijen, Juvincourt, Nivelles, Nordholz Plantlunne and Venlo were attacked. In addition, two *Day Rangers* (4th and 5th) and 27 escort sorties for bombers making daylight attacks on the Bordeaux area were completed during the month. No 515 Squadron contributed the remaining 91 sorties over 12 nights. During the course of these operations one Mosquito failed to return and attacks were made on the airfields at Cambrai/Epinoy, Chievres, Deelen, Gilze Rijen, Hoperhofen, St Dizier and St Trond, five *Day Rangers* and 50 escort sorties for daylight bombing raids on the Bordeaux (made on the 11th, 12th and 13th) were despatched in addition to the night work.

The *Mandrel* screen was operated on 16 nights during August, 199 Squadron and the 803rd now being supported by the half-dozen *Mandrel* B-17 aircraft of 214 Squadron. Six of these operations were in support of raids on Germany, five in support of raids on France and five spoofs. The French operations saw the screen set up over S.E. England to cover the Pas de Calais area and it was found that the presence of such jamming attracted enemy fighters into the area being affected. This phenomenon was later put to good use in spoof operations. August also saw the introduction of the technique of allowing the enemy to see the SWF throw a 'Breakdown' in the *Mandrel* screen. Again, 199 Squadron contributed aircraft to the SWF and between the 2nd and the 16th the squadron despatched 76 *Mandrel* and *Window* sorties, the 803rd flying 32 *Mandrel* patrols during the same period. Between the 16th and the 30th, 199 Squadron put in another 76 *Mandrel/Window* sorties while the 803rd contributed another 29 *Mandrel* patrols.

The SWF was out on seven nights during the month, three of which provoked an enemy response. The operation on the night of the 17/18th was a most striking example of Conditioning. A *Window* force, *Bullseye* aircraft and the *Mandrel* screen created the impression that Kiel was being attacked for the second night running. A total of 12 Staffeln of night fighters rose to meet the 'threat'. On the following night, a Main Force raid on Bremen was routed over the same area and was totally ignored by the German controllers in the belief that it was yet another spoof. Towards the end of August, the force's operations were curtailed by a shortage of the correct type of *Window*.

No 192 Squadron despatched 120 sorties during the month. Between the 2nd and the 16th, 44 operations were carried during which two Ju88s were claimed as being damaged. Enemy AI transmissions, the *Egon* system and signals traffic in the Calais/Sylt area were all investigated during this period. On the 4th, the squadron was put on 24-hour stand-by for surveillance flights to look for transmissions associated with *Big Ben* or the V-2. One of the unit's aircraft was detached to Farnborough during the early part of the month for trials with a captured enemy AI set,* and tests were carried out to determine the cause of interference being experienced on H2S sets.

Between the 16th and the 30th, the unit went on to complete a further 53 ELINT patrols during which one Mosquito was lost. Enemy R/T traffic was monitored and investigations were made into AI transmissions, *Würzburg*, *Freya*, *Seetackt* and *Mammut* radars, the *Egon* system, centimetric developments and the results of jamming operations against the enemy's signals in the 30 to 40 MHz band. *Big Ben* surveillance flights began towards the end of the month, 12 such sorties being made before the beginning of September.

In addition to the investigations, the squadron discovered a new EW radar (30 to 40 MHz band) on the Dutch coast and later went on to check the measures aimed at it as recounted above. A modified H2S set, code-named *Coal Scuttle*, was used to obtain bearings on a pulsed signal in the 10 to 30 MHz band of enemy origin. One of the unit's Halifax's made a lengthy investigation into radio/radar activity in the northern waters around Europe. A detachment of four P-38 aircraft from the 8th Air Force's 7th PR Group joined 192 Squadron at the end of the month and began daylight ferret flights (see page 82).

During the month 214 Squadron despatched a total of 103 sorties. This figure broke down into 40 *Jostle*, 27 *Mandrel* and 36 *Window* patrols. Between the 2nd and the 16th, 33 *Jostle* and *Mandrel* sorties were flown while between the 16th and the 30th, 34 *Jostle* and *Window* patrols were sent out. During this latter period, a B-17 failed to return from an operation to Russelheim. In the middle of the month, the squadron received the prototype modified *Jostle* for *Big Ben*

---

*On 13 July, a Ju88G-1 of 7/NJG 2 accidentally landed at Woodbridge in Essex. This windfall allowed the RAF to examine the latest enemy night fighter fitted with the SN-2 AI set and the FuG 227 *Flensburg* homer. The aircraft and its equipment were extensively tested at Farnborough. One of the direct results of these trials was the abandonment of *Monica* as a Main Force tail warning when it was discovered that FuG 227 could home on to it from a range of 45 miles (72 km).

jamming (see page 159).

Considerable electronic development and installation work was undertake during August. In the early part of the month, 214 Squadron's *Mandrel* aircra were fitted with *Mandrel III* and ten of its aircraft had H2S sets fitted. (With th demise of *Monica* as a tail warner for heavy aircraft, 214 Squadron now began t use the *Fishpond* facility in the H2S equipment for the purpose (see page 198 Additionally, one of 192's Mosquito aircraft was fitted with a *Monica IIIE*.

The latter part of the month, from the 16th onwards, was taken up wit BSDU trials with various homers and the AI Mk XV set. The introduction c SN-2 had led to an urgent requirement for a replacement for *Serrate*. The BSDl produced *Serrate IV* as a direct replacement for the earlier type (work on it star ing in May 1944) and also *Perfectos*, which gave a bearing on the enemy's Fu 25A IFF set after triggering it. Work on this device began at Radlett during th early summer of 1944, and details of these two devices may be found on pag 167. By the middle of August, the BSDU had completed a trial installatio of *Serrate IV* which was taken on operational flights and to Farnborough fc trials with the captured Ju88G-1. During these, the device proved to have range of 45 miles (72 km) when used against the forward SN-2 transmissior and 5 miles (8 km) when used against the set's tail warning capacity. *Perfect* was also tested against the Ju88 and proved to have a range of 15 miles (24 km The development of *Serrate IV* proved to be a protracted affair due to th enemy's constant switching of the frequency used by SN-2 in an attempt t overcome jamming. In the event, neither device entered service until late in th war, *Perfectos* becoming operational in November 1944 and *Serrate IV* in Januar 1945.

During the earlier part of the month, the BSDU undertook tests to cure th interference caused by *Monica IV* on the standard VHF R/T set (which we successful) and trials with the experimental *Serrate IIA* homer. As has bee mentioned, the unit undertook operational trials with new equipment whereve possible and between June and August 1944 despatched 11 such sorties. Eigl took place in June, all of which were evaluations of the *Monica IIIE* anti-V- range finder (see page 57). The remaining three were all *Serrate IV* sortie during which it was found that the device could not discriminate between th signals from the SN-2 and *Freya* sets. This only added to the other problem associated with this homer.

In June 1944, 100 Group received a sample of the American 3cm AN/APS- ASV radar then coming into service with the Fleet Air Arm. This device, alte natively known as *ASH* (or in the RAF usage AI Mk XV) was being used t that service as an interim AI set pending the availability of the purpose-bui AN/APS-6. Its handy pod mounting and the fact that it was centimetr prompted the Group to consider it as a replacement for its AI Mk IV equip ment. Ideally the Group would have liked to standardise on AI Mk X but th was not available in sufficient numbers. The BSDU initially considered moun ing the *ASH* pod on one of the wing bomb racks of the Mosquito but this wa superseded by a nose mounting developed by 218 MU. The nose machine gur in the Mosquito were displaced by this installation but this was not seen as disadvantage as all AI Mk X Mosquitos only carried the four belly-mounte cannon.

Flight trials began in the last week of August and the set proved to have maximum and minimum range of 19,000 and 600 ft respectively (5,846 m ar

185 m). On the strength of these trials, the Air Ministry approved the devices installation in the Mosquito VI aircraft of three of the Group's squadrons as an interim measure until the availability of AI Mk X. The set entered operational service in mid-November 1944.

In the event, AI Mk XV proved to be better suited to low-level work than AI Mk X. In service, the Group's navigators considered *ASH* to be vastly superior to AI Mk IV and appreciated its ability to operate in the face of *Window*, its clear single-tube presentation which allowed a watchful eye to be kept on other electronic equipment and its search scan, a product of its ASV origins, which made it a useful navigation aid in the same manner as H2S. Against this its slower scan speed and small upward cover were regarded as major drawbacks. The small size of its control box made its operation difficult and there was a tendency for ground returns to swamp a contact during turns. In addition, its 3 cm wavelength meant that heavy cloud produced a strong response, strong enough at times to make interception difficult.

On 23 August, 223 Squadron joined the Group for jamming duties. Based at Oulton, the unit was originally designated as the second *Jostle* unit but the emergence of the V-2 threat caused this to be changed to that of a *Big Ben* jamming squadron.* No 223 Squadron was to be equipped with Liberator aircraft (see page 241) supplied from 8th Air Force stocks, and the crews were initially drawn from Coastal Command B-24 OTUs. (Later, the unit's crews were trained by 1699 Flight. B-24 training began in September 1944.) By the end of August, 223 Squadron had nearly a full complement of aircraft, five of which were used for crew conversion.

The month ended on a happy note when the two AI Mk X squadrons returned to Swannington to resume full-time bomber support operations.

September saw a decline in the activities of the *Serrate* squadrons. A total of 240 such sorties were despatched of which 221 completed a patrol. Three aircraft failed to return and one Bf110 was claimed as destroyed. *Serrate* contacts had all but ceased during the month and this, coupled with the problems with AI Mk IV, made the re-equipment of these squadrons a matter of the greatest urgency. As an interim measure the unit's AI IVs had their frequencies changed from 193 MHz to 188 MHz during the month but this did not materially help the situation.

A new departure for the *Serrate* squadrons during September was the introduction of *Day Rangers* and escort duties with the Group's daylight *Big Ben* aircraft. An example of the latter type of operation came on the 11th when two of 239 Squadron's aircraft escorted B-17 HB772 of 214 Squadron during a patrol off the Low Countries.

The two AI X units, Nos 85 and 157 Squadrons, quickly resumed their bomber support role and despatched between them a total of 236 sorties during the month. No 85 Squadron contributed 117 to this total on 21 nights; 86 of these were high-level patrols which resulted in 22 AI contacts. From these, claims for four enemy aircraft destroyed, one probably destroyed and one damaged were made. The remaining 31 sorties were low-level patrols which resulted in 8 AI contacts and claims for two aircraft destroyed. No 157 Squadron despatched the remaining 119 sorties, again over 21 nights; 81 of these were high-level patrols which resulted in 25 AI contacts and claims for

---

*One source quotes that the squadron was *specifically* formed for *Big Ben* duties.

three destroyed and three damaged. Two Mosquitos failed to return from thes
operations. The other 38 sorties were all low-level patrols during which five A
contacts were reported and one enemy aircraft was claimed as being damaged
Throughout the month, both squadrons were being fitted out with *Monica I*
tail warning sets.

The known details of claims by these five squadrons during September are a
follows:

12/13th – Aircraft HR180 'B' of 141 Squadron, one Bf110 near Mannhein
12/13th – Aircraft 'A' of 85 Squadron, one Bf109
13/14th – Aircraft 'D' of 85 Squadron, one Bf110
17/18th – Aircraft 'J' of 85 Squadron, two Bf110s
27/28th – Aircraft 'J' of 85 Squadron, one Ju88
28/29 – Aircraft 'Y' of 85 Squadron, one Ju88

The two intruder squadrons, Nos 23 and 515, despatched a total of 23
sorties between them during the month. No 23 Squadron contributed 125 t
this total on 19 nights, from which two aircraft failed to return. The airfields a
Alhorn, Guterslow, Hanau/Langendiebach, Hopsten, Ober Olm, Paderborn
Quackenbruck, Stade and Usingen were attacked and claims for 16 aircra
destroyed (eight in the air, eight on the ground) were made. In addition, tw
Day Rangers were despatched and 12 of the squadron's aircraft acted as escort
for 192 Squadron *Big Ben* patrols on three days during the month (one of thes
operations taking place on the 14th and another on the 18th). No 51
Squadron's 107 sorties were despatched on 18 nights, the squadron losing tw
aircraft during these operations. The airfields at Bonn/Hangelar, Hesepe
Paderborn, Rheine, Twente and Westerland were attacked and claims for fiv
aircraft destroyed (two in the air and three on the ground) and three damage
(two in the air and one on the ground) were made. Eleven *Day Rangers* wer
despatched from which four aircraft failed to return; two more were interned i
Switzerland and eight of the squadron's aircraft acted as escorts for 19
Squadron *Big Ben* aircraft on two days during the month.

The *Mandrel* force received welcome reinforcement during September whe
171 Squadron was formed on the 7th. The new unit was to be equipped with 2
Halifax III aircraft but as these were not available one Flight of Stirlings wa
transferred from 199 Squadron to act as a nucleus. (The latter unit had bee
raised to three Flight status in August.) No 171 Squadron's first operationa
sortie occurred on the 15th and Stirling flights continued until 21 October whe
the first Halifax sortie was despatched (a *Window* sortie with the SWF whic
was, in fact, cancelled). Extended delays were experienced in obtainir
Mandrel/Window Halifaxes from the modification centre at St Athan and th
squadron was not fully equipped with the type until late November.

Between 29 August and 13 September, 199 Squadron and the 36th (th
803rd being thus redesignated on 14 August – see Chapter Four), despatched
total of 110 sorties, the 36th operating pure *Mandrel* patrols while 199 Squadro
combined this role with *Window* dropping for the SWF. From the 13th to th
27th, the *Mandrel* force despatched 161 sorties. This total was made up of 2
Window sorties with the SWF from 171 Squadron, 87 *Mandrel/Window* sorti
from 199 Squadron and 49 *Mandrel* sorties from the 36th. During this perio
199 and the 36th were used to give jamming support to the airborne landings
Arnhem.

An interesting view of the Mandrel *aerials on the undersurface of a Halifax. The line running down the left hand side of the fuselage is the beam approach aerial, the* Mandrel *antenna being those running down the centre line. The blister at the extreme rear is the* H2S *housing. The triangular object next to the beam approach aerial is the forward* Window *shute. (via D Wood)*

The *Mandrel* screen was operated on 19 nights during September. Nine of these operations were in support of major raids, nine in support of minor raids and one was a spoof. To prevent the enemy's EW radars in Holland seeing round the northern edge of the screen, it was lengthened to cover this area during the month.

The SWF was airborne on 12 nights during September and was now accompanied by the full repertoire of Bomber Command signals traffic. Two of its operations during the period were considered very successful; the first being on the 11/12th when the SWF and a group of mine laying aircraft were taken to be a major attack on either Berlin or Stettin. The following night the organisation was operating in the Karlsruhe area and provoked a large night fighter response. A major new innovation for the force during the month was the use of the *Mandrel* screen over Europe as part of its activities.

No 192 Squadron despatched a total of 155 ELINT sorties between 29 August and 27 September. The first serial took place between the former date and 13 September and comprised 52 patrols; 46 of these were *Big Ben* surveillance flights, the remaining six being a survey of radar cover in Norway in preparation for the attack on the *Tirpitz* which took place on 12 November. Between the 13th and the 27th, another 103 sorties were despatched. Again, these were mostly *Big Ben* patrols but some investigation work was carried out into the control systems of the enemy's HS 293 and *Fritz-X* guided bombs.

During September, 214 Squadron was heavily engaged in *Big Ben* work. Between 29 August and 13 September only 26 sorties were despatched. These were HF and VHF *Jostle* (from the 11/12th) and *Big Ben Jostle* (from the 9th) operation. A further 67 such sorties were completed between the 13th and the 27th with *Big Ben Jostle* predominating. During the early part of the month, the unit's aircraft were being fitted with *Carpet III* equipment. No 223 Squadron became operational on 19 September and between this date and the 27th despatched 15 *Big Ben Jostle* sorties by day and night.

Again, electronic development work and trials were to the fore during the month. By the 13th, six of 214 Squadron's B-17s had been fitted with *Big Ben Jostle* and a trial installation of *Mandrel* had been made in a Halifax. Work on automatic *Window* dispensers was well in hand and a prototype was being tested during the month. As part of the re-equipment programme for the *Serrate* squadrons, September saw *Monica* being installed in 239 Squadron's aircraft. The BSDU despatched six operational trial sorties during the month, three in connection with AI Mk X, one with *ASH*, one with *Perfectos* and one with *Monica IV*.

October saw the three *Serrate* squadrons despatch a total of 308 sorties of which 289 were completed, and all were flown at high level. This led to an increase in AI contacts of which no less than 111 were reported, although *Serrate* contacts were again almost non-existent, a mere five being reported for the entire month. Claims were made for the destruction of three Ju88s, one Bf110 and one FW190 and the damaging of another two Ju88s and a Ju188. In addition, *Night Rangers* were flown on four nights resulting in the destruction of a He111 and the few *Day Rangers* flown produced a claim for a seaplane being destroyed.

The two AI Mk X squadrons despatched 238 sorties between them during the month. No 85 Squadron's contribution was 80 high-level patrols and 37 low-level ones on 16 nights. The high-level patrols produced 29 AI and 16 *Monica* contacts (two of which were converted to AI) which resulted in claims for the destruction of four enemy aircraft. The low-level operations resulted in three AI and one *Monica* contact and the destruction of one aircraft. No 157 Squadron flew 83 high-level and 38 low-level patrols on 16 nights during the month. The high-level patrols yielded eight AI and seven *Monica* contacts and two aircraft were destroyed and another damaged. None of the *Monica* contacts were converted to AI. The squadron's low-level work produced three AI contacts.

By the end of the month it had become obvious that AI Mk X was best suited to high-level work. At altitudes between 1,500 and 2,000 ft (462 and 615 m) the set had its maximum range reduced to 3 miles (5 km). Of the three types of high level patrol, that is beacon patrols, stream escort and target area patrols, the latter proved to be the most effective in terms of enemy aircraft destroyed. It was also clear that although *Monica* was a very effective tail warner, it was very difficult to convert its contacts into AI ones.

Known details of the claims of these five squadrons during October are as follows:

6/7th – Aircraft NT234 'W' of 141 Squadron, one Ju88
15/16th – Aircraft PZ245 of 239 Squadron, one Fw190
15/16th – Aircraft 'D' of 85 Squadron, one Bf110
19/20th – Aircraft NT250 'Y' of 141 Squadron, one Ju88 near Karlsruhe
19/20th – Aircraft PZ175 'H' of 141 Squadron, one Ju88
19/20th – Aircraft 'Y' of 85 Squadron, one Ju88

19/20th – Aircraft PZ275 of 239 Squadron, one Bf110

The two intruder squadrons despatched a total of 173 sorties on 14 nights of the month. No 23 Squadron flew 97 of these and claimed one enemy aircraft destroyed. The airfields at Aalborg, Ardorf, Biblis, Flensburg, Kitzingen, Mark, Oberolm, Stade, Varel and Swischenahn were attacked. In addition, two *Day Rangers* and a daylight escort sortie (four aircraft for a daylight raid on the 4th) were sent out during the period. No 515 Squadron's total for the month was 76 sorties, which resulted in claims for two aircraft destroyed (one air, one ground) and two more damaged on the ground. The airfields at Biblis, Gutersloh, Nordholz, Oberolm and Schwabisch Hall were attacked. During daylight hours, the squadron despatched five *Day Rangers* (involving 10 aircraft) and contributed seven aircraft to the escort sortie of the 4th. The most notable of these operations was the *Day Ranger* of the 29th when two crews claimed between them nine aircraft destroyed and five more damaged in the Prague area. Known details of the squadron's claims are as follows:

8th – An aircraft of 515 Squadron claimed a Bf109 during a *Day Ranger*.
29th – Aircraft PZ344 of 515 Squadron claimed a Fw190
29th – Aircraft PZ344 of 515 Squadron claimed a Ju88
29th – Aircraft PZ217 of 515 Squadron claimed a Bf110

The *Mandrel* screen was operated on 12 nights during the month of which nine were in support of Main Force raids and three were spoofs. The screen was now being activated later than previously as the bombers were now flying at low level and in radio/radar silence only appearing in the enemy's radar cover as they climbed over the coast.

Between 27 September and 11 October, 171 Squadron despatched 26 *Window* sorties (despite difficulty in modifying their aircraft for this role), 199 Squadron despatched 64 *Mandrel/Window* sorties and the 36th despatched 29 *Mandrel* sorties. Between 11 and 24 October, 171 Squadron flew six *Mandrel* and 13 *Window* sorties and 199 Squadron another 60 *Mandrel/Window* sorties.

The SWF was operational on 11 occasions during the month, drawing aircraft from Nos 171 (39 sorties), 192 (11), 199 (8), 214 (84) and 223 (18) Squadrons. Two of its operations on the 19/20th and the 31/1st were regarded as being very successful. On the first occasion, enemy night fighters were drawn away from a raid on Stuttgart by the force's aircraft operating in the Frankfurt area and in the second, the enemy's interceptors were successfully drawn away from a raid on Cologne. VHF *Jostle* and H2S transmissions were now a normal part of the SWF's operations and the effect was further enhanced by the addition of *Carpet* and *Dina* in the second half of the month.

Pure *Window* operations were still found to be effective as demonstrated by operations on the 14/15th during a double raid on Duisburg and Brunswick. Unfortunately such operations could only be expanded at the expense of other jamming aircraft due to the constant lack of aircraft. Aircraft from the Group's fighter elements* were now involved in the force's sorties, an example being the

---

*Initially *Serrate* aircraft had escorted the SWF and *Serrate* and Intruder sorties had occasionally been despatched as feints in their own right. With the decline in enemy night fighter activity, the Group's fighters were brought into the SWF's operations on a larger scale from October 1944 to take advantage of the fighter reaction such operations provoked.

operation of the 7/8th when SWF *Windowers* were accompanied to Bremen by high- and low-level fighter patrols. No 8 Group also began to contribute some of its *Oboe* Mosquitos to the force's work to execute false target marking.

October saw 192 Squadron despatch a total of 181 ELINT sorties, from which one of the 7th PR Group's P-38 aircraft failed to return. Between 27 September and 11 November, 62 sorties were despatched. Some 39 of these were *Big Ben* patrols and another 15 were in connection with the V-1. The remaining eight were in connection with FuG 16 and *Egon* traffic, *Coal Scuttles*, determining the source of a 30.7 MHz signal and investigation into AI Mk IV interference. A further 82 sorties were made between the 11th and the 24th. Again, *Big Ben* patrols predominated (two to four aircraft) but work was done on AI signals in the 30 to 600 MHz band, *Egon* and FuG 25A traffic, AI Mk IV interference and, a new departure for the squadron, *Windowing* with the SWF.

No 214 Squadron ceased *Big Ben Jostle* jamming at the beginning of October and concentrated on HF and VHF *Jostle* jamming and *Window* dropping for the first half of the month, 62 such sorties being despatched between the end of September and 11 October, During the same period, eight of the unit's B-17s had been equipped with *Carpet III* and work had started on fitting *Dina*. Six aircraft had been completely fitted out with the last named device by the 25th. As such aircraft became available they were phased into operations and between the 11th and the 25th, 214 Squadron despatched a further 43 *Jostle*, *Carpet*, *Dina* and *Window* sorties. Problems were encountered with the *Dina* aerial array as it proved prone to snapping off when iced up.

No 223 Squadron continued its *Big Ben Jostle* operations during the month but was hampered by maintenance problems with its aircraft and a shortage of trained air and ground crews. Up to the 11th, 24 *Big Ben/Window* sorties had been flown, another 18 occurring between the 11th and the 24th. *Window* operations with the SWF were limited during the month because of a lack of qualified crews. On the latter date, *Big Ben Jostle* patrols were cancelled and the squadron was no longer required to maintain a 24-hour stand-by for such patrols. Considerable effort was put into the electronic re-equipping of the squadron's fighter elements during the month. By the 11th, 23 Squadron had begun training with AI Mk XV and at least one *ASH*-equipped Anson had been delivered to 1692 Flight to help in the training programme for this device. On the jamming side, a prototype *Carpet* fit (three *Carpet IIs* and three *Carpet IIIs*) was produced for 171 Squadron aircraft and work was carried out on *Window* chutes and magazines for Stirling aircraft. By the 25th, work was well ahead in fitting the *Perfectos* device into 169 Squadron's aircraft and 218 MU was working on the *ASH* installation for 141 Squadron. All of 85 and 157 Squadron's aircraft had been fitted out with *Monica IV* by this time and work was in hand installing the device in the first four Mosquito 30s destined for these units.

The BSDU despatched 15 sorties during October. These were in connection with AI Mk X, *Perfectos* and *Monica IV*. The results from *Perfectos* were very encouraging, one sortie with the device providing 12 contacts at ranges up to 40 miles (64 km) away from the carrier aircraft.

November saw major changes in the structure of the Group's fighter element. From the beginning of the month, the distinctions between the different roles performed by the various squadrons began to blur, a process which was to continue until the end of the war. The *Serrate* squadrons were in the throes of re-

Two views of the Luftwaffe's premier night fighter, the Ju88G. This particular Ju88G-6 of 5/NJG 4 was found by British forces near Hamburg in May 1945. Points of interest are the blister for the FuG 350 aerial above the cockpit, the nose antenna for the FuG 220 SN-2d AI set and the tail warning aerial for the same set under the tail fin. Note also the differing camouflage schemes carried by 3C-PN and the '88 in the background. (IWM)

equipment, ·169 Squadron replacing its *Serrate* homers with the *Perfectos* device while 141 was gearing itself up for the conversion to AI Mk XV. As in the previous month, the emphasis for these three squadrons was on high-level patrols. Plans were also being formulated to re-equip the two intruder squadrons, Nos 23 and 515, with *ASH* and to eventually re-equip 141, 169 and 239 Squadrons with AI Mk X. For convenience, details of all fighter activities will be given in statistical form by equipment from this point onwards.

Serrate/AI Mk IV (141 and 239 Squadrons)
Number of sorties despatched	190
Sorties completed	184
Aircraft lost	1
Number of *Serrate* contacts	0

Perfectos/AI Mk IV (169 Squadron):
Number of sorties despatched	106
Sorties completed	89
Aircraft lost	0
Number of *Perfectos* contacts	15
Number of *Perfectos* contacts converted to AI	3

Figures relating to all three squadrons;
Number of direct AI contacts	110
Claims	3 destroyed (2 air, 1 ground); 1 damaged

AI Mk X/*Monica* (85 and 157 Squadrons):
Number of sorties despatched	211
Sorties completed	185
Aircraft lost	1
Claims	17 destroyed; 3 probables; 3 damaged
Number of AI contacts	80
Number of *Monica* contacts	13
Number of *Monica* contacts converted to AI	5

These five squadrons also despatched 54 low-level sorties during the month.
Low level intruders (23 and 515 Squadrons):
Sorties despatched	182
Sorties completed	160
Aircraft lost	2
Claims	5 damaged (2 air, 3 ground)

Each of the squadrons operated on 12 nights during the month and a number of *Day Rangers* involving 12 aircraft were despatched.

Known details of the claims made by these seven squadrons during the month are as follows:

1/2nd – Aircraft 'R' of 85 Squadron, one Ju88
1/2nd – Aircraft 'N' of 85 Squadron, one Ju88, one Ju188 and one Bf110
1/2nd – Aircraft 'Q' of 85 Squadron, one unidentified enemy aircraft
4/5th – Aircraft TA401 'D' of 157 Squadron, one Bf110
6/7th – Aircraft 'N' of 85 Squadron, one Ju188
6/7th – Aircraft 'Y' of 85 Squadron, one Bf110
6/7th – Aircraft 'A' of 85 Squadron, one Ju88
6/7th – Aircraft TA391 'N' of 157 Squadron, one Ju188
6/7th – Aircraft TA404 'M' of 157 Squadron, one Bf110
10/11th – Aircraft TA402 'M' of 157 Squadron, one Ju88

11/12th – Aircraft 'R' of 85 Squadron, one Fw190
21/22nd – Aircraft MM630 'E' of 157 Squadron, one Ju88

The *Mandrel* screen was operational on 18 occasions during November, 171 Squadron contributing eight sorties to it and 199 Squadron, 97. In addition, the two squadrons were active in the SWF contributing between them 67 sorties. On the 25th, the 36th Bombardment Group finally returned to American control, concentrating its *Mandrel* sorties in support of the 8th Air Force from this point onwards. The split was gradually executed and for some months, the American units contributed aircraft to help out the Group (see page 80).

The SWF was active on 18 nights during the month, dividing its time between eight *Mandrel/Window* spoofs and ten diversions for Main Force raids. The operations undertaken on the nights of the 10/11th and the 28/29th were regarded as being very successful. Two new techniques were added to the force's repertoire during the period; namely saturation *Windowing* of a broad area and bombing on *Gee* by the Group's fighter units. The saturation *Windowing* grew out of a repeated series of attacks on the Ruhr area. The Germans had resorted to virtual standing patrols over the region whether it was under attack or not. To counter this, the SWF *Windowed* the entire Ruhr in order to blind the enemy as to a specific target in the area. This tactic was later expanded to *Windowing* when Main Force was not operating just to confuse the enemy.

High-level bombing on *Gee* indications by fighter units in concert with the SWF was carried out on the nights of the 27/28th and the 28/29th. On the first occasion, aircraft from 141 Squadron dropped 40 lb (18 kg) bombs on Cloppenburg, Quackenbruck, Lingen and Beilen. On the following night aircraft from the same squadron bombed Bonn. A total of 25 sorties was despatched on such operations and they were later expanded to include the dropping of flares and target markers as well as bombs.

No 192 Squadron despatched a total of 52 sorties during the month, 31 of which were by night and the remainder in daylight. Again, *Big Ben* patrols figured large but work was also done on recording enemy R/T traffic (which was hampered by difficulties with the recording devices used), investigating *Jagdschloss* and FuG 216 transmissions and trying to discover whether *Knickebein* was being used as a navaid for the Heinkel He111s air-launching V-1s over the North Sea. Again sorties were contributed to the SWF for *Window* dropping and a number of the unit's Mosquitos were being fitted with *Dina* for jamming duties during Main Force attacks.

The two *Jostle* squadrons, Nos 214 and 223, despatched a total of 233 sorties during November. No 214 Squadron flew 107 *Window/Jostle/Carpet/Dina* patrols with the SWF and a further 29 jamming sorties in support of Main Force raids while 223 Squadron despatched 97 *Window/Jostle/Carpet* and, from the middle of the month, *Dina* operations with the SWF. By the 21st, eight of the squadron's B-24s had been fitted out with *Dina*.

The re-equipment programme for the *Serrate* squadrons maintained its momentum during the month. By the 21st, 141 Squadron's aircraft were well on the way to being fitted out with AI Mk XV, which in their case had a tail-warning capacity. A prototype installation of the same AI set had been made in a 239 Squadron aircraft by this date but in the event the type was not to see general use with the unit. The installation programme for *Monica IV* in the AI Mk X squadron's Mosquito 30s was proceeding well, 16 such aircraft being fully equipped by the 21st. (These aircraft went to 85 Squadron.)

During the month it was decided to fit the *Loran* navaid to all the Group's heavy aircraft. Work was also proceeding on a prototype *ABC* installation for a B-24 which was scheduled for completion on the 22nd, and a further nine Halifaxes had been fitted out with *Mandrel* by the end of the month, with another eight nearing completion.

The BSDU despatched five operational trial sorties during the period, all of which were concerned with comparisons between the combination of AI Mk X with *Perfectos* and AI Mk IV also with *Perfectos*. During October and November, the unit also carried out work on a *Serrate IV* with a fitter for *Freya* signals and anti-jamming modifications to AI Mk IV and *Monica IV*.

With the closing of November, 100 Group had been operational for a full 12 months. Just as the first six months of its life had been fighter orientated, this second period from June had seen the jamming element predominate. By the close of the period, the Group's RCM campaign had reached maturity and was inflicting chaos and confusion amongst the enemy's night fighter system. At the same time, the fighter squadrons had been dogged by misfortune. The failure of *Serrate* and the loss of the AI Mk X squadrons to anti-Diver work had been grave setbacks from which the element was only just recovering. Unfortunately, both aspects of the Group's work had knitted together a little too late, for the Luftwaffe's night fighter arm had entered a steady decline from which it would not recover, crippled as it was by a lack of early warning, fuel and experienced crews. The remaining six months of the war would see the Group operating at full capacity against an ever weakening enemy – a true case of Overkill.

Chapter 4

The American Involvement:
January 1944 to May 1945

On 28 September 1940, Edward Bowen and John Cockcroft of the Tizard Mission revealed the Magnetron valve to a stunned American National Defence Research Committee. This, the core of centimetric radar development, galvanised the Americans into action, and from then on they were firmly wedded to the new technology. An American liaison team was soon sent to the Telecommunications Research Establishment at Malvern and in the course of time became aware of the centre's work on 'radio counter-measures'. This branch of radar work was also eagerly taken up.

With the formation of 100 Group in November, 1943, American personnel became involved in the operational application of such measures. On 17 January 1944, a small unit, known as the American Detachment, moved into Sculthorpe to train the air and ground crews of 214(SD) Squadron on the B-17. Two days later the unit, under the command of Captain G E Paris, became the Eighth Air Force's RCM Detachment. Initially, the unit was to confine itself to training activities whilst steps were being taken to integrate the American effort with that of the RAF, and for the latter service to provide the necessary electronic equipment. The first concrete step towards operations came on 10 February when six crews and their aircraft arrived at Sculthorpe from the 96th Bombardment Group (H) at Snetterton Heath. Work was immediately put in hand to modify these aircraft for night flying (exhaust flame dampers, etc) and to install *Gee* navigational equipment and *Mandrel* and *Carpet* jammers.

On 21 March, the American/RCM Detachment's B-17 conversion course for 214(SD) Squadron officially ended, although such activities actually continued until well into August 1944. (An RAF B-17 conversion flight, No. 1699, being formed for 100 Group in June.) On 28 March, the Detachment was redesignated the 803rd Bombardment Squadron (P). Captain Paris remained as the new unit's commanding officer. On this date, the squadron had a strength of six aircraft and nine crews.

Initially crew morale was low. All the unit's flying personnel had flown an operational tour with other squadrons. Only certain members were picked from each crew, the remainder being repatriated to America. This meant that new crews had to form, a situation which was not popular with men who had just gone through 25 operational flights with, say, a pilot whom they knew and trusted. The situation was only alleviated by the influx of new personnel at which time the squadron began to form its own identity.

On 25 April, Captain Paris relinquished command in favour of Major C A Scott. Paris now became the unit's operations officer. Further change came when on 16 May, Sculthorpe was closed and the 803rd and 214(SD) Squadrons moved to Oulton. During the period prior to the move, considerable thought had been given to the usage of the 803rd by the American authorities and by the second week in April, it was decided to allow the unit to be used in the support of RAF Bomber Command's operations. This meant that the squadron now became part of 100 Group in all but name, a situation which was to last until the following November.

At the time of the move, the squadron's aircraft were equipped as follows: one B-17 with three *Carpet* and one *Mandrel* jammers, two aircraft with nine *Carpet* and four *Mandrels*, two aircraft with six *Mandrels*, and an ELINT Ferret with S27 and one SCR 587 receivers. Training now went on apace to equip the unit for its operational role as part of the *Mandrel* screen with 199(SD) Squadron. Apart from the obvious familiarisation with jammers themselves, emphasis was laid on navigational training, especially *Gee*, and on imparting the RAF's night flying techniques.

Along with the other jamming Squadrons of 100 Group, the 803rd was held in readiness for the invasion of Europe. Its first operational sortie was made on the night of 4/5 June when a *Mandrel* screen was put up to mask the invasion fleet moving towards the coast of France. [A complete breakdown of the squadron's activities will be found at the end of this chapter.] This first mission was flown by four aircraft which took off at 2200 hrs and commenced jamming at 2235 hrs, continuing it until 0450 hrs. All returned safely. During the rest of the month, 803rd contributed 26 individual aircraft sorties to *Mandrel* operation on five nights. Tactics changed on 27/28th when the mission was flown at 19,000 ft (5,846 m) instead of 15,000 ft (4,615 m) as previously. Two aircraft returned early from this operation and one other became caught up with the bomber stream narrowly missing collisions on a number of occasions. All *Mandrel* screen operations were now flown at the higher altitude.

July operations opened on the night of the 4/5th when the 803rd despatched five aircraft. The squadron operated on 14 nights during the month, despatching a total of 57 individual aircraft sorties. Two of these returned early, one aircraft having an engine fire on the 9/10th and the other suffering a failure in its *Gee* equipment on 14/15th.

On 4th of the month, Major R F Hambaugh * was appointed liaison officer between the squadron and 100 Group. Up until the 12th, the 803rd had been solely operational on the B-17 but on this date the first B-24 sortie was flown, the squadron having converted completely by 28th. It had long been felt that the B-17** was not the ideal vehicle for electronic warfare and it was decided to standardise on the B-24 early in June. The Liberator was regarded as being more suitable because of its greater fuselage capacity. The first such machine was received on 22 June and the squadron received a total of 12 aircraft as follows:

B-24J 250665 'R4-K' received 22 June
B-24J 251226 'L' received 22 June
B-24H 251219 'I' received 23 June
B-24J 251232 'J' received 23 June
B-24J 250622 'N' received 30 June
B-24H 250385 'H' received 4 July
B-24H 251188 'O' received 4 July
B-24H 129143 'B' received 16 July
B-24H 27607 'A' received 16 July
B-24J 250671 'F' received 30 July
B-24J 251239 'C' received 1 August
B-24J 251308 'M' received 29 August

These aircraft were heavily modified for the electronic warfare role. B-24s 'A', 'B', 'C', 'F', 'H', 'I', 'J', 'L', 'N' and 'O' had floors installed in their right

*This officer later went on to command the squadron.
**Known B-17 serials are:
114 (*Jackal* installation), 039 (four, later six *Mandrels* and nine *Carpets*), 066 (as 039), 177 (as 039), 178 (six *Mandrels*), 353 (as 178), 363 (as 178), 438 (as 178), 518 (ELINT installation) and 743 (six *Mandrels* and ELINT installation).

rear bomb bays to carry *Mandrel III* equipment. These jamming bays were also fitted out with overhead lighting, oxygen and suit-heating points for the special operators. Each conversion took 42 hrs to complete. In addition, eight aerials for the *Mandrels* were fitted, three under each wing and two in the tail.

Aircraft 'M' was fitted out for ELINT duties. A similar compartment to the *Mandrel* type was fitted in her rear bomb bay to house the search equipment and operators. Two oxygen and suit-heating points were fitted for their comfort, and illumination was provided by three lamps. Three additional oxygen bottles were added to the aircraft's normal capacity to cover the additional requirement of the special operators. The search compartment was also fitted with a repeater compass. At a later date, 'M' was further modified to act as a *Carpet* trainer. This equipment was installed immediately aft of the flight deck, displacing the aircraft's oxygen supply. The oxygen bottles were now mounted in the forward bomb bay. The crews' ditching belts were also moved to the waist, just aft of the ventral turret well. This latter modification was also carried out on aircraft 'A', 'C', 'N' and 'O'. Part of the bomb-bay lighting on all these aircraft was eventually transferred to the floor of the radio operator's compartment in order that the W/O could see to tune the newly installed liaison transmitters mounted there. Aircraft 'A' and 'B' also had their waist windows enclosed.

July also saw the squadron expanding its activities. On the night of 17/18th, American aircraft took part in their first 'spoof'. Similar sorties were flown on 18/19th and 25/26th. From the former date, spare squadron aircraft were utilised as *Window* droppers during such deceptive operations.

The first August mission was despatched on the night of 6/7th when four aircraft were deployed. One of these returned early and was replaced by a reserve. The most important event of the month came on 14th when the squadron was merged with the 856th to become the 36th Bombardment Squadron (H). The new unit moved out of Oulton and became operational at Cheddington on the same day. The 803rd/36th operated as part of the *Mandrel* screen on 16 nights during the month, sending out 68 individual aircraft sorties. Four aircraft returned early and B-24 251232 'J' was fired on by an unidentified twin-engined aircraft; the squadron's first taste of combat. In addition to the *Mandrel* operations, four ELINT sorties were flown by 251308. The *Mandrel* missions broke down into six in support of RAF raids on Germany, five in support of raids on France and one spoof.

September saw no let up in *Mandrel* activities, the squadron being active in this role on 18 nights of the month, despatching 87 individual aircraft sorties. All such operations were in support of RAF Bomber Command raids, except that of 12/13th which was a spoof. One aircraft left station early on the night of 18/19th (250385 'H') and aircraft were fired on by enemy Flak during the missions of 12/13th and 16/17th. B-24 250385 'H' was attacked by an unidentified aircraft on the night of 6/7th. *Creeping Mandrel*, (the movement of the screen towards the enemy coast rather than it remaining stationary over fixed points), begun in July, was now a firmly established operational technique.

While operations built up, training continued unabated. Emphasis was still laid on navigation and *Gee* training; correct station keeping being vital to the effectiveness of the *Mandrel* screen. Work was also done in instructing special operators in the use of *Carpet* and *Mandrel* and latterly *Monica* and *Jostle*.

In October, the 36th made its first sortie in support of the 8th Air Force when

seven aircraft put up a *Mandrel* screen to cover the return of the dayligh
bombers on the 10th. The other 12 missions carried out during the period wer
in support of the RAF (nine for Main Force raids and three spoofs). Some 7
individual aircraft sorties were despatched for this purpose, from whic
number there were three early returns. The mission on the night of 21/22n
was recalled due to a deterioration in the weather and that of 31/1st resulted ir
three of the seven aircraft deployed being fired on by enemy aircraft.

At the end of the month, the squadron was equipped as follows:

Aircraft fitted with jamming compartments – B-24s 129143 'B', 250671 'F'
251188 'O', 251232 'J', 251239 'C' and 251308 'M' (ELINT).
Aircraft fitted with eight *Mandrel IIIs* – B-24 'J' (three aerials under each win
and two in the tail).
Aircraft fitted with two *Mandrels* and four *Dinas* – B-24s 'O', 'J', 'L', 'H', 'I', 'B'
'C', 'K' and 'F' (one *Mandrel* aerial under each wing and two in the tail).

All the above aircraft had the compass, altimeter and airspeed indicator, nor
mally mounted in the bomb aimer's position, moved to that of the navigator
Other modifications as already specified.

November saw a fundamental change in the squadron's role. From the 25t
of the month, involvement with 100 Group activities was gradually phased ou
and operations in support of the 8th Air Force began to predominate. Thes
took the form of a *Mandrel* screen set up to mask the R/T transmissions emanat
ing from the 8th's aircraft as they assembled into battle formation before settin
out from the enemy's hinterland. The first daylight screen was set up on 25th o
the month by six aircraft. Thereafter, sorties of this nature were undertake
every day until the 30th. Prior to 25th, 12 *Mandrel* patrols were flown in suppor
of Bomber Command, comprising 78 individual aircraft sorties. After the 25t
such patrols were continued, an American contribution being made to th
screen on each of the remaining nights of the month. November was also nc
table in that the squadron suffered its first losses. On the night of 9/10th, B-2
251226 'L' crashed in France, another B-24 failing to return on the followin
night. A third aircraft, 251219 'I' crashed whilst taking-off on the operation c
the 15/16th. These losses resulted in the deaths of eight crew members. By th
end of November, additional VHF sets had been installed in aircraft 25038
250622, 251188 and 251308 to enhance the squadron's spoof capability.

December saw a continuation of operations in support of the 8th Air Forc
VHF R/T screens were flown on 23 out of the 31 days of the month. Limite
involvement with RAF operations continued but on a much reduced scale. Ai
craft from the 36th Squadron were present in only nine *Mandrel* screens durin
the period, contributing one or two aircraft to each operation.

The 8th Air Force screen missions took three forms during this month, a
follows:

(1) *Mandrel* screens to mask the R/T traffic of assembling formations on 2
     occasions.
(2) Spoof missions of three aircraft attempting to deceive the enemy int
     thinking that a second formation was assembling, whereas in reality ther
     were none on the 1st and the 8th.
(3) *Mandrel* R/T screens which travelled some of the way to the target wit
     the main formations on the 9th, 10th and 18th.

The first type of mission was normally flown by between four and eight aircraft. Take-off would be at about 0630 hrs with the jamming commencing at 0700 hrs. The screen would be slowly advanced to a designated point over the North Sea or Northern France which would be reached at about 1030 hrs. At this point, jamming would cease and the aircraft would return home. The third type mentioned was an extension of this first technique in which the jamming aircraft flew in the van of the main formation well into enemy airspace. Spoof missions comprised the generation of jamming associated with bomber assemblies and the transmission of pre-recorded R/T chatter. This latter part of the operation was closely monitored by ground stations to check whether it was convincing or not.

On the 28th of the month, a new dimension was added to the unit's repertoire under the code-name *Jackal*. B-24 aircraft 230 'E', 385 'H' and 665 'K' took up station over the army's front line and for four hours orbited transmitting jamming signals directed against the enemy's AFV net. Aircraft 622 'N' kept station with the formation and by means of an S27 search receiver monitored the effectiveness of the jamming. *Jackal* transmissions were stopped when conventional bomber forces were near due to their interference with the instrument bombing equipment of such aircraft.

The month ended on a sad note when aircraft 251232 'J' flew into a hill near Valley in North Wales on the 22nd, killing nine of her 11-man crew.

The opening month of 1945 saw the virtual cessation of operations with the RAF. A total of 24 operations were flown during January of which only two (those of the 1/2nd and 2/3rd) were in support of Bomber Command. Seven *Jackals* were completed and 133 individual aircraft sorties were despatched in total, seven of which returned early.

By the end of the month considerable changes in equipment had taken place. During the month 60 SCR 522 *Jackal* transmitters were received and installed in B-24 aircraft, 250665, 250476, 251230, 251685, 295221 and 401609. All these aircraft had had their ventral turrets removed and all but 295221 carried three *Carpet Is* in addition to the *Jackal* equipment; 250665, 251230, 251685 and 295221 had *Dina* installations as well. Three of the *Jackal* aircraft, 250476, 251685 and 295221, were fully fitted out with jamming compartments. Two aircraft, 251311 and 251315 were fitted out with *Jostle*. This device was being tested as an alternative to the SCR 522 equipment, to which it was deemed superior, but was never used operationally. In addition to the *Jostle*, each of these aircraft carried three *Carpet Is* and had had their ventral turrets removed.

Mandrel III equipment was removed from all the squadron's aircraft during this period to be replaced by an unspecified variant of the device in aircraft 250385, 250665, 250750, 250844, 251546 and 295221. Aircraft 250665 and 295221 have already been described, and this last installation made them the most powerful jamming aircraft in Europe. Aircraft 250385, 250750, and 250844 also carried *Dina* installations. Aircraft 251188, 251239, 251308 and 251576 carried a fit of ten *Dinas*, 251188 and 251308 also having had their ventral turrets removed. Two ELINT aircraft, 250622 and 250671 were also on hand. Aircraft 671 had no ventral turret and a *Dina* installation, whilst 622 was fitted with *Carpet* and a search compartment. Finally, aircraft 251239 and 250495 were in the process of being converted into jammers. Aircraft 495 had had a jamming compartment installed and her ventral turret removed, whilst 239 had only reached the stage of having the under turret removed.

The main event of February came on 27th, when the squadron moved to Alconbury, its final wartime base. Operationally, the squadron despatched 150 individual aircraft sorties on 24 screening patrols for the 8th Air Force. Two aircraft were lost during the period, 251239 failing to return on 5th and 250385 crashing during take-off on 19th.

The pattern remained much the same during March with the exception of a splitting of effort after the 16th between screening R/T transmissions and actually jamming the enemy's radar during bomber assembly period. Some 28 such operations were carried out during the period. In addition, aircraft 41507 flew on 14 days to monitor the effects of jamming transmissions.

Early in the month, a detachment of three ELINT Droop Snoot P-38 aircraft from the 7th Photographic Group (R) came under the squadron's control. These aircraft flew six missions during the period, monitoring enemy radar in Holland and along the front-line in Germany. During these operations, one of the P-38s was lost as was B-24 250844 which crashed on take-off on 20th. Previously, the P-38 detachment had been based at Foulsham, alongside 192(SD) Squadron, from which place it had been operating since August 1944. P-38 operations continued until 19 April, by which time a further two sorties had been flown, one to the Munich area and one to the Baltic. VHF screening sorties were flown on 18 days, usually by four aircraft and a single B-24 ELINT sortie was made.

As far as it is known, no sorties were flown during May before the German surrender on the 8th. By this time, the squadron had become part of the 482nd Bombardment Group and had returned to the USA by the end of the following month.

Although, the 803rd/36th Squadron provided the major American contribution to the bomber support campaign, three other 8th Air Force units became involved during 1944/45.

The first of these was the Intruder Detachment based at Little Snoring. The unit was formed sometime in March 1944 and comprised one P-38 and two P-51 aircraft under the command of Major T Gates. Earlier in the year, HQ 8th Air Force expressed its willingness to allow some of its escort fighter force to be used to supplement to work of the intruder element of 100 Group. Air Commodore R Chisholm acted as the Group's Liaison officer and it was arranged to form a small unit for training and trials after which further allocations could be made.

The Detachment became operational on the night of 24/25 March when Major Gates took one of the P-51s to Berlin and back. Nine more sorties were made before the end of the month. Working closely with 515(SD) Squadron, a further 21 sorties were despatched during April, ten of which were completed. By the end of the month, it had become obvious that the American single-seat fighters were unsuitable for night intruder work and the Detachment was duly disbanded. Plans for large-scale USAAF help in this direction were shelved as a result.

In February 1945, the 8th Air Force once more came to the aid of 100 Group, this time in the form of 857th and 858th Bombardment Squadrons (H). These two squadrons, part of the 492nd Bombardment Group (H), began bombing operations as part of the *Special Window Force* during the month. By the following month (at the end of which the 857th was disbanded) the American unit dropping 240 tons of explosive out of a monthly total of 320 tons. The 858th con tinued such operations during April (358 tons of bombs dropped overall by the force), but was not involved in the final mission of the war on the night of 2/3 May.

Thus ended the American contribution which had been characterised by a constant willingness to help which is warmly remembered by the Group's personnel. The importance of the 803rd/36th Squadron's efforts between June and November 1944 cannot be overstressed. The *Mandrel* screen was regarded by 100 Group as one of its most effective measures and during the period in question, the American unit shared the operational burden equally, with the Group's *Mandrel* Squadron, No 199. The equality of effort was continued until the RAF's second *Mandrel* Squadron, No 171, was able to take over in October/November 1944.

Again, in the early spring of 1945, when the Group was in need of more aircraft to enhance the effect of the Special *Window* Force's operations, the 8th Air Force supplied machines which Bomber Command could not. Finally, American industrial might and technological expertise came to the aid of the campaign by providing much needed jamming equipment, such as American *Mandrel*, *Carpet III*, *Dina II* and *Piperack*, which was of the greatest help to the over-stretched British electronics industry.

Perhaps the only disservice the American RCM effort did for 100 Group came when the 36th Squadron began to operate a daylight *Mandrel* screen in support of 8th Air Force bomber assemblies. It is most probable that this constant use of the *Mandrel* screen contributed materially to the enemy's ability to operate his fighter control system effectively in the face of it, simply by giving him added practice in doing so. That the *Mandrel* screen became less effective as time went on is without doubt; the post-war trials code-named *Post Mortem* proved this conclusively (see Chapter 5).

The following table details the activities of the 803rd/36th Squadron on a day by day basis between, May 1944 to March 1945. The letters BC indicates RAF Bomber Command. Mention of a *Window* force and/or an OTU (Operational Training Unit) feint does not indicate a spoof operation unless the entry specifies the mission as such. Such additional activities were a normal part of masking the bomber's approach route.

Month	Day	Night	Number of aircraft Despatched	Remarks
May 44	27		One	B-17 '743' used to plot the polar diagram of the radar station at Bawdsey.
June 44	3		One	B-17 '518' used to gauge the field strengths from the Bawdsey and Sizwell stations over enemy territory (Brussels)
		5/6	Four (B-17)	First operational *Mandrel* sortie. In support of the D-Day landings.
		16/17	Six (B-17)	*Mandrel* in support of BC. Sixteen aircraft from 199(SD) Squadron.

Month	Day	Night	Number of aircraft Despatched	Remarks
		17/18	Five (B-17)	*Mandrel* in support of BC. Six aircraft from 199(SD) Squadron.
		22/23	Five (B-17)	*Mandrel* in support of BC. Ten aircraft from 199(SD) Squadron. One B-17 returned early. Feint by BC OTU aircraft.
		27/28	Five (B-17)	*Mandrel* in support of BC. Flown at 19,000 ft (5,791 m) instead of 15,000 (4,572 m) as previously. Two B-17 returned early.
		28/29	Five (B-17)	*Mandrel* in support of BC.
July 44		4/5	Five (B-17)	*Mandrel* in support of BC. Fourteen aircraft from 199(SD) Squadron. Twelve jamming centres. Feint by BC OTU aircraft.
		7/8	Five (B-17)	*Mandrel* in support of BC. Fourteen aircraft from 199(SD) Squadron.
		9/10	Five (B-17)	*Mandrel* in support of BC. Fourteen aircraft from 199(SD) Squadron. One B-17 returned early with an engine fire.
		12/13	Five (B-17/B-24)	*Mandrel* in support of BC. First B-24 sortie. Twelve 199(SD) Squadron aircraft.
		14/15	Five (B-17/B-24)	*Mandrel* in support of BC. Twelve aircraft from 199(SD) Squadron. One US aircraft suffered a *Gee* failure. *Window* force from 199/214(SD) Squadrons. Feint by BC OTU aircraft.
		17/18	Five (B-17/B-24)	*Creeping Mandrel* in support of BC. Thirteen aircraft from 199(SD) Squadron. *Window* force of fourteen 100 Group aircraft. Feint by 100 BC OTU aircraft.
		18/19	Four (B-17/B-24)	*Creeping Mandrel* in support of BC. Sixteen aircraft from 199(SD) Squadron. *Window* force and BC OTU feint.
		20/21	Four (B-17/B-24)	*Mandrel* in support of BC. Fourteen aircraft from 199(SD) Squadron. *Window* force.
		21/22	Three (B-17/B-24)	*Mandrel* in support of BC. Eight aircraft from 199(SD) Squadron.

Month	Day	Night	Number of aircraft Despatched	Remarks
				Window force of twelve 100 Group aircraft.
		23/24	Five (B-17/B-24)	*Mandrel* in support of BC. Twelve aircraft from 199 and 214(SD) Squadrons. *Window* force and BC OTU feint.
		24/25	Three (B-17/B-24)	*Mandrel* in support of BC. Eight aircraft from 199(SD) Squadron. *Window* force of twelve 100 Group aircraft and BC OTU feint.
		25/26	Three (B-17/B-24)	*Creeping Mandrel* in support of BC. Fifteen aircraft from 199(SD) Squadron. *Window* force of seven 100 Group aircraft.
		28/29	Three (B-24)	*Mandrel* in support of BC. Fourteen aircraft from 199(SD) Squadron. *Window* force of nine 100 Group aircraft.
		29/30	Three (B-24)	*Mandrel* in support of BC.
August 44		6/7	Four (B-24)	*Mandrel* in support of BC. One aircraft returned early and was replaced by a reserve. All aircraft landed away from base.
		7/8	Five (B-24)	*Mandrel* in support of BC. One aircraft returned early. All aircraft landed away from base. The operations of 6/7 and 7/8 were supported by *Ground Mandrel* at Hastings and Dover.
		8/9	Four (B-24)	*Mandrel* in support of BC. One aircraft returned early and was replaced by a reserve.
		9/10	Four (B-24)	*Mandrel* in support of BC.
		10/11	Four (B-24)	*Mandrel* in support of BC.
		11/12	Four (B-24)	*Mandrel* in support of BC.
		12/13	Five (B-24)	*Mandrel* in support of BC. One aircraft returned early after a *Gee* failure.
		13/14	Three (B-24)	*Mandrel* in support of BC.
		16/17	Four (B-24)	*Mandrel* in support of BC.
		17/18	Two (B-24)	*Mandrel* in support of BC.
		18/19	Six (B-24)	*Mandrel* in support of BC.
		25/26	Six (B-24)	*Mandrel* in support of BC. All aircraft recalled early.
		26/27	Seven (B-24)	*Mandrel* in support of BC.

Month	Day	Night	Number of aircraft Despatched	Remarks
		27/28	Six (B-24)	*Mandrel* in support of BC.
		29/30	Four (B-24)	*Mandrel* in support of BC. Aircraft 251232 'J' was fired on by an unidentified twin-engined aircraft.
		30/31	Six (B-24)	*Mandrel* in support of BC.

In addition to the above, four ELINT missions were flown by the Squadron during the month.

Month	Day	Night	Number of aircraft Despatched	Remarks
September 44		1/2	Four (B-24)	*Mandrel* in support of BC. Six aircraft from 199(SD) Squadron.
		5/6	Four (B-24)	*Mandrel* in support of BC. Six aircraft from 199(SD) Squadron.
		6/7	Four (B-24)	*Mandrel* in support of BC. Six aircraft from 199(SD) Squadron. Aircraft 250385 'H' was fired on by an unidentified aircraft. In support of a *Window* spoof.
		8/9	Four (B-24)	*Mandrel* in support of BC. Eight aircraft from 199(SD) Squadron.
		9/10	Four (B-24)	*Mandrel* in support of BC. Ten aircraft from 199(SD) Squadron.
		10/11	Three (B-24)	*Mandrel* in support of BC
		11/12	Five (B-24)	*Mandrel* in support of BC.
		12/13	Six (B-24)	*Creeping Mandrel* in support of BC. Five of the aircraft were fired on by Flak. In support of a *Window* spoof.
		13/14	Six (B-24)	*Mandrel* in support of BC.
		15/16	Seven (B-24)	*Creeping Mandrel* in support of BC.
		16/17	Five (B-24)	*Creeping Mandrel* in support of BC. Screen set up twice. One aircraft fired on by Flak.
		17/18	Six (B-24)	*Mandrel* in support of BC.
		18/19	Seven (B-24)	*Creeping Mandrel* in support of BC. Aircraft 250835 'H' returned early. *Window* force.
		22/23	Four (B-24)	*Creeping Mandrel* in support of BC. Spoof operation.
		23/24	Six (B-24)	*Mandrel* in support of BC. Screen operated in two parts.
		25/26	Three (B-24)	*Mandrel* in support of BC.
		26/27	Four (B-24)	*Mandrel* in support of BC.
		28/29	Five (B-24)	*Mandrel* in support of BC.

Month	Day	Night	Number of aircraft Despatched	Remarks
October 44		5/6	Five (B-24)	*Creeping Mandrel* in support of BC.
		6/7	Seven (B-24)	*Mandrel* in support of BC.
		7/8	Six (B-24)	*Mandrel* in support of BC. Special *Window* Force operation.
	10		Seven (B-24)	In support of an 8th AF operation. One aircraft returned early.
		14/15	Seven (B-24)	*Mandrel* in support of BC.
		15/16	Six (B-24)	*Mandrel* in support of BC.
		19/20	Seven (B-24)	*Mandrel* in support of BC. This operation was regarded as being extremely successful.
		21/22	Eight (B-24)	*Mandrel* in support of BC. One aircraft returned early and the others were recalled.
		23/24	Six (B-24)	*Mandrel* in support of BC. One aircraft returned early.
		24/25	Six (B-24)	*Mandrel* in support of BC.
		26/27	Six (B-24)	*Mandrel* in support of BC. One aircraft returned early.
		30/31	Seven (B-24)	*Mandrel* in support of BC.
		31/1	Seven (B-24)	*Mandrel* in support of BC. The screen was operated twice. Three aircraft were fired on by unidentified aircraft.
November 44		1/2	Seven (B-24)	*Mandrel* in support of BC.
		2/3	Seven (B-24)	*Mandrel* in support of BC.
		4/5	Six (B-24)	*Mandrel* in support of BC. The screen was operated twice.
		6/7	Eight (b-24)	*Mandrel* in support of BC. All aircraft recalled.
		9/10	Seven (B-24)	*Mandrel* in support of BC. Aircraft 251226 'L' crashed in France.
		11/12	Seven (B-24)	*Mandrel* in support of BC. Northern and Southern screens. Northern – two 36 and two 199 aircraft. Southern – five 36 and six 199 aircraft.
	12		One (B-24)	Test flight of SCS 51 (precision bombing through overcast equipment) at 25,000 ft (7,620 m).
		15/16	Five (B-24)	*Mandrel* in support of BC. Aircraft 251219 'I' crashed on take off.
	18		One (B-24)	*Mandrel* and *Dina* jamming test against VHF communications in connection with 8th AF operations.

Month	Day	Night	Number of aircraft Despatched	Remarks
		18/19	Five (B-24)	*Mandrel* in support of BC.
		20/21	Five (B-24)	*Mandrel* in support of BC.
		21/22	Six (B-24)	*Mandrel* in support of BC.
		23/24	Six (B-24)	*Mandrel* in support of BC. One aircraft returned early.
	25		Six (B-24)	VHF screen in support of 8th AF.
		25/26	Three (B-24)	*mandrel* in support of BC.
	26		Six (B-24)	VHF screen in support of 8th AF.
		26/27	Three (B-24)	*Mandrel* in support of BC.
	27		Five (B-24)	VHF screen in support of 8th AF.
		27/28	Three (B-24)	*Mandrel* in support of BC.
	28		Eight (B-24)	VHF screen in support of 8th AF. Three of these aircraft acted as a spoof.
		28/29	Two (B-24)	*Mandrel* in support of BC.
	29		Seven (B-24)	VHF screen in support of 8th AF. One aircraft returned early.
		29/30	Two (B-24)	*Mandrel* in support of BC.
	30		Six (B-24)	VHF screen in support of 8th AF.
		30/31	Two (B-24)	*Mandrel* in support of BC.
December 44	1		Seven (B-24)	VHF screen in support of 8th AF. Three of these aircraft acted as a spoof.
		1/2	One (B-24)	*Mandrel* in support of BC.
	2		Six (B-24)	VHF screen in support of 8th AF.
		2/3	Two (B-24)	*Mandrel* in support of BC.
	3		Seven (B-24)	VHF screen in support of 8th AF.
	4		Eight (B-24)	VHF screen in support of 8th AF.
		4/5	Two (B-24)	*Mandrel* in support of BC.
	5		Nine (B-24)	VHF screen in support of 8th AF. One aircraft returned early.
	6		Eight (B-24)	VHF screen in support of 8th AF.
		6/7	Two (B-24)	*Mandrel* in support of BC.
	7		Eight (B-24)	VHF screen in support of 8th AF.
	8		Ten (B-24)	VHF screen in support of 8th AF. Three of these aircraft acted as a spoof and another one (from the screen) returned early.
	9		Ten (B-24)	VHF screen in support of 8th AF. On this occasion the screen moved with the bombers.
		9/10	One (B-24)	*Mandrel* in support of BC.
	10		Eight (B-24)	VHF Screen in support of 8th AF. On this occasion the screen moved with the bombers. One aircraft returned early.

Month	Day	Night	Number of aircraft Despatched	Remarks
	11		Nine (B-24)	VHF screen in support of 8th AF.
	12		Eight (B-24)	VHF screen in support of 8th AF. One aircraft returned early.
		12/13	One (B-24)	*Mandrel* in support of BC.
	13		Three (B-24)	VHF screen in support of 8th AF.
	15		Six (B-24)	VHF screen in support of 8th AF. One aircraft returned early.
	16		Five (B-24)	VHF screen in support of 8th AF.
		17/18	One (B-24)	*Mandrel* in support of BC.
	18		Nine (B-24)	VHF screen in support of 8th AF. On this occasion the screen moved with the bombers. One aircraft returned early.
		18/19	One (B-24)	*Mandrel* in support of BC.
	19		Eight (B-24)	VHF screen in support of 8th AF.
	23		Two (B-24)	VHF screen in support of 8th AF.
	24		Five (B-24)	VHF screen in support of 8th AF.
	25		Eight (B-24)	VHF screen in support of 8th AF.
	28		Ten (B-24)	Six aircraft provided VHF screen in support of 8th AF, one of which returned early. Three aircraft flew the first *Jackal* sortie. One ELINT aircraft with the *Jackal* force.
	30		Five (B-24)	VHF screen in support of 8th AF.
		30/31	One (B-24)	*Mandrel* in support of BC.
	31		Seven (B-24)	Five aircraft provided VHF screen in support of 8th AF, one of which returned early. Two aircraft flew a *Jackal* sortie.
January 45	1		Seven (B-24)	VHF screen in support of 8th AF.
		1/2	One (B-24)	*Mandrel* in support of BC.
	2		Seven (B-24)	Four aircraft provided VHF screen for 8th AF. Three aircraft flew a *Jackal* sortie.
		2/3	One (B-24)	*Mandrel* in support of BC.
	3		Four (B-24)	VHF screen in support of 8th AF.
	5		Ten (B-24)	Eight aircraft provided VHF screen in support of 8th AF, three of which returned early. Two aircraft flew a *Jackal* sortie.
	6		Five (B-24)	VHF screen in support of 8th AF.
	7		Seven (B-24)	Five aircraft provided VHF screen in support of 8th AF, one of which returned early. Two aircraft flew a *Jackal* sortie.

Month	Day	Night	Number of aircraft Despatched	Remarks
	8		Six (B-24)	VHF screen in support of 8th AF. One aircraft returned early.
	9		Five (B-24)	VHF screen in support of 8th AF.
	10		Four (B-24)	VHF screen in support of 8th AF.
	13		Six (B-24)	VHF screen in support of 8th AF.
	15		Six (B-24)	VHF screen in support of 8th AF.
	16		Five (B-24)	VHF screen in support of 8th AF.
	17		Seven (B-24)	VHF screen in support of 8th AF.
	18		Seven (B-24)	VHF screen in support of 8th AF.
	20		Eight (B-24)	VHF screen in support of 8th AF.
	21		Six (B-24)	VHF screen in support of 8th AF. One aircraft returned early.
	23		Five (B-24)	VHF screen in support of 8th AF.
	24		Six (B-24)	VHF screen in support of 8th AF. One aircraft returned early.
	26		Three (B-24)	VHF screen in support of 8th AF.
	28		Five (B-24)	VHF screen in support of 8th AF. One aircraft returned early.
	29		Five (B-24)	VHF screen in support of 8th AF.
	31		Seven (B-24)	VHF screen in support of 8th AF.
February 45	1		Seven (B-24)	VHF screen in support of 8th AF.
	2		Six (B-24)	VHF screen in support of 8th AF.
	3		Seven (B-24)	VHF screen in support of 8th AF.
	5		Nine (B-24)	VHF screen in support of 8th AF. One aircraft, 251239, FTR.
	6		Eight (B-24)	VHF screen in support of 8th AF.
	7		Six (B-24)	VHF screen in support of 8th AF.
	8		Six (B-24)	VHF screen in support of 8th AF.
	9		Six (B-24)	VHF screen in support of 8th AF.
	10		Six (B-24)	VHF screen in support of 8th AF.
	11		Six (B-24)	VHF screen in support of 8th AF.
	14		Seven (B-24)	VHF screen in support of 8th AF.
	15		Seven (B-24)	VHF screen in support of 8th AF.
	16		Seven (B-24)	VHF screen in support of 8th AF.
	17		Six (B-24)	VHF screen in support of 8th AF.
	19		Two (B-24)	VHF screen in support of 8th AF. Aircraft 250385 crashed on take-off.
	20		Seven (B-24)	VHF screen in support of 8th AF.
	21		Seven (B-24)	VHF screen in support of 8th AF.
	22		Seven (B-24)	VHF screen in support of 8th AF.
	23		Seven (B-24)	VHF screen in support of 8th AF.
	24		Seven (B-24)	VHF screen in support of 8th AF.
	25		Seven (B-24)	VHF screen in support of 8th AF.
	26		Six (B-24)	VHF screen in support of 8th AF.
	27		Six (B-24)	VHF screen in support of 8th AF.

Month	Day	Night	Number of aircraft Despatched	Remarks
	28		Six (B-24)	VHF screen in support of 8th AF. One aircraft returned early.
March 45	1		Six (B-24)	VHF screen in support of 8th AF.
	2		Five (B-24)	VHF screen in support of 8th AF.
	3		Four (B-24)	VHF screen in support of 8th AF. One aircraft returned early.
	5		Two (B-24)	VHF screen in support of 8th AF.
	6		Two (B-24)	VHF screen in support of 8th AF.
	7		Five (B-24)	Four aircraft provided VHF screen in support of 8th AF. One aircraft 410507 flew an ELINT sortie.
	8		Five (B-24)	Four aircraft provided VHF screen in support of 8th AF. 410507 flew an ELINT sortie.
	9		Four (B-24)	VHF screen in support of 8th AF.
	10		Five (B-24)	Four aircraft provided VHF screen in support of 8th AF. 410507 flew an ELINT sortie.
	11		Five (B-24)	Four aircraft provided VHF screen in support of 8th AF. 410507 flew an ELINT sortie.
	12		Five (B-24)	Four aircraft provided VHF screen in support of 8th AF. 410507 flew an ELINT sortie.
	14		Five (B-24)	VHF screen in support of 8th AF. One aircraft returned early.
	15		Five (B-24)	VHF screen in support of 8th AF. One aircraft returned early.
	16		Thirteen (B-24)	Three aircraft provided VHF screen in support of 8th AF. Nine aricraft provided radar screen in support of 8th AF. 410507 flew an ELINT sortie.
	17		Fourteen (B-24) One (P-38)	Three aircraft provided VHF screen in support of 8th AF. Nine aircraft provided radar screen in support of 8th AF. 410507 flew an ELINT sortie as did the P-38.
	18		Thirteen (B-24)	Three aircraft provided VHF screen in support of 8th AF, one of which returned early. Nine aircraft provided radar screen in support of 8th AF. 410507 flew an ELINT sortie.
	19		Fourteen (B-24) One (P-38)	Four aircraft provided VHF screen in support of 8th AF, one of which

Month	Day	Night	Number of aircraft Despatched	Remarks
				returned early. Nine aircraft provid radar screen in support of 8th AF. 410507 flew an ELINT sortie as did the P-38.
	20		Eleven (B-24)	Three aircraft provided VHF screer in support of 8th AF. Aircraft 25084 crashd on take-off. Eight aircraft provided radar screen in support of 8th AF.
	21		Eleven (B-24)	Three aircraft provided VHF screer in support of 8th AF. Seven aircraft provided radar screen in support of 8th AF. 410507 flew an ELINT sortie.
	22		Four (B-24)	Three aircraft provided VHF screer in support of 8th AF. 410507 flew ar ELINT sortie.
	23		Eleven (B-24) One (P-38)	Three aircraft provided VHF screer in support of 8th AF. Seven aircraft provided radar screen in support of 8th AF. 410507 flew an ELINT sortie as did the P-38.
	24AM		Nine (B-24)	Three aircraft provided VHF screer in support of 8th AF. Six aircraft provided radar screen in support of 8th AF.
	24PM		Three (B-24)	VHF screen in support of 8th AF.
	25		Three (B-24) Two (P-38)	Three aircraft provided VHF screer in support of 8th AF. The two P-38s flew ELINT sorties.
	26		Four (B-24) One (P-38)	Three aircraft provided VHF screer in support of 8th AF. 410507 flew ar ELINT sortie as did the P-38.
	27		Thirteen (B-24) One (P-38)	Three aircraft provided VHF screer in support of 8th AF. Nine aircraft provided radar screen in support of 8th AF. 410507 flew an ELINT sortie as did the P-38.
	30		Thirteen (B-24)	Three aircraft provided VHF scree in support of 8th AF. Nine aircraft provided radar screen in support of the 8th AF. 410507 flew an ELINT sortie.
	31		Three (B-24)	VHF screen in support of 8th AF.

April and May 1945: No precise figures are available for these two months.

Chapter 5

Overkill:
December 1944 to May 1945

December 1944 was dominated by the weather, which severely limited the Group's activities during the month. The fighter squadrons were further hampered by their large-scale re-equipment programme. Of the three *Serrate* units, only 169 Squadron could be considered truly operational; 141 Squadron completing its conversion to AI Mk XV and 239 Squadron commencing its re-equipment with the AI Mk X-carrying Mosquito 30 aircraft. The two latter units managed to despatch a few sorties before the end of the month, 141 Squadron flying its first AI Mk XV operation on 21/22nd, but the main burden fell on 169 with its AI Mk IV/*Perfectos* combination.

The two intruder units, 23 and 515 Squadrons, were also busily engaged in converting to and training with AI Mk XV which, combined with the weather, contrived to reduce greatly their operations during the month. Thus it was left mainly to the AI Mk X squadrons, Nos 85 and 157, to harry the enemy, which they did most successfully, claiming a total of 35 enemy aircraft destroyed between the 1st and the 31st. Statistics for the seven squadrons' operations during December are as follows:

AI Mk IV/*Serrate* (141 and 239 Squadrons):
Serrate contacts   65

AI Mk IV/*Perfectos* (169 Squadron):
Perfectos contacts   51
Perfectos contacts converted to AI   30
These three squadrons despatched a total of 116 such sorties which resulted in no claims being reported.

AI Mk X/*Monica* (85 and 157 squadrons):
Sorties despatched   280
Sorties completed   239
Aircraft lost   1
Claims   35 destroyed; 2 probably destroyed;
                                                 3 damaged

AI contacts   95
Monica contacts   15
Monica contacts converted to AI   6
In addition to these high-level patrols, the squadrons despatched four low level sorties.
Intruders (23 and 515 Squadrons):
Sorties despatched   128
Sorties completed   112
Aircraft lost   1
Claims   3 destroyed (2 air, 1 ground); 3
                                                 damaged (ground)

Twenty-seven of these sorties were flown by AI Mk XV equipped aircraft which resulted in five contacts and one claim (31st/1st).

Known details of the claims for December are as follows:

2/3rd – Aircraft 'A' of 85 Squadron, one Bf110
2/3rd – Aircraft MM671 'C' of 157 Squadron, one Ju88
4/5th – Aircraft MM671 'C' of 157 Squadron, one Ju88
4/5th – Aircraft 'C' of 85 Squadron, two Bf110s

4/5th – Aircraft 'B' of 85 Squadron, one Bf110
4/5th – Aircraft 'D' of 85 Squadron, one Ju88
6/7th – Aircraft 'O' of 85 Squadron, one Bf110
6/7th – Aircraft MM671 'C' of 157 Squadron, one Bf110 and one Ju88
12/13th – Aircraft 'A' of 85 Squadron, one Ju88
12/13th – Aircraft 'O' of 85 Squadron, two Bf110s
12/13th – Aircraft 'Z' of 85 Squadron, one unidentified enemy aircraft
17/18th – Aircraft MM627 'H' of 157 Squadron, one Bf110
17/18th – Aircraft MM653 'L' of 157 Squadron, one Bf110
18/19th – Aircraft MM640 'I' of 157 Squadron, one He219
21/22nd – Aircraft TA401 'D' of 157 Squadron, one Ju88
22/23rd – Aircraft 'B' of 85 Squadron, two Ju88s and one Bf110
22/23rd – Aircraft 'P' of 85 Squadron, one Bf110
22/23rd – Aircraft TA404 'M' of 157 Squadron, one Ju88
23/24th – Aircraft TA404 'M' of 157 Squadron, one Ju88 near Koblenz
23/24th – Aircraft 'N' of 85 Squadron, one Bf110
24/25th – Aircraft MM671 'C' of 157 Squadron, one Ju88
24/25th – Aircraft TA404 'M' of 157 Squadron, two Bf110s
24/25th – Aircraft MM676 'W' of 157 Squadron, one Bf110
24/25th – Aircraft 'A' of 85 Squadron, one Bf110
31/1st – Aircraft RS518 of 515 Squadron, one Ju88
31/1st – Aircraft 'E' of 85 Squadron, one Ju188
31/1st – Aircraft 'R' of 85 Squadron, one Ju88 and one Ju188
31/1st – Aircraft RS507 of 23 Squadron, one Ju88. (This was the Group's fir
AI Mk XV victory.)

A feature of the month's fighter operations was the introduction of the Clo
Patrol in late November/early December. This technique came about throu
the success of AI Mk X patrols around Main Force targets and consisted
each fighter being given a position around the target at a distance of six to t
miles (10 to 16 km) from it. Each aircraft then patrolled in towards and o
from the target along this track during and after the raid. In addition, it w
now decided to utilise 23 and 515 Squadrons, when they had completed conve
sion to the AI Mk XV set, in the high-level role when the weather was too ba
for intruder work in order to gain the maximum use from them.

The Group's heavy jamming squadrons received welcome reinforcement
the end of December when 462 (RAAF) Squadron moved into Foulsham on t
29th for *Window* and *ABC* duties. This unit was the last to join 100 Group befc
the end of hostilities. Its move from 4 Group initially caused problems in that
took some time to convince the Australian air crew that their new role w
worthwhile, the majority of them feeling that they had not come thousands
miles from their homeland to drop pieces of tin foil all over Germany, rath
than bombs.

For the operational heavy squadrons, December had been a busy mont
The *Mandrel* screen had been used on 18 nights during the month and had er
ployed 219 individual sorties. No 171 Squadron contributed 64 of these, 199, 1
and the 36th Squadrons contributing nine. The SWF was also operational
18 occasions during the month. All the heavy squadrons, with the exception
No 462, contributed aircraft to the force as follows: 171 – 47 sorties, 192 –

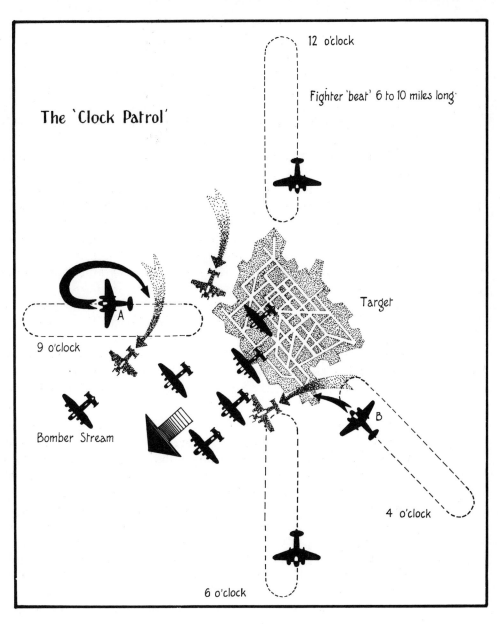

The 'Clock Patrol'

12 o'clock

Fighter 'beat' 6 to 10 miles long

Target

9 o'clock

Bomber Stream

B

4 o'clock

6 o'clock

The Clock Patrol. *Aircraft A is about to commence the* Whiting *manoeuvre while B is entering the classic AI stern chase.*

sorties, 199 – 5 sorties, 214 – 85 sorties and 223 – 71 sorties.

The spoofs undertaken on the 5/6th, 12/13th and the 23/24th were considered to be most successful and overall 160 tons (128 tonnes) of *Window* were dropped by the force. Again, the fighter element was active with the SWF and 41 sorties were despatched during which bombs were dropped on *Gee* indications. Two examples of this type of operation occurred on the 15/16th and the 17/18th. On the first occasion, five aircraft of 239 Squadron bombed Giessen. Aircraft HR 203 marked the target with yellow indicators for the others, who discharged eight 500 lb (227 kg) bombs. HR 203 itself contributed one 250 lb (113 kg) and one 500 lb (227 kg) bombs as an addition to this total. On the second occasion, the same squadron despatched four aircraft to bomb

Mannheim. PZ179 flown by Flying Officer Smith marked the target wit ground and sky indicators for the other three who dropped 250 lb (113 kg) an 500 lb (227 kg) bombs.

No 192 Squadron despatched 128 sorties during December. Two of the unit Mosquitos had been fitted with the *Dina* and *Piperack* (see pages 157 and 16C jammers and a number of these sorties were jamming operations in connectio with Main Force raids. Eventually, all the squadron's Mosquitos were to b fitted with these devices. The majority of the unit's work however was sti ELINT sorties. Enemy AI, *Würzburg* and *Jagdschloss* transmissions wer investigated, as was the possible use of pulse communication.he search fo navaids for the He111/V-1 combinations was continued and tests were carrie out with a TRE 3 cm homing device against H2S Mk III transmissions.

The two *Jostle* squadrons, Nos 214 and 223, despatched a total of 204 sorti during the month. No 214 contributed 122 to this total, made up of 85 oper; tions with the SWF and 37 in support of Main Force, and 223 Squadron co tribuh2, made up of 71 operations with the SWF and 11 in support of Ma Force. The two squadrons were now operating *Carpet*, *Jostle* and *Pipera* jamming equipment. The installation of *Dina* and *Piperack* jammers in the ai craft of 214 Squadron is a somewhat confused story. The two devices were bo American products developed from the *Mandrel* family. *Dina* carried tl American designation AN/APT 1 and was designed to affect enemy radars the 95–210 MHz band. Some sets of this type were modified to cover the 69 93 MHz range used by the SN-2 AI set. In this guise AN/APT 1 was known *Piperack*.

As had been stated, 214 Squadron's B-17s were at one time fitted with tl *Airborne Grocer* device. This was removed because of its vulnerability to bein homed on to. Although the internal equipment associated with this device wa removed, there is photographic evidence to suggest that its four Yagi aeria were not. Further, there is some evidence that these aerials were employed the later *Piperack* installation. This is a doubtful proposition in that the offici records* specifically state that *Piperack* used wing-mounted whip aerials, description which is backed up by photographic evidence of one of the unit B-17s so equipped. Further, *Piperack* was used to give overall jamming cover Main Force aircraft, a role for which the highly directional properties of a Ya aerial would be most unsuitable. In view of this there would seem to be only or use to which these aerials could have been put, that is for the *Dina* installatio This solution benefits from the fact that the set's aerials did give trouble and may be that the Yagis were used as an interim array while the problems with tl true aerial array were worked out. It must be stressed that these observatio are conjectural, no hard evidence being available. The author would be mo grateful to hear from anybody who can shed further light on this intriguir little mystery.

January 1945 saw no let-up in the programme of re-equipment for tl Group's fighter squadrons. Nos 169 and 239 were now in the throes of conver ing to AI Mk X, No 169 receiving its first Mosquito XIX so equipped on tl 14th and despatched its first sortie with this combination on the 21/22n No 239 Squadron received Mosquito 30 aircraft during the period upc

*Public Records reference AIR 20/1492.

which it became operational at the end of the month. During the re-equipment, both squadrons managed to despatch a number of high-level patrols with AI Mk IV-carrying aircraft.

No 141 Squadron continued its conversion to AI Mk XV and despatched an increasing number of high-level patrols with the device during the month while Nos 23 and 515 Squadrons were almost completely re-equipped with this radar and used it exclusively in low-level work throughout January. A further programme was initiated at about this time to fit *Monica IV* to the aircraft of these three squadrons but in the event it appears that only 141 Squadron used it operationally.

January also saw the start of the wide scale use of *Perfectos* and *Serrate IV*. It had proved very difficult to convert *Perfectos* contacts into AI Mk IV ones so it was decided to cease such operations. Again, 169 Squadron's *Perfectos Is* had proved to be inadequate in direction finding. This had been overcome in the Mk II model which entered service with 85 Squadron in November and 169 in January. A further sub-type of the device, the IB, was also being fitted to AI Mk XV aircraft, entering service in December 1944. No 157 Squadron was being fitted out with the *Serrate IV* homer (see page 167) during January and was operational with the device by the end of the month, although no such contacts were reported and in fact no victories were attributed to the device before the end of the war except two claimed by a BSDU aircraft during a sortie on 13/14 February.

The new year saw further changes in fighter tactics. During January and February there was a marked increase in enemy fighter activity and the AI Mk X squadrons resumed route escort for the bombers. This was successful as long as the aircraft so equipped remained above the stream where interference from H2S and *Window* were at a minimum. The intruder squadrons now divided their time between high- and low-level patrols, (the Group now describing all its fighter activities by these two categories). The lack of low-level contacts led these squadrons into a concentrated attack on enemy airfields during this period. The particular airfield would be illuminated with flares and attacked with HE and incendiary bombs.

The operational statistics for these seven squadrons during January are as follows:

AI Mk X – High level (85, 157, 169 and 239 Squadrons):

Sorties despatched	177
Sorties completed	154
Aircraft missing	0
Claims	11 destroyed; 3 damaged (2 air/1 ground)
AI Mk X contacts	44
Monica contacts	9

AI Mk XV – High level (141 Squadron):

Sorties despatched	84
Sorties completed	74
Aircraft missing	0
Claims	3 destroyed; 1 damaged
AI Mk XV contacts	13
Monica contacts	18 (approximately)
Monica contacts converted to AI	1

AI Mk XV – Low level (23 and 515 Squadrons)
Sorties despatched   78
Sorties completed   72
Aircraft missing   2
Claims   3 destroyed (2 air, 1 ground)

AI Mk XV contacts   6
AI Mk IV – High level (169 and 239 Squadrons)
Sorties despatched   40
Sorties completed   34
Aircraft missing   1
Claims   0
AI Mk IV/Non radar – Low level
Sorties despatched   47
Sorties completed   43
Claims   1 destroyed (ground)

In addition, two daylight escort sorties were despatched resulting in one Fw19
being claimed as damaged.

Known details of these claims are as follows:

1/2nd – Aircraft TA393 'C' of 157 Squadron, one Ju88
2/3rd – Aircraft 'X' of 85 Squadron, one Ju88
2/3rd – Aircraft 'N' of 85 Squadron, one Ju188
5/6th – Aircraft 'B' of 85 Squadron, one Ju88
5/6th – Aircraft TA394 'A' of 157 Squadron, one He219
14/15th – Aircraft HR294 'T' of 141 Squadron, one unidentified enemy aircra
15/16th – Aircraft MM653 'L' of 157 Squadron, one Bf110
16/17th – Aircraft 'R' of 85 Squadron, one He219
16/17th – Aircraft HR200 'E' of 141 Squadron, one Bf110
16/17th – Aircraft HR213 'G' of 141 Squadron, one Bf110
17/18th – Aircraft TA446 'Q' of 157 Squadron, one Ju188

At the beginning of the New Year, Fighter Command returned to the bombe
support role. With the decline of Luftwaffe attacks on Great Britain during th
latter half of 1944, four squadrons of night fighters were released for operation
with Bomber Command. Details of these units are as follows:

151 Squadron Equipped with Mosquito VI and 30 aircraft, this unit bega
         installing *Monica* equipment at the end of 1944 for bombe
         support work. The first such sortie took place on 21 Februar
         and high- (Mosquito 30) and low-level (Mosquito VI) patrol
         were continued until May 1945.

307 Squadron Equipped with Mosquito 30 aircraft, this unit of the Polish Ai
         Force began bomber support operations in December 1944
         January 1945. Like 151, its aircraft were fitted with *Monica* an
         high- and low-level patrols were flown until May 1945.

406 Squadron Equipped with Mosquito 30 aircraft, this unit began bombe
         support operations in late August/early September 1944. High

and low-level patrols were continued from this date until May 1945.

456 Squadron Equipped with Mosquito 30 aircraft, this unit began bomber support operations in March 1945 and continued these on a full time basis until May 1945.

The introduction of these squadrons to the bomber support role provided welcome reinforcement to the fighter element of 100 Group. What level of success they achieved is not clear and details of only four claims by 406 Squadron are known for certain, these being:

1/2 January – Aircraft MM732, one Ju88 and aircraft NT283, one Bf110
15/16 April – Aircraft NT283, one Ju88 near Prenzlau
24/25 April – Aircraft MM727, one Ju88 near Wittstock

The Group's heavy squadrons were also hampered by the weather in January 1945. In fact only ten Main Force attacks were made during the month so bad were conditions. The *Mandrel* screen was used on 12 occasions with a total of 147 sorties being despatched. No 171 Squadron contributed 56 to this number, 199 Squadron eighty-nine and the 36th two. The night of the 2/3rd marked the last sortie the 36th was to fly with Bomber Command. Ten of these operations were in support of Main Force and two were spoofs. On the 28/29th, the aircraft which had formed the screen continued when it was closed down to act as a *Window* force for the first time.

The SWF was active on 11 nights during the month with the heavy squadrons despatching a total of at least 216 sorties to its activities. This total was made up as follows: No 171 Squadron, 36 *Window* sorties; 192 Squadron, 10 *Window*/bombing sorties; 199 Squadron, one *Window* patrol; 214 Squadron 38 *Window*/jamming sorties; 223 Squadron, 45 *Window*/jamming sorties; and 462 Squadron, 86 *Window*/bombing sorties. Bombing was a new departure for the force's heavy squadrons and was inaugurated by 462 Squadron on the 7th. Target marking for these operations was undertaken by Mosquitos from 8 Group or from 100 Group's fighter element.

The introduction of bombing by the heavy aircraft of the force allowed it for the first time to simulate 5 Group attacks. Proximity target indicators and flares would be dropped by Group Mosquitos after which a normal bombing attack would be delivered directed by a Master Bomber using 5 Group frequencies and R/T patter.

No 192 Squadron despatched a total of 85 sorties during the month which included seven by the American P-38 detachment and 10 *Window*/bombing sorties with the SWF (carried out exclusively by Halifax aircraft). The remaining 68 sorties were divided between *Piperack* jamming in support of Main Force (*Piperack* became operational on the 13/14th) and investigations into *Bernhard* (see page 197) and centimetric transmissions. The *Piperack* aircraft also made recordings of VHF R/T and W/T traffic during Main Force raids. The two *Jostle* squadrons, Nos 214 and 223, despatched a total of 133 sorties during January. No 214 contributed 38 *Window*/jamming sorties to the SWF and 34 jamming sorties in support of raids on 17 targets, while 223 Squadron flew 45 sorties with the SWF and 16 jamming sorties in support of raids on 10 targets. In all cases, both squadrons provided *Jostle*, *Carpet* and *Piperack* jamming. The two squadrons also began using *Gee* during the month, its use being practical during intervals in the jamming cover.

The Group's newest heavy squadron, 462, began operations on 1 January and had despatched 85 *Window*/bombing sorties by the end of the month. January also saw the installation of the first *ABC* equipment in a 462 Squadron aircraft, although the squadron was not to use it operationally until March.

February saw no let up in the Group's fighter activities, a total of 313 AI Mk X and 361 Mk XV sorties being despatched during the period. High-level patrols were flown with both types of radar while the low-level ones were flown almost exclusively with the AI Mk X equipment. Statistics for the month's operations are as follows:

	High level AIX	Low level AIX	High level AIXV	Low level AIXV
Sorties despatched	287	26	169	192
Sorties completed	264	26	161	177
Aircraft missing	1	0	1	1
AI contacts	51	3	30	20
AI claims	9 destroyed 2 damaged	1 probably	None	1 destroyed
Visual claims	None	None	None	1 damaged
Ground claims	1 damaged	None	None	2 damaged

Known details of these claims are as follows:

1/2nd – Aircraft MV557 'Y' of 85 Squadron, one Bf110
1/2nd – Aircraft NT309 of 239 Squadron, one Bf110
2/3rd – Aircraft MT548 'Z' of 85 Squadron, one Ju88 near Wiesbaden
8/9th – Aircraft NT361 of 239 Squadron, one Bf110 near Hamm
8/9th – Aircraft NT330 of 239 Squadron, one Bf110 near Goch
14/15th – Aircraft MT532 'S' of 85 Squadron, one Ju88

The *Mandrel* screen was operational on 12 nights during the month, 17 Squadron despatching 117 sorties towards its activities with 199 Squadron weighing in with 79. The SWF was equally active with the Group's heavy squadrons contributing 238 sorties towards its patrols, as follows: 17 Squadron, 11 *Window*/bombing sorties (the squadron starting bombing operations during February); 192 Squadron, 18 *Window*/bombing sorties; 21 Squadron, 48 *Window*/jamming sorties; 223 Squadron, 57 *Window*/jamming sorties; and 462 Squadron, 104 *Window*/bombing sorties.

The SWF feinting operations began to lose their effectiveness during this period because of the depth of penetration of Main Force attacks, giving the enemy opportunity to distinguish between real and fake raids. Towards the end of February, the force was augmented by aircraft from the 492nd Bombardment Group of the 8th Air Force who went on to shoulder a major part of the force's bomb dropping.

No 192 Squadron despatched 152 ELINT/*Piperack* sorties during February. *Bernhard*, 120 to 130 MHz pulse transmissions, SN-2 signals in the 60 to 110 MHz band and EW signals in the 30 to 70 MHz band were all investigated. Additionally, work was done on the jamming of *Gee* and *Loran* by the enemy checks were made on the effectiveness of *Fidget* and *Jostle* jamming and recordings made of enemy VHF/R/T and W/T traffic. The squadron also resumed *Big Ben* patrols during the month following the resumption of V-2 attacks on London. (The main weight of the V-1/V-2 offensive having been switched to Antwerp during the period between November 1944 and January 1945.)

No 214 Squadron, apart from its work with the SWF, despatched 43 *Jostle/Carpet/Piperack* sorties in support of Main Force raids during the month. At the same time, the squadron's *Piperack* fit was modified to six transmitters instead of two so that the whole of the SN-2's operating band could be covered. During the same period, 223 Squadron despatched 58 direct support sorties for Main Force and on the 20/21st suffered its second loss (the first being on 14/15 January) when a B-24 failed to return.

March saw the despatch of 383 AI Mk X sorties and 261 with AI Mk XV. No 141 Squadron was in the process of being re-equipped with the Mosquito 30 which began on the 15th of the month and which was completed by 3 April. The squadron flew its first sortie with this aircraft on 8 March. As a whole, the Group's fighter units flew bombing and flare dropping sorties in support of the SWF; anti-intruder patrols over the UK when there was an upsurge in such activity on the part of the Luftwaffe (see page 215) and Flak suppression sorties in support of 8 Group Mosquito operations, as well as the normal high- and low-level patrols. Towards the end of the month, the Group began long-range control experiments with its fighter units. The aircraft were fitted with SCR 274 receivers with a range of 500 miles (805 km). Group operational control would thus be able to transmit in-flight intelligence, but unfortunately there were few opportunities to use this technique before the end of the war.

Statistics for the month's operations read as follows:

	High level AIX	Low level AIX	High level AIXV	Low level AIXV	Other Sorties
Sorties despatched	347	36	48	213	11
Sorties completed	335	33	48	202	None
Aircraft lost	2	1	0	3	1
AI contacts	62	2	6	9	None
AI claims	10 destroyed* 2 damaged	None	1 destroyed	1 probable 1 damaged	None
Visual claims	1 destroyed	None	None	1 destroyed	None
Ground claims	None	None	None	3 destroyed 9 damaged	None

*Four of these claims resulted from *Perfectos* contacts which were converted into AI ones.

Known details of the above claims for March are as follows:

6/7th – Aircraft NT361 of 239 Squadron, one Ju88 near Chemnitz
8/9th – Aircraft PZ288 of 23 Squadron, one Fw190 near Stendal
8/9th – Aircraft MT555 of 85 Squadron, one Ju188 near Hamburg
15/16th – Aircraft NT309 of 85 Squadron, one Ju88 near Musburg
17/18th – Aircraft NT330 of 239 Squadron, one Ju188 near Nuremburg

An in flight view of a Mandrel *equipped Halifax of 199(BS) Squadron based at North Creake. This particular aircraft is a B III, serial number P.N 375, coded* EX-F. *(via J Scutts)*

18/19th – Aircraft NT364 'K' of 157 Squadron, one Ju88
19/20th – Aircraft MT548 'Z' of 85 Squadron, one Bf110
19/20th – Aircraft NT271 of 239 Squadron, one He219
21/22nd – Aircraft NT324 'T' of 85 Squadron, one Bf110 and one He219

With 199 Squadron completing its conversion to the Halifax III during the month, (this process having severely restricted its activities during February) four of the Group's six heavy squadrons were now mounted on the type. The two *Jostle* squadrons, Nos 214 and 233, would have re-equipped with the Halifax had it been possible to mount the device in such an aircraft, since the Group had decided to standardise on the Halifax as its heavy RCM platform. The *Mandrel* screen was used on 20 occasions during March in the execution of which 171 Squadron despatched 144 sorties and 199 Squadron 123 sorties. The SWF was operational on the same number of nights during the period, dropping 200 plus tons (160 tonnes) of *Window* and 320 tons (255 tonnes) of bombs, 240 tons (192 tonnes) of which were despatched by the 492nd Bombardment Group. The heavy squadrons contributed a total of 381 sorties to the force's activities during the month, this total breaking down as follows: 171 Squadron, 44 *Window*/bombing sorties; 192 Squadron, 13 *Window*/bombing sorties; 199 Squadron, 51 *Window* sorties (probably in concert with bombing); 214 Squadron, 75 *Window*/jamming sorties; 223 Squadron, 85 *Window*/jamming sorties; and 462 Squadron, 113 *Window*/bombing sorties. To aid the SWF's activities when it was operating away from the main bomber stream, the Group began broadcasting its own meteorological details during the month.

An ABC equipped Halifax, serial number P.N 451/G, of 462(BS) Squadron photographed in a 'graveyard' at York on Boxing Day, 1945. The camouflage is interesting in that the unit markings are incomplete. The yellow fin stripes are a carry over from the squadron's days with 4 Group. (via J D Rawlings)

Jamming support was provided for Main Force attacks by aircraft of 192, 214 and 223 Squadrons during the month. No 192 Squadron despatched 21 *Piperack* sorties, 214 Squadron contributed 41 *Carpet/Jostle/Piperack* sorties and 223 Squadron flew 19 similar operations. No 462 Squadron also became operational in the *ABC* role during March, the first such sortie being flown on the 13/14th. In fact, the unit only managed to despatch 16 *ABC* sorties before the end of the war. In addition to its *Piperack* jamming and *Window*/bombing sorties, 192 Squadron made investigations into *Bernhard* transmissions, signals from an unknown source in the 30 to 40 MHz band, SN-2 transmissions, the jamming of *Loran* and into the general efficiency of British jamming. In addition, recordings were made of enemy VHF R/T and W/T transmissions. In total, the squadron despatched 160 sorties during the month.

The first three months of 1945 saw losses amongst the heavy squadrons beginning to rise. No 223 Squadron lost a Liberator on 20/21 February and B-24 'B' was shot up in the Oulton circuit during March, probably on the night of the 3/4th, but managed to land safely. On the same night, 171 Squadron lost one of its Halifaxes to an intruder. By far the greatest losses were, however, suffered by 214 Squadron, which lost no less than eight B-17s between 8 February and 22 March.

March also saw an automatic *Window* dispenser finally placed in production but there is some doubt as to whether such a device entered general service before the end of the war. There is evidence that at least 199 Squadron was equipped with a dispenser in the last months of the war.

April saw the Group's fighter squadrons despatch a total 753 sorties; 457 of these were AI Mk X operations and 241 were with AI Mk XV. In addition to the normal high-and low-level patrols, a number of anti-Flak patrols were made in support of mining operations in Norwegian waters. On the 4/5th, 141 Squadron despatched its first Mosquito 30 sortie, three such aircraft operating on this night. On the 13/14th, 515 Squadron despatched its first Master Bomber sortie. This role grew out of the needs of the general airfield attack which began in April, 23 and 515 Squadrons acted as markers for the other

Mosquito squadrons. No 515 Squadron's mode of operation was to drop green target indicators for 141 and 169 Squadrons to bomb on using 500 lb (227 kg) high explosive and 250 lb (113 kg) incendiary bombs. The Group's Mosquito 30s began bomb carrying on the 17/18th and the airfield attacks took on a new dimension on the 18/19th when seven of 141 Squadron's aircraft dropped Napalm on Neubiburg, Under the codename *Firebash*, attacks of this nature were made on Neubiburg, Flensburg, Schleswig and Lübeck, the usual aircraft load being two 100-gallon (455 litres) drop tanks filled with Napalm. During April, at least 13 attacks of all types were made on airfields.

Statistics for the month's operations read as follows:

	High level AIX	Low level AIX	High level AIXV	Low level AIXV	Other sorties
Sorties despatched	360	97	15	226	55
Sorties completed	336	96	15	222	51
Aircraft missing	2	0	0	1	1
AI contacts	32	5	2	3	0
AI claims	3 destroyed 1 probable 2 damaged	2 destroyed 1 damaged	None	1 destroyed 1 damaged	None
Visual claims	1 destroyed	None	None	3 destroyed	None
Ground claims	None	None	None	5 destroyed 10 damaged	2 destroyed 1 damaged

Known details of these claims are as follows:
5/6th – Aircraft 'C' of 85 Squadron, one Ju188 near Magdeburg
7/8th – Aircraft 'Q' of 85 Squadron, one Fw190
9/10th – Aircraft NT494 of 85 Squadron, one Ju88 near Lutzendorf
10/11th – Aircraft RS575 of 515 Squadron, one Ju188
11/12th – Aircraft NT331 of 239 Squadron, one He111
14/15th – Aircraft NT334 'S' of 85 Squadron, one He219 near Kiel
16/17th – Aircraft PZ398 of 515 Squadron, one Ju52/3m near Schlesheim
17/18th – Aircraft MV557 of 85 Squadron, one Fw190
23/24th – Aircraft 'Z' of 85 Squadron, one Ju88
25/26th – Aircraft RS575 of 515 Squadron, one Do217

April saw the distinctions between the various roles of the heavy squadrons merge. *Mandrel* operations were now flown with the bomber stream; either with the aircraft forming a screen ahead of the Main Force or, as on three occasions during the month, mingled in with it. The two *Mandrel* squadrons had their establishments increased by four aircraft each during this period.

The SWF also operated as part of Main Force feinting ahead of the stream and carrying out full scale raids on diversionary targets. During the course of these operations 358 tons (286 tonnes) of bombs and 184 tons (147 tonnes) of *Window* were dropped. Again, aircraft from the 492nd were involved in the

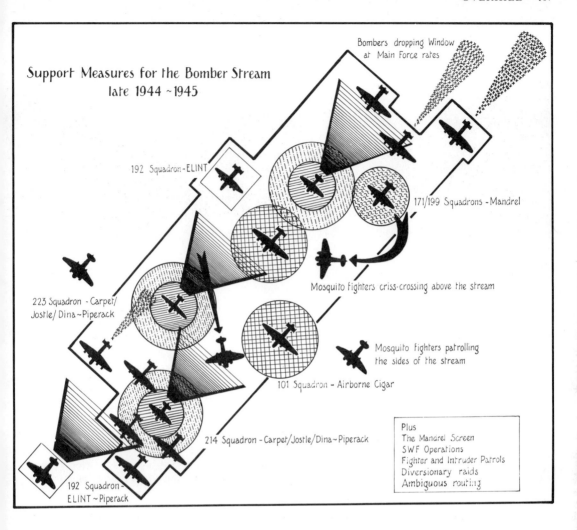

Support Measures for the Bomber Stream
late 1944 ~1945

Bombers dropping Window
at Main Force rates

192 Squadron-ELINT

171/199 Squadrons - Mandrel

Mosquito fighters criss-crossing above the stream

223 Squadron - Carpet/
Jostle/ Dina ~ Piperack

Mosquito fighters patrolling
the sides of the stream

101 Squadron - Airborne Cigar

214 Squadron - Carpet/Jostle/Dina ~ Piperack

Plus
The Mandrel Screen
S W F Operations
Fighter and Intruder Patrols
Diversionary raids
Ambiguous routing

192 Squadron -
ELINT ~ Piperack

force's operations as were aircraft from 4 and 6 Groups. These latter formations contributed to the SWF on very few occasions, supplying a maximum of 20 to 24 aircraft on any one occasion.

The only other event of note during the month was 223 Squadron's conversion to the B-17. The squadron had long had problems in servicing its B-24 aircraft which had also proved to be too slow to keep up with the British aircraft they were called upon to fly with. The squadron's first B-17 sortie was despatched on the night of the 19/20th.

The beginning of May saw the German forces in total disarray and on the verge of surrender. The month was only eight days old when this indeed happened and Field Marshal Von Runstead surrendered all German forces in the West of Field Marshal Montgomery on Luneberg Heath. As a consequence 100 Group was only able to fly one operation before the cease-fire, this being on the night of the 2/3rd. On this date, 86 of the Group's aircraft gave support to a Main Force raid on Kiel. Known details of this operation are as follows:

23/141 Squadrons Honn and Flensburg were attacked with Napalm and incendiaries by these two squadrons. The raid was controlled by Squadron Leader Griffiths of 515 Squadron

A Jostle equipped Fortress B III, serial number KJ 109, of 223(BS) Squadron photographed at 51 MU at Lichfield post war. The aircraft is illustrated again on page 238. (via J D Rawlings)

	flying RS513, and 141 Squadron contributed 13 aircraft to the operation.
169 Squadron	Aircraft from this squadron attacked Schleswig and Westerland. (Unknown units of the Group also made a Napalm attack on Jagel.)
199 Squadron	This unit despatched a total of 17 sorties comprising four *Mandrel/Window* sorties over the North Frisians, eight *Mandrel/Window*/bombing sorties over Kiel and five *Mandrel/Window* sorties over Schleswig. A third Halifax in the Frisian force returned early and two of the Kiel force were lost.
214 Squadron	This unit despatched 11 *Window*/jamming sorties over the Kiel area.
223 Squadron	This unit despatched 9 (four B-17s, five B-24s), *Window*/jamming sorties.
462 Squadron	This unit despatched 10 sorties in a spoof against Flensburg (probably involving 223) comprising three jamming sorties and seven *Window*/bombing ones.

In this way, the Group finished its wartime operations but the onset of peace did not bring any let up in operations. It was to be involved in a major series of investigative exercises in the following month to discover its own effectiveness. These exercises were code-named *Post Mortem* and are fully described in the following chapter.

An interesting sidelight on this investigation work came in the late summer of 1945 when the Group had the chance to dissect a German night fighter on British soil. In the immediate post-war period, RAF teams earmarked various captured enemy aircraft for evaluation and these were gradually brought to England. High on their list were night fighters and eventually some 33 aircraft of this nature were either brought or were marked for delivery to the UK. This number was made up of 14 Ju88s, possibly eight Bf110s, six He219s, one radar equipped Fw190, one radar equipped Si204 trainer and three Me262B-1a/U1s.

The spoils of war. A Heinkel He219A-2 seen at Farnborough in October 1945. Along with some thirty other German night fighters, this aircraft was brought to the UK for evaluation. The 'V1' painted below the cockpit indicates the type of AI radar fitted. (via J Scutts)

One of the Ju88s, a G-6 sub-type carrying the Werke Nummer 622983 and the code '4R-RB', indicating that it was operated by NJG 2, was delivered to the BSDU sometime in July or August. Captured at Schleswig and equipped with FuG 218 and FuG 350, the aircraft was damaged in a landing at Foulsham on 12 September. After repair, it was passed to the Central Fighter Establishment at West Raynham on 4 October.

Chapter 6

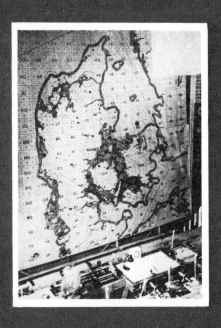

Post Mortem:
25 June to 7 July 1945

With the ending of the European war, the various agencies which had been most closely involved with the bomber support campaign began the planning of a major evaluation of the enemy's defensive system. This evaluation was to be carried out in two distinct phases: a series of exercises against the German radar network in Denmark to test the effectiveness of the various measures, and an in-depth interrogation of *Luftflotte Reich's* night fighter personnel.

At the end of hostilities, most of the radar network in Denmark remained intact. The decision was taken to re-activate the various stations and to fly a series of exercises over the area employing all the varieties of electronic counter-measures which had been used operationally during the later stages of the war. The overall exercise was code-named *Post Mortem*.

On 12 June, Wing Commander G Keighley, (HQ Fighter Command) and Wing Commander W Jennings (HQ 60 Group) arrived at Schleswig to make preliminary arrangements for the exercise with HQ 83 Group and *Luftflotte Reich,* the Luftwaffe organisation which was to provide the ground personnel to man the various radars. The Keighley/Jennings mission's main task was to ensure that the activation of a sufficiently large portion of the defensive organisation for the period of the exercise would not seriously interfere with the general disarmament programme. Having satisfied itself on this point, the mission reported to the Air Ministry on the 18th that, providing certain problems could be overcome, (the transportation of the necessary RAF observers into the area being the major of these) the exercise could begin on the 25th. Accordingly, the Air Ministry issued *Exercise Post Mortem, Operation Order No 1 Flying Plan*, the gist of which was as follows:

> A series of exercises was to be carried out in daylight which would simulate a bomber stream and supporting feint force approaching across the North Sea to a 'target' at Flensburg. The exercises were to be flown over two routes, 'A' Northern and 'B' Southern. Route 'A' was to allow the radar network to view the approaching force obliquely, whilst 'B' was to give it a direct view. A third route, 'C', was to be used in Exercise 10, details of which were to be unknown to the radar stations. Post Mortem was to begin on 25 June and end on 7 July. The following aircraft were to be employed:

> (a) A main bomber force (with Pathfinders)
> (b) Window spoof forces
> (c) *Mandrel* aircraft mounting screens
> (d) *Mandrel* aircraft accompanying the main bomber forces and the *Window* spoofs
> (e) Special jamming aircraft.

The actual numbers and type of aircraft to be deployed were detailed in an appendix, as follows:

Exercise	BC Aircraft	100 Group Aircraft
One	200	None
Two	200	None
Three	200	None
Four	200	20 *Mandrel* aircraft forming a screen.
Five	200	20 *Mandrel* aircraft forming a screen. Six *Mandrel* and four *Piperack/Jostle/Carpet* aircraft dispersed throughout the main force and the 20 strong *Window* force (provided by 100 Group).

Exercise	BC Aircraft	100 Group Aircraft
Six	None	Approximately 24 *Window* aircraft.
Seven	None	20 *Mandrel* aircraft forming a screen. Approximately 24 *Window* aircraft.
Eight	None	20 *Mandrel* aircraft forming a screen. 24-strong *Window* force. Four *Piperack/Jostle/Carpet*, four *ABC/Jostle/Carpet* and six *Mandrel* aircraft with the *Window* force.
Nine	200	20 *Mandrel* aircraft forming a screen. 45-strong *Window* force.
Ten	200	20 *Mandrel* aircraft forming a screen. Two *Window* forces totalling 48 aircraft. 14 jamming aircraft.
Eleven	None	Approximately 20 Mosquito bombers ⎫
		⎬ 8 Group
Twelve	None	Approximately 20 Mosquito bombers ⎭
Thirteen	None	22-strong *Window* force accompanied by six *Mandrel* aircraft in pairs at 15-mile intervals.
Fourteen	None	28-strong *Window* force including six *Piperack* aircraft.

Schedule

Exercise 1

The main bomber force was to fly at 17,000 to 20,000 ft (5,182 to 6,096 m) over Route A. Operational height was to be gained outside enemy radar cover and there was to be no *Window* cover. This exercise was to be a 'control' to see what the radar network could do in the absence of jamming. In addition, H2S was to be used from take-off to ascertain the range at which its transmissions could be picked up.

In all subsequent exercises current BC restrictions on radar transmissions were to be observed. This eliminated the use of such aids west of 07° 30'.

Exercise 2

The main bomber force was to fly at 2,000 to 3,000 ft (610 to 914 m) until 6° east, when it was to climb to 17,000 to 20,000 ft (5,182 to 6,096 m) before crossing the enemy coast. The flight plan was to conform closely to those of recent bomber operations. *Window* was to be dropped as soon as the bombers came within the enemy's radar cover. The exercise was to be flown over Route A and was designed to discover the effectiveness of a low/high approach flight.

Exercise 3

The main bomber force was to fly at 17,000 to 20,000 ft (5,182 to 6,096 m) over Route B. This exercise was to discover the effectiveness of *Window* dropped at main force rates.

Exercise 4

A *Mandrel* screen was to be set up off the German coast line through which a bomber force would emerge on its way to the target. The Exercise was to be flown over Route B and *Window* was to be dropped from the point of passage through the *Mandrel* screen. Number 4 was to be an evaluation of the effectiveness of *Mandrel*.

Exercise 5

This was to be a repetition of the previous exercise with the addition of a

Window feint and *Mandrel*, *Jostle*, *Piperack*, *ABC* and *Carpet* jamming support for the main bomber force and the *Window* feint. This exercise was to be the first one in which the enemy radar system was subject to the full weight of Bomber Command's electronic counter-measures.

Exercise 6

A *Window* force simulating a main force of 200 heavy bombers was to fly at 18,000 ft (5,486 m) over Route B. No other form of jamming was to be used and the aircraft were to be spread over a 10 mile (16 km) front with a length of $6\frac{1}{2}$ minutes. The exercise was designed to discover the effectiveness of a *Window* spoof.

Exercise 7

This was to be a repetition of the previous exercise with the addition of a *Mandrel* screen.

Exercise 8

This exercise, flown over Route B, was to be a simulation of Exercise 5 by a spoof force backed by a *Mandrel* screen, *Window* and other jamming techniques

Exercise 9

The main bomber force was to fly at 17,000 to 20,000 ft (5,182 to 6,096 m) over Route A. A *Window* force was to precede the main force through a *Mandrel* screen and adopt the area fan formation which had been used during late war operations over the Ruhr. The aim of the exercise was to discover the effectiveness of large-scale *Windowing* when the enemy knew the general area under attack but not the precise target.

Exercise 10

The main bomber force was to fly at 17,000 to 20,000 ft (5,182 to 6,096 m) over Route C. Two *Window* forces were to accompany the bombers which, after emerging from the *Mandrel* screen, were to feint in different directions. Full jamming support was to be provided. No warning as to route or which were real or spoof forces was to be given to the operators and the exercise was to be regarded as the major test of the enemy's system. The flight plan of the RAF aircraft involved was to be as close as possible to that of a fully supported late war raid. Exercise 10 was to be the last one involving main force aircraft.

Exercise 11

A force of 20 No 8 Group Mosquito aircraft were to fly at or above 25,000 ft (7,620 m) over Route A. No form of jamming was to be undertaken and the exercise was designed to evaluate the enemy's ability to track high speed, high altitude aircraft.

Exercise 12

This was to be a repetition of Exercise 11 flown at 2,000 to 3,000 ft (610 to 914 m).

If time allowed, the following two exercises were to be flown:

Exercise 13

A *Window* force accompanied by *Mandrel* aircraft was to fly at 18,000 ft (5,486 m) over Route A. This exercise was to be a comparison with Exercise 6.

Exercise 14

This was to be a repeat of the previous exercise but replacing *Mandrel* with *Piperack*. The aim was to ascertain the effect of *Piperack* against ground radars.

Timing

(a)   H-hour was to be regarded as the time at which the first aircraft reached Flensburg.

(b)   When two exercises were to be carried out on the same day, timing was to be such that the two forces should pass one another 3° east in order to eliminate mutual interference.

(c)   The exercise order was to be adhered to wherever possible in order to allow the observation of a steady build-up in electronic counter-measures.

Programme

Day One: Exercise 1 at H hour and Exercise 4 at H plus $2\frac{1}{2}$ hours.
Day Two: Exercise 2 at H hour and Exercise 6 at H plus 2 hours.
Day Three: Exercise 4 at H hour and Exercise 7 at H plus 1 hour.
Day Four: Exercise 5 at H hour and Exercise 8 at H plus 2 hours.
Day Five: Exercise 11 at H hour and Exercise 12 at H plus 2 hours.
Day Six: Exercise 8.
Day Seven: Exercise 9.

The night fighter control room at Grove in Denmark. The map on the left hand side of the picture is printed on a ground glass screen divided up into the Luftwaffe's standard fighter grid. The staggered tiers of seats on the left were occupied by female operators who projected spots of light on to the map representing the aerial situation for the fighter controllers on the other side of the screen. (via D Wood)

Day Eight: Exercise 10
Day Nine: Exercise 13 at H hour and Exercise 14 at H plus 2 hours.
The order went on to detail exactly which parts of the Danish radar chain were to be used. The following German Air Force installations were to be used:

(a) The Jagddivision control centre at Grove.
(b) The radar stations *Faun, Ringelnatter* and *Star*.
(c) The Observer Corps Centre at Kolding and its associated posts.
(d) The 'Y' Service stations at Tamariske or Strohblume and Veilchen or Geiss-blatt.

This brief list belies the actual extent of the network which was used. Three categories of radar stations existed for the Germans which may conveniently be described as first, second and third class. Third class sites consisted of a single equipment which passed its information directly to a first class site. A second class site consisted of a group of radars and was responsible for constructing an overall picture of the air situation on site which was passed to the first class site. In addition, all such sites were equipped for *Himmelbett* fighter control (see Appendix 3). The first class sites were responsible for correlating all received information, adding any material from its own radars and passing the completed picture on to the Jagddivision control centre. Again, a first class sight had a GCI facility.

The stations *Faun, Ringelnatter* and *Star* were all first class sites. Their seven dependent second class sites, (*Adler* and *Fledermaus* – *Faun, Lama* and *Buffel* – *Ringelnatter* and *Auster, Robbe* and *Ameise* – *Star*), were also activated. Although no third class sites were used, this gave a total of 16 *Freya*, ten *Würzburg* – *Reise*, two *Drehfreya*, six *Wassermann*, three *Mammut* and two *Jagdschloss* equipments in operation.

A representative Observer Corps layout comprising 21 posts reporting into the *Flugwach Kommando* at Kolding and the two 'Y' stations at Veilechen and Tamariske completed the network for the exercise. The Kolding centre reported to *Faun* whilst the 'Y' stations reported directly to the *Jagddivision* control centre at Grove. This was not the usual procedure but was the most convenient arrangement for the duration of *Post Mortem*.

The final link in the German defensive chain, interceptor aircraft, were excluded from the exercise, the occupying authorities feeling, perhaps with some justification, that Luftwaffe aircrews might use the opportunity to make one last attack or to defect to neutral Sweden, a tempting alternative to the POW cage. Thus, the first of many artificialities crept into the exercise in that the RAF was unable to evaluate the effectiveness of its measures against the ground-to-air control channels.

On 23 June, 131 RAF observers arrived at Grove and Schleswig airfield from where they dispersed to the various radar stations and control centres. Later on the same day, Air Commodore W Pretty and Group Captain R Hiscox arrived at Schleswig and were taken by Wing Commander Keighley to the headquarters of *Luftflotte Reich* which was presently situated some 10 miles (16 km) outside Schleswig in a concentration of caravans dispersed throughout a pine forest. Here, the RAF team interviewed General Major Boner, Chief Signals Officer of the German organisation. Boner was responsible for the activation and manning of the various stations and was able to report that the necessary arrangements had progressed well and that the Danish authorities would have completed all telephone connections by the next day. He requested to be allowed to be stationed at

Grove for the duration of the exercise. This request being granted, the British/German party departed for Grove, from where, on the night of the 24th, a signal was despatched informing the Air Ministry that all was ready for the exercise to begin on the morning of the 25th.

In describing the results of the various exercises, it has proved impossible to establish whether the order laid down in *Post Mortem* Order No 1 was adhered to, so it has been deemed wise to describe the operations in their numerical order. The summary should be read in conjunction with the schedule.

A Summary of Observations of the Various Exercises of Post Mortem

Exercise Number	Radar Plots	Y Service Details	Effects of *Window*	Effects of *Mandrel*	Effects of other Jammers	General Remarks
One	First recorded plot at 0813 hr from a *Mammut* at *Auster*.	First plot at 0825 hr. 10 cm signals were plotted throughout the exercise. At 0935 hr, H2S plots indicated that the bomber force had divided. One aircraft using IFF against orders was accurately tracked throughout the exercise.	Although *Window* was not used, six sites reported its use on 11 occasions during the exercise.	*Mandrel* was not used.	No other jammers were used.	The reporting of *Window* was put down to misinterpretation of the scale of the aircraft used and probably contributed to a consistently lower number of aircraft being reported than there actually were. Height reports were in the main correct. Mosquito aircraft were reported where there were none but the main force was correctly identified as being made up of four-engined aircraft. Grove consistently placed the main force ahead of its actual position.
Two	The low approach used on this exercise cut down the early warning range considerably.	One IFF plot intermittently shown from 1135 hr. (An aircraft was found to be using the device against orders.) Large numbers of H2S plots recorded, as were a small number of *Monica* ones. (No *Monica* sets were in use.)	*Window* was reported by all radar stations other than *Auster*. No *Window* was in fact used.	*Mandrel* was not used.	No other jammers were used.	The reporting of *Window* was felt to be due to the sudden appearance of a large number of aircraft plotted as they climbed up into the radar cover. No explanation for the *Monica* plots could be offered. Once the aircraft had been picked up on radar, Grove plotted the track of the force fairly accurately, although making it on a much broader front than in reality. On two occasions completely spurious tracks away from the main formation appeared.
Three	First recorded plot at 1130 hr from the *Wassermann* at *Ringelnatter*. Aircraft were reported to be dropping *Window*.	H2S and IFF plots accurately tracked the bomber formation.	*Window* was reported by all radar stations and the areas of *Window* infection were for the most part accurately plotted.	*Mandrel* was not used.	No other jammers were used.	The use of *Window* completely threw the control system. After the initial radar pick up, Grove plotted a spurious track for 20 jamming aircraft. Between 1219 and 1237 hr total confusion reigned, the controller eventually deciding that the bombers were travelling west whereas they had actually turned south. This southward track was accurately plotted by the Y

Exercise Numbers	Radar Plots	Y Service Details	Effects of *Window*	Effects of *Mandrel*	Effects of Other Jammers	General Remarks
						service but the information was discounted in the face of a total lack of radar conformation.
Four	First recorded plot at 1350 hr from the *Wassermann* at *Ringelnatter*.	*Mandrel* transmissions first plotted at 1331 hr. At 1334 hr, Tamariske reported the first H2S plot.	Areas of *Window* infection were accurately plotted.	The *Mandrel* Screen was not fully effective because of bad weather and technical failures in two aircraft which resulted in gaps in the frequencies covered between 1323 and 1540 hr. *Mandrel* had the following effects on the various radars: *Wassermann* – No effect other than a slowing in the plot rate on those with a capacity to change frequency. Single frequency *Wassermanns* reported wide-scale jamming but were able on occasions to plot through it. *Freya* – Completely jammed. *Mammut* – Completely jammed. *Jagdschloss* – Able to plot through gaps in the screen. *Würzburg* – Not affected.	No other jammers were used.	The presence of the *Mandrel screen* delayed rather than confused the Grove plot. The first indication that a raid was developing came at 1350 hr but continuous plotting was not started until 1424 hr. Y service attempts to plot the *Mandrel* jamming centres were unsatisfactory. This was felt to be due to the fact that only two such stations were operational. The height of the bomber force was plotted accurately from 1424 hr onwards.
Five	First recorded plot at 1358 hr from the *Wassermann* at *Auster*.	H2S plots recorded at Veilchen at 1526 hr and at Tamariske from 1531 hr onwards. Such plots were then recorded continuously throughout the exercise.	*Window* used throughout the operation. The combined effect of this jamming was: *Wassermann* – Those at *Robbe* and *Auster* plotted fairly well despite the jamming, though the plot was not continuous. Those radars of this type at *Lama*, *Ringelnatter* and *Buffel* were all seriously affected, none being able to produce any information of value. *Freya* – All sets of this type were 100 per cent effectively jammed throughout the exercise. *Mammut* – Equipment of this type at *Auster* and *Buffel* were able to give early warning of the approach of the jamming screen but once the	*Mandrel* Screen set up.	*Jostle*, *ABC*, *Piperack* and *Carpet* jamming.	Despite the intensity of interference which affected most of the radars feeding information to Grove, a track was established by 1511 hr and was maintained from there on with reasonable accuracy. The diversionary force was not plotted at all and the estimate of the numbers of aircraft involved in the main force was totally inaccurate. The first useful height indications were only received when the aircraft

Exercise Number	Radar Plots	Y Service Details	Effects of *Window*	Effects of *Mandrel*	Effects of Other Jammers	General Remarks
			Mandrel screen was in action they could no longer plot. The *Mammut* at *Auster*, however, managed to continue plotting the longest, being effective until 1526 hr. *Jagdschloss* – Both radars of this type were effectively jammed for the duration of the exercise. *Würzburg* – All sets of this type were severely affected by the combination of *Window* and electronic jamming. The only plots emanating from such radars during the course of the exercise were those of aircraft flying outside the main areas of interference.			were about 25 miles from the coast. After the main force had crossed the coast, Grove's estimate of its timing was fairly accurate. Most of the plots received were on aircraft at the head of the stream where the jamming was least intense.
Six	First recorded plot at 1517 hr from the *Wassermann* at *Buffel*.	H2S plot recorded at 1515 hr at Veilchen. From 1525, such plots were recorded continuously. From 1647 hr, *Monica* plots were established.	*Window* used throughout the exercise.	*Mandrel* was not used.	No other jammers were used.	From the first radar plot at 1517 hr until 1555 hr Grove correctly estimated the number of aircraft involved to be 20. At this point, *Window* began to confuse the issue and accurate plotting virtually ceased. All radars reported their inability to distinguish between the bombers and *Window*. Estimates of the numbers of aircraft began to fluctuate, a final figure of 60 to 100 aircraft being arrived at. The bomber's track was followed with reasonable accuracy, as was their operating height.
Seven	Exercise not carried out.					
Eight	First recorded plot at 1711 hr from the *Wassermann* at Auster.	H2S plot recorded at 1725 hr. Plotting continued until 1810 hr.	*Window* used throughout the exercise.	*Mandrel* screen set up.	Jammers of an unspecified nature used.	This exercise was flown almost immediately after No 5. The results were prejudiced by the fatigue of the German personnel (the *Jagdschloss* operators had been on stand-by for five hours by the time of the second exercise). The situation was further complicated by technical failures at *Star*, *Ringelnatter* and *Auster*. These factors combined with the heavy weight of jamming led Grove into a totally inaccurate estimation of the situation. A totally erroneous plot was produced and all functioning radars reported severe interference.
Nine	First recorded plot at 1529 hr from the *Wassermann* at *Robbe*.	H2S plot recorded at 1548 hr at Veilchen. Thereafter accurate plots were maintained for the duration of the exercise.	*Window* used throughout the exercise. The measures affected the following radars: *Wassermann* – All such sets were affected to a lesser or greater degree. *Freya* – Effective against all such sets except those operating on 52 and 57 MHz. *Mammut* – Some sets of this type were rendered ineffective, others not. *Jagdschloss* – Although affected all equipments of this type remained operable. *Würzburg* – All sets of this type were heavily affected.	*Mandrel Screen* set up.	No other jammers were used.	Despite the disruption caused by the jamming, Grove managed to establish a fairly accurate track for the bombers. It was deemed that the broad-front *Windowing* was not a success but that this may have been because the controller was becoming familiar with the routing of the exercises.

Exercise Number	Radar Plots	Y Service Details	Effects of *Window*	Effects of *Mandrel*	Effects of Other Jammers	General Remarks
Ten	First recorded plot at 1420 hr from the *Wassermanner* at *Robbe*.	10 cm plots were recorded.	*Window* used throughout the exercise. The combined effect of this jamming was similar to that of Exercise 9.	*Mandrel* screen set up.	Jammers of an unspecified nature were used.	The Grove plot began at 1514 hr, at which time it was reasonably accurate. As the exercise progressed this accuracy fell away. The target was plotted as being Flensburg when it was in fact Copenhagen. This was in part due to the *Window* force which did in fact head in the general direction of the former location but then turned away northwards. A diversion to Kiel was all but ignored.
Eleven	First recorded plot at 0922 hr from the *Mammut* at *Buffel*.	H2S plot recorded at 0920 hr at Veilchen.	No *Window* was used during this exercise.	*Mandrel* was not used.	No other jammers were used.	The Grove plot indicated three separate incoming raids but this was in part due to it not being equipped to handle the tracking of individual aircraft. All the various radars proved to be able to track the aircraft successfully within their own range limitations.
Twelve	First recorded plot at 0924 hr from the *Mammut* at *Buffel*.	No plots recorded during the exercise.	No *Window* was used during this exercise.	*Mandrel* was not used.	No other jammers were used.	The Grove plot only gave a general indication of the area over which the aircraft were operating. The controller thought that raids were being carried out against Westerland, Flensburg, Hadersleu and Esbjerg, whereas in fact all the aircraft concentrated on Flensburg. Radar performance was generally adequate but with a noticeable reduction in pick-up range.
Thirteen	Exercise not carried out.					
Fourteen	Exercise not carried out.					

In the event, only 11 of the planned 14 exercises were flown, bad weather seriously delaying the flight plan. As the observers were required to leave the Continent by 7 July and those exercises which had been flown by the 5th having provided more than enough information, it was decided to terminate *Post Mortem* on the latter date. All RAF personnel involved were back in the UK by the 7th.

Before considering the conclusions which were drawn from the exercise, a number of factors relating to the local conditions under which the radar network was operating should be examined. The great majority of the German personnel involved co-operated willingly. This was especially true of the higher ranks who were most anxious to demonstrate their professional skill. The only exception was in the case of the female plotters at Grove who appeared disgruntled and who were deemed responsible for certain delays and omissions in the passing of plots. Generalmajor Boner was of the opinion that the radar station crews were of average quality whilst the staff at Grove showed a low degree of competence at all levels. These views were endorsed by the British observers. This latter point may be explained to an extent by the fact that the radar network in Denmark had not had to handle a major raid for at least eighteen months and even then, it had never been faced with the full weight of the RAF's electronic counter-measures. In view of this it may be concluded that the exercise was probably more effective than it would have been if handled by personnel from areas which had received greater attentions from Bomber Command.

In confirmation of this, the best performance was turned in by the *Star* Group of stations who, during the war, had reported to the *2nd Jagddivision* control centre at Stade, near Hamburg; an area of the Reich which had been attacked regularly. The British observers fully agreed with this viewpoint.

The routing of the various exercises also helped to falsify the effectiveness or otherwise of the various measures in that only two alternative flight plans were used in 10 out of the 11 exercises. Once the German controllers had realised this, it became obvious that plots were being produced by mental dead reckoning when accurate radar information was lacking.

Although the area of the network activated was considered adequate to give a representative picture, it was notably lacking in observer posts and Y stations. The latter category was particularly important in that the Germans had come to rely more and more on the reception of aircraft transmissions as an accurate means of plotting bomber forces in the face of heavy jamming. Under fully operational conditions, Grove would have received information from six such stations plus a general picture of the air situation from the route tracking organisation in Berlin.

Finally, the comparatively small geographical scope of *Post Mortem* favoured the RAF. Normally the time spent by the bombers over enemy territory had been much longer, allowing the German controllers to make more considered decisions as to the enemy's intentions.

Bearing these points in mind, the post-exercise report contained the following conclusions:

(1)   Tracking of raids

It was felt that the German system was designed to give a general picture of large-scale attacks and was not equipped to deal with the tracking of single aircraft. [This refers to the *Zahme Sau* system.] During all the exercises involving heavy bombers, Grove was able to track the formations with reasonable accuracy. The only exception was Exercise 10 when a change in track was not immediately appreciated.

(2)   Long-range warning
Variations in radar performance were noted during the different exercises. Pick-up range was noticeably better against high altitude formations.

(3)   Value of low approach
Exercises 2 and 12 were held to prove the value of such an approach. A low-level penetration of the area of radar cover was found to halve the pick-up range.

(4)   Effects of the *Mandrel* screen

(a)   During the course of the exercise, the long-range radar cover consistently gave warning of the approach of *Mandrel*-equipped aircraft approximately $1\frac{1}{2}$ hours before the bomber force reached its target. The controller at Grove stated that the presence of this type of jamming was a useful indicator of impending activity. The Chief Operations Officer stated that under operational conditions, fighter aircraft would not have been scrambled until the main force had been detected.

(b)   In all cases when the *Mandrel* screen was used, there were sufficient gaps in the frequency cover to allow certain of the radars to plot the activity behind the screen. The *Wassermann* device proved to be the most resistent to this form of jamming.

(c)   The *Mandrel* screen proved to be relatively disappointing in its ability to reduce the enemy's early warning time. Its presence, however, added greatly to the controller's problems in correctly assessing the character of the raid.

(5)   Effect of *Window*
It was found that *Window* had profoundly affected the whole of the German radar and control system. It had forced the abandonment of the *Himmelbett* system. When the measure was employed, radar was employed to plot the infected areas in the hope that the bombers' track could be deduced from the resultant pattern. It proved to be impossible to determine accurately the numbers of aircraft flying in the face of such jamming, and to be very difficult to distinguish feint forces from the main bomber stream.

The Y Service
This system proved to be highly efficient, especially in the detection of 3 to 10 cm signals. As a whole, it was deemed to provide information of the utmost value which was incorporated into the overall picture with the minimum of delay.

Observer system
This was regarded as being inferior to the British system. Plotting was found to be inaccurate and the transmission of information laggardly. The Germans placed much greater reliance on other sources of information.

Plotting
It was found that the primary aim of a Jagddivision controller was to determine the position of the bomber formation. Spoof and diversionary attacks were to be ignored at all times so as to avoid waste in the interception effort. During the last months of the war, the correct plotting of the bomber stream became even

more important in the face of the critical aviation fuel shortage (allowing onl
50 to 80 sorties per night against a usual average of 200). In thes
circumstances, it was felt that the bomber support campaign had bee
particularly successful although a greater supply of fuel would most probabl
have reduced its effect.

Interceptors

Interrogation confirmed that the effective control of interceptor aircraft ha
been one of the defensive systems' most serious problems. On many occasions
it had proved impossible to hear the running commentary (see Appendix 3) a
all and despite the use of multiple frequency transmissions, only the mos
experienced crews could operate efficiently.

Identification

The Germans found no great difficulty in differentiating between friend and fo
except when the interceptors were mingled with the bomber stream. The size c
the bomber streams made them readily identifiable and the use of four-engine
bombers made air-to-air recognition very easy.

Effectiveness of Counter Measures

A definition of 100 Group's aims in 1945 was contained in a statement issued b
the Group's headquarters on 14 March 1945, as follows:

(1)   To deny the enemy use of GCI.
(2)   To deny the enemy early warning of raids.
(3)   To prevent the enemy obtaining a clear picture of operations over hi
       territory.
(4)   To make things as difficult as possible for the enemy night fighte
       attempting to carry out interception of bombers.
(5)   To get enemy night fighters airborne unnecessarily by means of fein
       attacks involving him in waste of effort and material and also conditionin
       him to certain fighter deployments from the point of view of future targets

With these points as a criteria, the RAF observers came to the following conclu
sions:

(1)   The combination of *Window* and electronic jamming rendered the clos
       control of night fighters from the ground impossible.
(2)   The only reduction in radar warning range came with the use of a lo
       approach. When using a high altitude approach with jamming cover, th
       Wassermann device was able to give adequate warning because of gaps i
       the frequency cover and the use of incorrect frequencies in the *Mandr*
       screen.
(3)   Any form of jamming was rendered valueless unless radio/radar silenc
       was strictly observed because of the efficiency of the German Y servic
       [This point was most forcibly stressed in the report.]
(5)   Interrogation proved the effectiveness of the jamming of the ground-to-a
       control channels.
(6)   *Post Mortem* could provide no evidence of conditioning of the enemy
       defensive system.
       It was felt that the exercise as a whole provided the most striking evidenc
       of the accuracy of the RAF's electronic intelligence with regard to th
       German radar devices.

During the same period as the *Post Mortem* exercises were being carried ou
an interrogation team led by Air Commodore R Chisholm was interviewin

Luftflotte Reich personnel to ascertain the conditions under which that organisation's night fighter force had been operating. The team comprised 12 officers drawn from 100 Group personnel and was based at Schleswig. Two German signals officers were co-opted as guides and the first session was with the Staff of *Luftflotte Reich*. The aims were much the same as the observers in Post Mortem proper but with a greater emphasis on fighter tactics.

This first meeting proved that the Luftwaffe was keenly aware of 100 Group, even to the extent of compiling dossiers on the formation's senior officers. However, it became obvious that the *Luftflotte* Staff were somewhat out of touch with day-to-day events and could not supply the required information. Therefore, it was decided to pursue the questioning at Geschwader and fighter controller level. The fighter controllers provided ample evidence of the difficulties under which the Luftwaffe had been operating its night fighter force during the last eighteen months of the war.

Of more interest to this team was the discovery of personnel from 10/NJG 11 and NJG 4 at Schleswig. From crews of NJG 11 much was learnt about the operation of the Me262 as a night fighter and an example of the Me 262B-1a/U1 radar-equipped variant was examined. Amongst other aircraft discovered was the Bf110G-4 flown by Heinz Wolfgang Schnaufer, the Luftwaffe's leading night fighter *Experten*.

Schnaufer, the Kommodore of NJG 4, was interrogated over a two-day period. At various points he was reluctant to divulge information and had to be

The Corkscrew. *This was the standard fighter evasion manoeuvre developed by Bomber Command for the protection of its heavy bombers. The course of the manoeuvre was as follows: 1 – Any member of the crew was empowered to give the order for evasive action with the words 'Corkscrew, port (or starboard), go!' on becoming aware of the imminence of a fighter attack. 2 – The pilot banked the aircraft in the direction instructed. 3 – The aircraft was put into a dive. 4 – The aircraft was pulled out of the dive and a climb in the opposite direction was begun. 5/6 – The aircraft was banked in the opposite direction and another dive begun. 7 – An opposite climb was begun. 8/9 – The fighter having been thrown off, the bomber resumed its original flight path. This constant changing of direction, speed and attitude was designed to make accurate deflection shooting very difficult and proved to be very effective in doing so.*

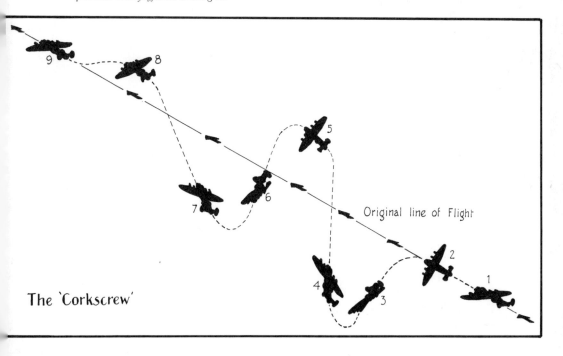

The 'Corkscrew'

threatened before answering fully. His interrogators were impressed by his knowledge of Bomber Command tactics. It became clear that the four-engined bomber, once in visual range of a competent night fighter crew, had little chance of escape unless it adopted the corkscrew manoeuvre. Schnaufer admitted that a corkscrewing bomber was an extremely difficult target, citing a fruitless 45-minute chase he had had with just such an aircraft.

The interrogation team interviewed as many of the Geschwader's air crew as possible and accumulated ample evidence of the Group's successes. The jamming of airborne radar and R/T and W/T links were often mentioned but the greatest talking point was the potency of the RAF's Mosquito fighter aircraft. Although small in number, the fear of such aircraft had reached tremendous proportions. Every loss, from whatever cause, became attributable to the Mosquito, indeed in the eyes of the crews interviewed, the type had been endowed with almost magical properties!

Quick visits to Grove and Copenhagen rounded off the team's work. Although it compiled a separate report, the gist of their findings was incorporated in the main report and may be found in the extracts quoted previously.

With the ending of *Post Mortem* on 5 July, 100 Group was rapidly run down. The first unit to be disbanded was 239 Squadron on 1 July. Two days later 141(SD) Squadron was transferred to Little Snoring. Its previous base, West Raynham, passed out of the Group's control on the 20th, its new owners being 12 Group, Fighter Command. The end of the *Post Mortem* also led to a rapid run down in the Group's heavy squadrons. The first units to go were Nos 17 and 214 Squadrons, the former unit being disbanded on the 27th whilst the latter was remustered as part of the MEAF on the same day. (The jamming unit was disbanded, 614 Squadron taking over its number at the same time. Two days later, 199 and 223(SD) Squadrons were disbanded, the last of the heavy units hanging on until 24 September, when 462(SD) Squadron, RAAF, was wound-up.

The specialist units fared little better, the first to be disbanded being the Bomber Support Development Unit on 21 July. On the 30th, 1694 Flight ceased to exist and 192(SD) Squadron followed on 22 August. No 80 Wing, the originators of radio counter-measures disappeared on the same day as 462(SD) Squadron.

The fighter units joined the general rush to disband. No 239(SD) Squadron has already been mentioned, the next to leave the Group being 169 Squadron which was disbanded on 10 August. Six days later, 157 Squadron followed suit closely followed by 141 Squadron on 7 September. The last of these squadrons No 23, went on 25 September. (The remaining fighter squadron, No 85, had reverted to Fighter Command immediately after the end of the European War.

The run down of squadrons led to the re-allocation of airfield control. On 3 September, North Creake, Oulton and Swannington passed into the care of 4 Group, Maintenance Command. The Group's last flying unit, its Communications Flight, ceased to exist on 17 October and on 10 November, Foulsham came under 40 Group control, while Swanton Morley passed into the hands of 25 Group, Flying Training Command.

With no units remaining, the Group itself was disbanded on 17 December having existed for little short of 25 months. In that time it had developed the new science of electronic warfare to a level hardly credible a scant three year earlier. It is perhaps fitting that it disappeared as quickly as it had begun, having fought a most ethereal war of bluff and counter bluff.

Chapter 7

Confound and Destroy?

With the official disbandment of 100(SD) Group in December 1945, the RAF's involvement with radio counter-measures virtually ceased. The dawn of the age of nuclear weaponry rendered the Allied strategic airforces virtually obsolete since the payload of one heavy bomber could now be as destructive as that of five hundred a year earlier. This, coupled with the advent of the jet bomber and the electronic backwardness of the only potential enemy, Soviet Russia, led the Air Ministry in the early post-war years to consider any form of bomber support unnecessary. Perhaps as lip service to the prodigious effort put into electronic warfare during the latter war years, a Radio Warfare Establishment was set up at Watton on 21 September 1945, but work in this field was continued on a very limited basis until the worsening of the Cold War in the early 1950s.

This initial belief that bomber support was no longer necessary, left the assessment of the wartime campaign started in *Post Mortem* incomplete and it is perhaps only now that any judgements as to the success or failure of the campaign can be made. The overall purpose of such operations was in broad terms to render the Luftwaffe's night fighter arm and its associated signals organisation ineffective to the point where Bomber Command's losses in men and machines were compatible with the continuation of the sustained strategic offensive against Germany. To this end, bomber support operations developed into two quite distinct elements; offensive operations against the enemy's night fighters and defensive ones involving deceptive tactics and electronic warfare to shield the bombers from detection by the German radar system. Both these elements will be considered separately but the reader's attention is first directed to the German system and what effect the campaign had on it.

national basis in 1932. Broadly similar in concept to the Royal Observer Corps, the *Flugmeldedienst* was primarily concerned with air raid warning for specific targets rather than the provision of an overall picture of the air situation. The service was made up of observer posts (*Flugwachen* or *Fluwas*) situated around the larger towns. A given number of *Fluwas* would report to a Central Observer post (*Flugwachkommando* or *Fluko*) from which the collated information would be passed on to the Air Force, Civil Authorities and the Railways.

In 1939, this organisation was taken over by the appropriate *Luftgau* (an airforce regional administration) and its personnel were combined into Aircraft Reporting Companies (*Flugmeldekompanien*). The embryo radar chain was also incorporated into the system and all plots from such sources and the *Fluwas* were passed to the relevant *Fluko* for collation and onward transmission.

Thus it will be seen that the radar stations (*Flugmeldemessstellungen* or *Flummess*) were initially used for early warning rather than for controlled interception. When this latter role took on greater importance during 1940/41 a secondary system had to be grafted on to the existing one to allow the particular station to communicate directly with the fighter organisation. The growth of the controlled interception role also led to the *de facto* separation of the radar system from the *Flugmeldedienst*, although it remained under it for administrative purposes.

In the later summer and autumn of 1943, the radar chain reverted to the early warning role with the introduction of the *Zahme Sau* interception technique. This reorganisation led to a change in the method employed for information collation. Those radar stations fitted out for fighter control (see page 216) now passed their information to special Night Fighter Area HQs (*Jagen*). Whereas

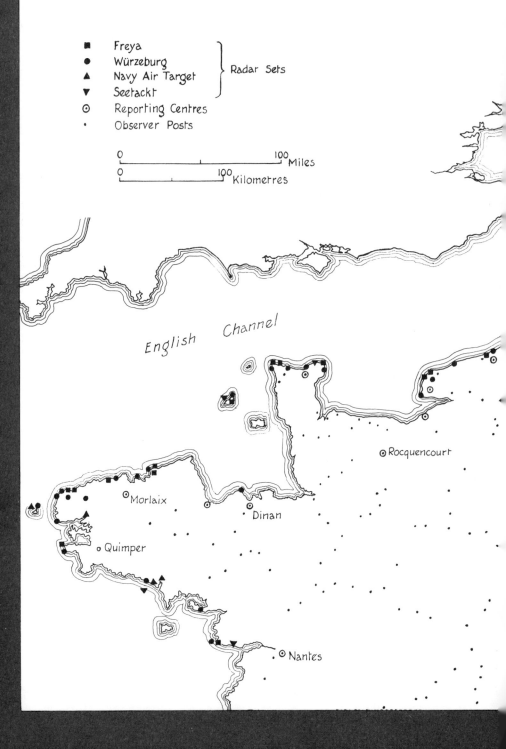

Coastal Radar Installations
March 1942

■ Freya
● Würzeburg
▲ Navy Air Target } Radar Sets
▼ Seetackt
⊙ Reporting Centres
• Observer Posts

0   100 Miles
0   100 Kilometres

English Channel

⊙ Rocquencourt

⊙ Morlaix

⊙ Dinan

○ Quimper

⊙ Nantes

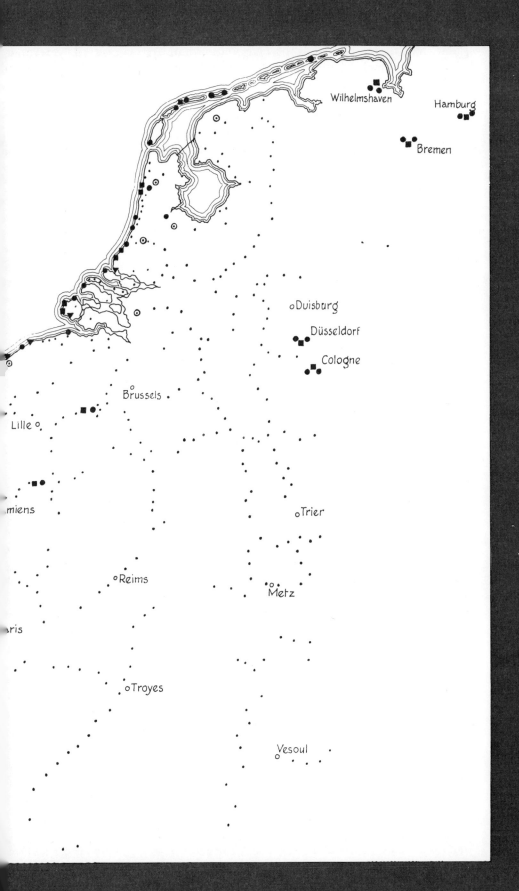

radar information passed to the *Flugmeldienst* had been converted from range, bearing and height to the Fighter Grid (the Luftwaffe using a grid reference to convey such information to its interceptors) at *Fluko* level, this function was now performed at the radar site. In addition, the *Fluwas* now reported to a designated radar station (*Kleinfluko*) who processed their data and combined it with their own for onward transmission to the *Jagen* and the *Hauptfluko*. This latter organisation corresponded to the original *Fluko* but with a great emphasis on air raid warning for the civilian population and industry than before.

It will be seen that from 1940/41, the introduction of radar controlled interception brought about a cumbersome reporting system. The same information was passed to the military and civilian authorities in different forms, a state of affairs which latterly created two virtually independent systems. Rationalisation of this situation came about in February 1944 when the *Flugmeldedienst* came under the control of the relevant *Jagddivision* (the administrative and operational control of all fighter units in a given area). At this time, all radar sites were given one of three classifications: *Flummess Erster Ordnung* (First Class), *Zweiter Ordnung* (Second Class) or *Dritter Ordnung* (Third Class).

A First Class site could comprise a *Jagdschloss*, a *Wassermann*, two *Würzburg-Riese*, three *Freya*'s (one or more fitted with AN*) and two lines to the Y-Service. This combination was used for simultaneous early warning and fighter control. A Second Class site was the old controlled interception set up equipped with two *Würzburg-Riese* and a *Freya* AN. Its primary role was fighter control, being used for general surveillance when not so occupied. All remaining sites were given Third Class status and usually comprised coastal locations equipped with a single *Wassermann*, *Mammut* or *Freya*. They combined the roles of reporting shipping movements with general air surveillance.

The *Fluko* system was replaced with a new organisation, the Preliminary Plotting Centre (*Vorauswertung*). This operated on a more limited level than its predecessor, being responsible for collating the information from a limited number of *Fluwas*, passing this on to its designated *Erster Ordnung* site and issuing local air raid warnings. The key element in this revised system was the First Class site. This acted as a collation point for the data produced by all the agencies in its designated area, i.e. Second and Third Class sites, the *Vorauswertung*, the Y Service, *Jagddivision* situation reports and those from First Class sites in the vicinity. From this mass of information, the given *Erster Ordnung* station produced a 'running commentary' for its area which was in turn passed on to the *Jagddivision* for incorporation into the Divisional 'running commentary' and for onward transmission to the interested civilian agencies. Overall, this was the system in operation at the end of the war.

The foregoing is a brief account of the ground organisation against which the RCM campaign was directed. That such measures were effective is beyond doubt in that the abandonment of radar-controlled interception was brought about by the application of electronic jamming, notably the introduction of *Window*. The post-February 1944 organisation was in fact tailored for operations in an environment heavily polluted by jamming and where, as a conse-

---

*The AN designation indicated that the individual *Freya* was capable of having information translated directly from its CRTs rather than passing the raw data to be processed at a *Seeburg* Table (see page 216).

quence, close ground control of interceptors was impossible.

Having established the profound effect electronic warfare had on the German radar system, the campaign's effects can now be considered in detail. In 1945, Germany possessed five major ground radars, namely *Jagdschloss*, *Wassermann*, *Würzburg-Reise*, *Freya* and *Mammut*. Against these, the RAF employed four major measures, *Mandrel*, *Piperack*, *Carpet* and *Window*. The *Post Mortem* exercises provided hard evidence of their effectiveness or otherwise.

Of all these measures, *Window* proved to be the most dynamic. All the available German radars were affected to a greater or lesser extent. It was instrumental in bringing down the *Himmelbett* system (see page 216) although the introduction of the bomber stream had already rendered it obsolete if still able to operate. From its introduction into service the German system was reduced to plotting the areas of *Window* jamming in order to deduce the track of the bombers from the resulting pattern. During *Post Mortem*, the German operators proved unable to determine with any accuracy the numbers of aircraft flying when *Window* was used or to be able to distinguish between feint and real forces with any certainty. The only real defence against such jamming was a change in the affected radar's wavelength. This the Germans seem to have had some difficulty in carrying out. The interrogation report on General Martini, head of the Luftwaffe's Signals branch, has this to say on the subject:

> 'The very nature of the high frequency war with counter-measures, measures to overcome counter-measures and constant changes in the apparatus, led to demands on the wireless industry which it could not meet.'

Eventually, Germany did manage to produce models of the various radars with variable wavelengths and considerable effort was put into utilising the Doppler effect (under the code-name *Laus*) to specifically counter *Window*. Unfortunately, the *Laus* scheme met a certain amount of resistance from the actual operators. An intelligence report on a captured signals officer from the 53rd Signals Regiment has this to say on the subject:

> 'Some operators of the *Würzburg* and *Freya*, although agreeing that they experienced interference from *Window* . . ., maintain that because *Window* travels more slowly than an aircraft, an experienced operator can distinguish the flight of the aircraft against the tracks of the *Window*. The officer P/W however, is sceptical about all anti-*Window* devices and believes that the German radar authorities are seriously perturbed by it.'

In any event, *Window* remained a problem for the Germans right up to the end of the war, although the freer *Zahme Sau* technique was better able to cope with it than was the *Himmelbett*.

Post Mortem indicated that *Mandrel* was not as effective as had seemed probable. The *Wassermann* radar proved to be particularly resistant to this form of jamming and the operators maintained that there were usually sufficient gaps in the frequency cover to allow at least one radar type to 'see' through it. The chief Operations Officer at Grove indicated that the presence of *Mandrel* jamming had, in the light of experience, proved to be a useful indicator as to the imminence of enemy activity.

Exercise Four, Five and Nine of *Post Mortem* used combinations of measures. In the first of these, Four, *Window* and *Mandrel* were used and the RAF observers felt that the overall effect was one of delay rather than outright

Luftwaffe Radar Installations
in Europe 1944/1945

■ First Class Site
▲ Second Class Site
● Third Class Site

MEERAUGE

BRACHVOGEL
SCHLOSSHUND
KREUZOTTER
NASHORN
GRASMÜCKE

BOCK

LEOPARD   HIRSCH
PIROL
STIER
HEIMCHEN
LAUS
MAKRELE
SEESTERN

KONDOR   KOBRA
LOWENFELS
SCHNEPFE
DOBERMANN
NEUNAUGE
REIF
MILAU

SAN
HORNCHEN   STIEGLITZ
STRANDLAUFER   KANINCHEN   TONFELS

WINDHUND   EICHFELS
WALFISCH

HUHN   BAR
KONRADSBURG
TRAMPELTIER   FLAMINGO
TIRSTEINT
HOCKERSCHWAN   LINDENSTEIN   LAHNBURG
BIRKHAHN   SONNBERG   PERLHUHN
DOHLE
KEMPERSTEIN
R
ROSSBERG
RUH   LIEBENBERG

WARTENSTEIN
ENSITTICH   PINSCHER(RIND)
KORNBERG   WURM
MISTKAFER   KRANSTEIN
HEUPFERD
PLATTBERG
SEIDENSPINNER   RATIBOR
NEBELHORN
KORALLE

IN   ENGERLING

CHSE

TAPIR
BRUMBAR
HER(HAHNCHEN)   BLUTEGEL   KLEIBER   MILBE
NEUFUNDLÄNDER
REHPINSCHER   PAPAGEI
HOLZWURM   WACHTEL
PFAU   MUSTANG   ALPSPITZE
RIEN·KAFER   MOLCH
GAISBERG
TAUBE   KEILER

EGRUBE   STEINFELS
SCHIMMEL
ANDER   SAATKRÄHE
HUND   KALB
SKORPION

0   100 Miles
0   100 Kilometres

confusion. Exercises Five and Nine on the other hand, threw the full weight of electronic measures against the system. In both cases, the *Freya* sets were rendered almost completely useless as were the *Würzburgs*. The *Mammuts* were able to operate until the start of *Mandrel* jamming although in the latter exercise (Nine), the cover was patchy. The *Jagdschloss* sets behaved in much the same way, being effectively jammed in Exercise Five and patchily so in Nine. The *Wassermanns* proved to be the only radars capable of operating effectively in the face of concentrated jamming and even these succumbed to a certain extent in Exercise Nine.

Thus we have a picture of a system in which the radar element was highly unreliable and at times little more than useless. Against this, however, it should be remembered that the system was optimised for producing a broad picture rather than specifics and that its radar component was only negated if all the jamming measures were fully operational. This was not always the case. The newness of the technology, the haste with which many of the jammers were produced and the difficulty of operating such equipment under operational conditions led to frequent breakdowns and misapplication of the various measures which allowed the Germans to 'see'. In addition, the demise of radar as a primary means of obtaining data led to the increasing importance of the *Horchdienst*, the Luftwaffe's Listening or Y-Service. This service was divided into three branches, the *Y* which monitored enemy signals traffic, a jamming branch (*Funkmessstörung*) and a radar interception service (*Funkmessbeobachtung*).

In the Western theatre, two Signals Regiments, the 350th and the 351st operated this service. These two units were divided into *Kompanien* for administrative purposes and *Zugen* and *Truppen* for operational ones. The structure of a typical Kompanie was as follows. The particular unit, the 19th company of the 351st Regiment, was sub-divided into three HQs each controlling two sub-stations. In addition to these, the unit controlled six mobile units. Each of these was equipped with two direction-finding sections (*Meter-Peilung*) each with *Samos* (90 to 470 MHz), *Dohmeyer F* (200 to 500 MHz) and *Dohmeyer G* (up to 1,000 MHz) receivers, two *Naxburg* trailers for *Oboe* tracking and two anti-*Bumerang* (ABG 23 and ABG 24) jamming transmitters for use against *Oboe*.

Two Y-Stations were operational during *Post Mortem* and were equipped as follows:

Veilchen:
This station had four towers to carry its receivers, the first of which was 65 ft (20 m) high carrying a horn-type aerial for the reception of signals in the 2.6 to 4 cm band. Bearings from this receiver were accurate to within 3°. The second tower, which was 48.75 ft (15 m) high, also carried a horn-type aerial for the reception of 8 to 12 cm signals. Again accuracy was in the region of plus or minus 3°. The third tower was the same height as the second but carried two dipoles backed by a reflector. These fed a *Samos* (90 to 470 MHz) and a *Fano* (400 to 800 MHz) receiver which gave an accuracy of bearing of between 1° and 3°. The remaining tower served a further *Samos* receiver.

Tamariske:
This station had three towers, all of which were 48.75 ft (15 m) high. The first of these carried a vertically-polarised aerial feeding a *Samos* receiver while a second one carried an aerial array at 45° to feed another *Samos*. The final tower carried two horn-type aerials feeding two *Korfu* receivers, one of which covered

the 2.5 to 4 cm band while the other received the 8 to 12 cm band.

From these details, it will be seen that the Y-Service was very well equipped to cover virtually the entire spectrum of receivable enemy transmissions. The reliance Bomber Command put on its electronic navigational aids such as H2S and *Gee* made this Y ability increasingly important to the Germans. Bomber Command was quite capable of deceiving or blinding the radar components of the system but it could only deceive the Y-Service by switching off *all* the transmitting equipment in its aircraft. This posed an almost insoluble problem for, without its navigational aids, the Command could not find its targets. A partial solution was the imposition of total radio/radar silence until the stream had crossed the enemy coast, instituted in late 1944, but the depth of penetration occurring in this period tended to negate this somewhat. Worse, the crews were lax about maintaining such conditions, the chief offence being the indiscriminate use of IFF (see page 18). Martini had this to say on the subject to his post-war interrogators:

> 'The General had heard the explanation from British bomber pilots that they kept their IFF switched on to dowse searchlights, but he did not believe it. He thought that there must have been some important reason for this procedure which allowed the Germans to pick up the approach of RAF bombers. He asked whether it was maintained with the object of eventually being of some value to night fighter escort aircraft. He pointed out that it was of exceedingly great value to the Germans.'

The RAF observers during *Post Mortem* were greatly impressed by the performance of the Y-Service and it is the author's opinion that the availability of such accurate and unjammable information went a long way towards the negation of the advantages brought about by the successful jamming of the German ground radars.

Overall then, we have a picture of a detection system flexible enough to overcome the worst effects of jamming by the use of whichever element was least affected at any given time. In this sense, the bomber support campaign may be seen to have failed in its objective of denying the enemy a picture of what was happening in his airspace. Against this, however, it may be said that the campaign denied the Germans close ground-control of their interceptors, which in any case was rendered obsolete tactically by the introduction of the stream and more importantly, it rendered the *Zahme Sau* technique incapable of reaching its full potential.

The introduction of the stream made the *Zahme Sau* style of running battle inevitable whether or not jamming had been introduced. That *Zahme Sau* could be successful is without doubt as shown by the losses suffered by Bomber Command in the spring of 1944. The weight of jamming rendered the system more loose than it would have to have been in order to reach its full potential. Jamming was only a part of this process and other factors, which will be discussed later, seem to have had much greater importance.

No mention has yet been made of the other side of the German system, the interceptor aircraft and their R/T and W/T links with the control centres. (Details of the three interception techniques, *Himmelbett*, *Wilde Sau* and *Zahme Sau* will be found on pages 216 to 220.)

The Luftwaffe succeeded in bringing into service four families or individual types of AI radar, namely the FuG 202/212 family, the FuG 216/217/218 *Neptun* family, FuG 220 and FuG 240. The major RAF measure against all these was the ubiquitous *Window* backed by a number of airborne and ground-based transmitters. FuG 202/212 was completely overwhelmed by *Window*. The metric wavelength *Neptun* family and FuG 220 were also heavily affected by the measure. Only the provision of variable wavelengths in the later FuG 217, 218 and 220 equipments in 1944 gave some respite from the intensity of the jamming. Even then, it must be said that really successful operations could only be carried out by crews with the most experienced radar operators.

The *Zahme Sau* technique slightly offset this problem in that the 'running commentary' gave the crews a broad indication of where the enemy was and even if an aircraft's radar was completely useless, it could be still brought into the stream where the crew could search visually, with a good chance of success. AI jamming proved, in fact, to be a double-edged weapon in that experienced crews found that a concentration of jamming indicated the position of the bombers quite clearly. Some units even resorted to using their best crews as 'pathfinders', flying in formation with other crews and leading them to the bombers.

The remaining AI radar, FuG 240, remained unjammed by virtue of its centimetric wavelength but never entered service in significant numbers.

The increasing pressure of AI jamming and the wide scale employment of electronic aids in the bombers led to the introduction by the Luftwaffe of a number of airborne homing devices, the most important of which were FuG 227 and FuG 350. There was and still is no real answer to a homing device short of removing the offending transmission being homed on to. This was the case with these two devices and they continued to take a toll of bombers as long as there were transmissions for them to detect.

Serious though the interference with AI radar was, more serious was the jamming of the R/T and W/T links between the interceptors and the ground. *Zahme Sau* relied totally on the ability to convey updated information to the interceptors by radio at all times. The same had been true with the *Himmelbett* system, were the fighter was totally reliant on broadcast instructions until it was within AI radar or visual range. The RAF was quick to recognise this factor as the weakest link of all in the whole German system and put great effort into producing a whole range of R/T and W/T jammers, the most notable of which were *Airborne Cigar* and *Jostle IV*.

Although the effectiveness of such jammers was never actually tested post-war, interrogations of ex-Luftwaffe personnel indicated that such jamming was a major problem. Various remedies were evolved ranging from multi-channel broadcasts, so that if one was jammed the aircrew could tune into another which was free, to totally bizarre schemes such as using a force's broadcasting station to play certain types of music to indicate the position of the stream. The executive order for this novel scheme read as follows:

'In agreement with the Generalkommando of Jagdcorps I, the following arrangements have been brought into force in the area of *Luftwaffe Befehishaber Mitte* for transmission of the fighter commentary from the broadcasting station at Mühlacker:

(1) In the event of enemy air penetration, a music programme will be broadcast by the Forces transmitter *Annemarie*, interspersed with orders to fighters. This will be additional to the Korps and Divisional fighter commentary.

(2) The music programme will be divided into:
   (a) Wuerlitzer organ music, (b) Marches, (c) Xylophone music, (d) Violin music, (e) Piano music, (f) Soldier's songs, (g) Waltzes and (h) Accordion music.

(3) The main zones to be defended are divided into eight large areas, each of·which is allotted the name of the W/T beacon placed in that area.

(4) The following areas have been laid down:
   (a) *Quelle*, (b) *Kurfürst*, (c) *Phillip* (for Kassel area), (d) *Otto*, (e) *Nine*, (f) *Ten*, (g) *Berta* and (h) *Ponto*.

(5) The following music is to be taken as code denoting these areas:
   (a) *Quelle* – Wuerlitzer organ.
   (b) *Kurfürst* – Marches.
   (c) *Phillip* – Xylophone.
   (d) *Otto* – Violin.
   (e) *Nine* – Piano.
   (f) *Ten* – Soldier's songs.
   (g) *Berta* – Waltzes.
   (h) *Ponto* – Accordion.

(6) If, for example, an enemy formation flies into the *Quelle* area, the Forces transmitter *Annemarie* will play cinema organ music as long as the formation remains in that area.

(7) As long as the fighter units are receiving their orders by means of Korps and Divisional commentaries, they will continue to fly according to the instructions given in these commentaries.

(8) If the Korps and Divisional commentaries are jammed, orders will be transmitted by the radio station *Annemarie*.

(9) If ground to air reception of the Korps and Divisional commentaries proves impossible and no orders are given out by *Annemarie*, fighters will fly to the area indicated by the type of music broadcast by *Annemarie* and will assemble near the W/T beacon in that area.

(10) The areas *Quelle*, *Kurfürst*, *Phillip* and *Otto* are subdivided into northerly and southerly halves.

(11) (a) If the enemy formation is in the northern half of those areas, each piece of music played will be announced individually.
   (b) If the enemy formation is in the southern half of the area, two pieces of music will be announced at a time.

(12) If enemy aircraft do not enter the areas laid down in paragraph 4, the radio station *Annemarie* will broadcast its usual dance music.

(13) If a number of large formations penetrate into Reich territory, the Generalkommando of *Jagd Korps* I will decide what music is to be played.

(14) The frequency on which *Annemarie* transmits is at present 968 Kc/s. Any change in frequency will be advised in good time.

(15) This instruction comes into force on 26th December 1943 at 15.00 hours.

Solutions such as those described and the RAF's habit of frequently interrupting jamming transmissions to stop them being homed on to, which allowed clear reception on even jammed channels at certain times, ensured that the aircrews received some sort of information. Again, post war interrogation made it clear that, as with AI jamming, only the most able crews were success-ful under such conditions. It is interesting, however, to note in this context, one POW's comments when he was asked the usual reasons for an interceptor not making contact with the bombers; he cited three reasons in order of importance:

(1)   Confusion due to diversionary attacks;
(2)   Bad navigation on the part of the night fighter;
(3)   British interference with the commentary.

As with the jamming of the ground system, the interference with the Luftwaffe's airborne electronics seems to have caused very serious problems but ones which were by no means insoluble. The jamming seems once more to have inhibited rather than brought about the collapse of the system it was aimed against, and yet the system did finally break-down in the autumn of 1944. It is the author's view that the final collapse of the Luftwaffe's night fighter defence system was due to factors unrelated to the bomber support campaign with one exception, the Mosquito fighter aircraft.

In the summer of 1944, the Allies invaded France and by the autumn of that year had pushed the German forces out of most of that country. The loss of France's coastline facing England punched a gigantic hole in the radar chain which was never to be fully plugged. A new network was hastily cobbled together on the German frontier but there was not enough equipment available to make it really effective, and more importantly it cut the time in which a raid could be plotted drastically. This meant that feint operations became more effective because the German controllers had less time to distinguish between the real and the fake threat. On deep penetration raids the system could still work, but attacks on areas such as the Ruhr gave no leeway for error. In fact so desperate was the situation, the only defence such a region could be provided with was standing patrols and luck.

At the same time as preparations were under way for the invasion, the Allied strategic air forces began to turn their attention to oil targets. By this stage in the war, Germany was almost totally reliant for fuel on what she could produce within her own borders. As the attacks mounted the fuel supply, which had never really been adequate, became critical. In consequence, the number of night fighters which could be despatched on any night dropped dramatically. Controllers became more and more wary of committing their meagre force until the enemy intention was clear, in order not to waste precious fuel. The net result was that the level of interceptions dropped markedly.

Aircrew training was also vitally affected by the fuel famine, virtually ceasing by 1944. This meant that no adequately trained replacements were available to fill the gaps in the strengths of the front-line units. So abyssmal was the level of training given to new crews at this stage that a two-tier system of aircraft use had to be instituted. All crews were divided into 'A' and 'B' classifications. 'A' crews were the experienced ones who were given the best aircraft fitted with the latest equipment and who were scrambled to intercept the bombers. 'B' crews were held in reserve or were used for night ground-attack work. At this point morale began to crack.

As the use of the experienced crews increased so did their casualty rate. Many of the Luftwaffe's best night fighter pilots had been in combat for perhaps three years and the hazards of night interception increasingly took their toll. Once an *Experten* had been incapacitated there was no one to replace him. The remaining crews could barely fly let alone get through the jamming and find the bombers.

It was at this point that 'Mosquito phobia' broke out. It had long been known in Germany that the RAF was using Mosquito fighters to harry the Luftwaffe's night interceptors and as the attacks from this source, both in the air and on the ground increased, panic began to appear. The fear of interception caused crews to take risks they would not normally have taken. Low flying caused an increasing number of accidents as did attempts to land on unlit airfields when intruders were about. In truth many of these accidents resulted from inexperience but all were attributed to the Mosquito. Morale sank lower and lower, a process which was not helped by increasing calls for night fighters to make night ground-attack sorties for which they were not trained and which proved to be extremely dangerous to execute.

It is the author's contention that it was these factors which defeated the Luftwaffe's night fighter organisation and not the bomber support campaign. The campaign itself may be regarded as a holding operation which kept losses down to an acceptable level rather than one which soundly defeated the enemy. On being asked whether he considered the jamming campaign a success, Sir Robert Cockburn stated that he felt that it was, in that it allowed Bomber Command tactical flexibility which it would have otherwise lost through the increasing casualties inflicted on it. He went on to say that certain measures, such as *Window*, were so effective initially that Bomber Command was seduced by the success to the point where its tactics would not function without an RCM element.

Air Vice-Marshal Addison's reply to the same question was a most definite 'yes' in terms of the saving of human life. Addison went on to discuss the role of the campaign and it emerges that his operational philosophy was one of attack. He gives the impression that he was not particularly concerned whether a particular measure worked, being more interested in making his Group's presence felt and subduing the enemy by constantly frightening and worrying at him. In essence, he saw the campaign as one of attrition, constantly wearing the enemy down by ever increasing pressure. In this, he mirrored the prevailing operational mood of the entire Command.

Having considered the effect the campaign had on the enemy, let us now take a look at the bomber support units themselves. As has been indicated, these fall into two distinct categories, the heavy airborne jamming units and the offensive fighter units. As a general remark, it should be noted that the campaign always had the highest priority in aircraft, equipment and man-power within the resources available.

The heavy units were equipped with five types of aircraft, the Stirling, Liberator, Fortress, Halifax and Lancaster. (192 Squadron also operated Wellingtons and Mosquitos in the ELINT role.) Addison would have liked to standardise on the Lancaster but the entire production of this type was required for bombing operations. Of the remaining four aircraft types, the Stirling and the Liberator were the least satisfactory.

The Stirling was used as a carrier for the *Mandrel* device, the operation of which made performance demands really beyond the type's capabilities. It was replaced by the Halifax which was an altogether more suitable electronic warfare platform in terms of performance and fuselage capacity. It was eventually hoped to standardise on this latter type for all the heavy squadrons

within 100(SD) Group but this did not prove possible because the type could
not carry the *Jostle* device. The size of *Jostle* was the main reason for retaining
the two American types, the Fortress and the Liberator, both aircraft having
the capacity to carry it. As has been said, the Liberator was altogether
unsatisfactory in that the aircraft supplied to 100(SD) Group had previously
been used by American units and in consequence manifested all the problems
associated with aircraft which had logged many flying hours. This is not to say
that the B-24 was a poor electronic warfare platform, indeed the American
RCM unit (803rd/36th) appreciated the type for its capacious fuselage and
standardised on it. It was simply that the RAF aircraft were too old to meet the
performance criteria demanded of them and proved difficult to keep serviceable.

The reasons for the use of the Fortress have been discussed in detail on pages
37 and the type presented no major problems in service. It was retained for its
ability to carry *Jostle* and eventually replaced the Liberator in this role. Thus,
by the end of the war, the Group's jamming squadrons were equipped with two
types of aircraft, the Halifax and the Fortress.

The major problems encountered by the heavy jamming squadrons were the
sensitivity of the electronic equipment and the demands made on navigational
skill by their role. There were frequent breakdowns in equipment, especially
amongst the *Mandrel* units, and the crews were constantly made aware of the
need to be in the right place at the right time. No 100(SD) Group's records
contain numerous references to navigational training programmes and to
problems with this or that squadron's performance in that area. Electronic aids
such as *Gee/Loran* and H2S were of help but were often interfered with by the
operation of the jamming equipment itself.

The jammers presented another hazard in that they were liable to be homed
on to. That the Command was well aware of this danger is shown by Signal
Instruction Number 23 of 1 July 1944, referring to the use of *Jostle*, which read
as follows:

'Introduction:
  (3) The installation in aircraft of 214 Squadron comprises the following:
      An HF transmitter rapidly tunable to any frequency in the 3 to 6 mc/s
      and radiating 2 kW of power, and a precision wavemeter is provided
      to accurately divine the enemy frequency.
  (4) Jamming is controlled by the station at Kingsdown, who notify *Jostle*
      aircraft which frequencies are to be jammed.

Execution:
  (6) *Jostle*-equipped aircraft are to be available for every major raid.
214 Squadron Operations:
  (8) The Duty Signals Officer, Bomber Command, is to be informed, as
      early as possible, of the following:
      (1) The number of *Jostle* aircraft available for operations.
      (2) The order of flight in the bomber stream, by aircraft letter.
      (3) The collective call-sign for *Jostle* aircraft.
      (4) The identification number of the wavemeter in each aircraft.
      If *Jostle* aircraft are covering a number of separate bomber forces, the above
      details must be given separately for each force.

Kingsdown Control:

(10) Jamming instructions will be broadcast on 4090 kc/s, Kingsdown using sign A7Z. Wireless operators are to listen to this at all times except when receiving 100 Group's half-hourly broadcast and Bomber Command's navigational transmissions.

(11) The frequency to be jammed will be signified by the broadcast of the appropriate wave meter reading.

(13) Jamming on the designated frequency will be continued until orders to the contrary are received.

(14) Jamming is to be lifted during Group and Command transmissions and is to be applied in 60 second cycles with a 15 second break between to allow reception of jamming orders and to prevent the enemy homing on to the transmissions.

Examples of orders from Kingsdown:
B8070, B8070, B8070;
Jostle aircraft B is to begin jamming transmissions on a wave setting of 80.70.
B00, B00, B00;
Jostle aircraft B is to cease jamming transmission.'

The Germans certainly developed and used airborne homing devices which were capable of giving a bearing on various of the RAF's jamming transmissions. There is no hard evidence as to whether such devices materially increased the losses suffered by the jamming squadrons. No 101 and 214 Squadrons incurred particularly heavy losses, some of which were probably attributable to this cause.

As has been suggested earlier, the jamming units were most successful when involved in diversions rather than direct electronic jamming. Unfortunately, there were never really enough aircraft available to give true credibility to the spoof. An inverse ratio developed whereby more aircraft were needed to simulate the complexities of the Command's transmissions and fewer resources of trained crews and fully equipped aircraft were available. This state of affairs was never fully resolved and was not helped by the blind alley of *Big Ben* operations. As has been recounted, *Big Ben* was designed to counter the non-existent radio control of the V-2 bombardment rocket. During the latter half of 1944 and again in early 1945, squadrons were tied up in this work which could have well been used elsewhere. It is dangerous to be over critical with hindsight, for the V-2 was immune to any sort of interception and any method of stopping it had to be pursued. Indeed, signals of the type thought to be connected with the rocket were picked up and jammed, their existence justifying the continuance of such operations.

Closely allied to the airborne jamming units was the electronic intelligence element, latterly represented by 192 Squadron. Airborne data gathering of this kind proved to be a vital element in providing an up-to-date picture of the enemy's defences. So useful was the information gleaned in this way that the ELINT units were used more and more for purposes outside the scope of the bomber support campaign as time went on. Examples of these other uses included the mapping of the Norwegian radar chain in preparation for the final aerial attack on the *Tirpitz*, the search for *Big Ben* transmissions and investigations into navigational aids used by the He111s air launching V-1s in early 1945.

With regard to the bomber support campaign, ELINT proved of the greatest value and the *Post Mortem* observers noted with some satisfaction that a close look at the German defensive system produced no equipment which was unknown to them.

The fighter element of bomber support operated with reasonably consistent success throughout the campaign. Initially, some problems were encountered with the aircraft available but the appearance of the Mosquito solved these. In this aircraft, the bomber support campaign found the almost perfect escort fighter/intruder. It was heavily armed, manoeuvrable, could take heavy damage, had an adequate range and a performance envelope superior to most of the aircraft it was ranged against. Initially, 100(SD) Group was issued with Mosquito II fighters which were old and mechanically unreliable because of this. Overhaul and re-engining of these aircraft and the introduction of later marks ironed out early difficulties with the type and, fitted with centimetric radar, the Mosquito was without doubt the supreme interceptor operating in the night skies of Europe during the middle war years.

Four types of AI radar, the Mks IV, VIII, X and XV, were carried by the fighter element in the campaign. AI Mk IV proved to be the least successful. It was heavily affected by *Window* and, because of its metric wavelength, had difficulty in following a target near the bomber stream or the ground because the 'blip' was obscured by all the extraneous clutter picked up by the set. There is evidence to suggest that the Germans jammed the set from mid-1944, degrading its performance even more. A change in wavelength did little to help the situation and the type was replaced with centimetric sets as quickly as possible.

Centimetric AI, with its attendant advantages of being fairly resistant to *Window* and the ability to follow much smaller target movements, was available in 1943 but was not released for use over enemy territory until the late spring of the following year. The first such set to be used was the Mk VIII but its use was extremely brief since, at the time of its entry into bomber support service, it was already being replaced by the superior Mk X.

AI Mk X, an American product, proved to be an outstanding radar and most of 100(SD) Group's fighter squadrons were eventually equipped with it. It proved to be resistant to *Window*, although care had to be taken when using it near the bomber streams because a combination of the former measure and H2S transmissions did affect it. At low level its range was greatly reduced and its relatively short wavelength made it susceptible to weather interference; bad rain storm could clutter the CRTs and make tracking difficult.

AI Mk XV, another American product, was initially used as a substitute for AI Mk X when the latter was in short supply. It originated as an ASV radar and this heritage created certain disadvantages when it was used in the AI mode, i.e. its relatively slow scan pattern made the tracking of a violently moving target difficult. It did, however, prove to be better able to operate at low level than the AI X and its ASV background allowed it to be used in a similar way to H2S for navigation. As with AI X, weather interference proved to be a problem.

All these AI sets were prone to break down, this being especially true for AI Mk IV. The following figures relating to the instances of radar failure against sorties flown by one AI X crew may give the reader some idea of the scale of the problem:

In a tour of 45 sorties there were:

Two instances of damage to own aircraft.

Three instances of mechanical failure in own aircraft.

Five instances of radar failure in own aircraft.

In addition to AI, three other electronic aids, *Serrate*, *Monica* and *Perfectos*, were employed to bring the fighters into contact with the enemy. The first of these, *Serrate*, was a homing device designed to give a bearing on the enemy's FuG 202/212 AI sets. In service, it proved most successful until such time as the sets it was directed against passed out of use, but the need to convert the *Serrate* contact to an AI one to complete the interception proved to be a major weakness, especially with AI Mk IV. More often than not, contact was lost during the switch over. *Serrate* was later developed to home on to FuG 220 transmissions, but this was so protracted as to give the new model little change to prove itself.

Monica, originally a tail-warning device for bombers, was used by the fighter units in much the same way except that they tried to close with the contact rather than to evade it. The procedure was to allow the 'bogey' to approach to within 1,800 ft (549 m) and then swing round through 360° and try and pick him up on the forward AI in order to make an interception. As will be appreciated, a manoeuvre of this nature required a skilled pilot and radar operator to be successful.

Perfectos was the most sophisticated of the three in that it triggered the enemy's FuG 25a IFF set and having thus established the 'bogey's' identity with 100% certainty, gave a bearing and range reading on the transmission. Unfortunately, the Germans suspected that their IFF transmissions were being homed on to and adopted the simple expedient of switching off their sets, thereby cancelling out *Perfectos'* usefulness at a stroke.

Initially, navigation proved something of a problem for the bomber support fighter units. Most of the crews had previously served in defensive squadrons which had operated over friendly territory where a fix could always be obtained if there seemed to be any danger of getting lost. Now they were being called on to fly deep into enemy territory, often to specific locations. Training the crews for this took time. The introduction of *Gee* helped greatly in this direction but again it took time to train a man to use it. More subtly, the increasing weight of electronic gear being carried put a considerable strain on the radar operator in a Mosquito. Not only did he have to watch the radar set, the tail warner and the homer but he had to operate the *Gee* set and tell the pilot what course to follow as well!

This quantity of plumbing in the cockpit also caused problems of space. The Mosquito's cockpit was relatively small and had never been designed to carry a radar set. Conditions now became chaotic – the only place the *Gee* equipment would fit was behind the pilot's seat which meant that the radar operator had to kneel on his seat and operate the set over the back of it! It became a standing joke in 100(SD) Group that to be a radar-operator in a Mosquito you had to be no more than 5 ft tall. Obviously, working in such conditions did not help matters and it says much for the endurance of the crews that they were so successful.

A final point to note concerning the fighter units of 100(SD) Group is that the crews initially had some difficulty settling down to their new Command

structure. Mostly coming from Fighter Command, they needed some while t
adapt to the more stolid ways of Bomber Command. Whereas previously the
had been used to a fairly informal method of operations they were now expecte
to conform to their new Command's more strict and doggedly determine
ways. This caused some friction which was not helped by difficulty in findin
the enemy. The influence of Chisholm, a fighter man himself, helped enor
mously in this direction and in any case the nature of the Group's work mean
that it was left pretty much to its own devices and soon worked out its ow
operational method. Indeed, by late 1944, the Group can be said to hav
become rather an exclusive club altogether.

At this point, the reader has been given some insight into the high and lov
points of the campaign from both the RAF and the Luftwaffe points of view an
the question must be asked, what was achieved?

If the campaign was primarily aimed at cutting down Bomber Command'
casualties, as it certainly was, then it must be seen as a success. A look at th
chart below will show that the introduction of electronic counter-measure
produced a sharp drop in casualties and continued to suppress them until suc

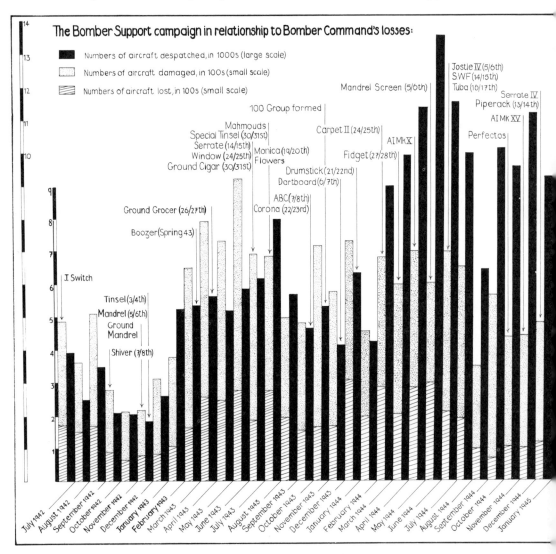

time as the Luftwaffe was no longer a force to be reckoned with. The combination of jamming and deception allowed Bomber Command to continue its offensive when a head-on battle of attrition would have destroyed it. That the Luftwaffe was quite capable of doing this is demonstrated by the 44,000 plus aircrew who did not come back, in spite of ever increasing support for them in one form or another.

The activities of the bomber support units did not, however, materially contribute to the Luftwaffe night fighter arm's eventual collapse other than through the contribution of the fighter squadrons. As has been shown, however great the weight of jamming or deception thrown against it, the German system was flexible enough to continue operating in one form or another. That such operations made life all the more difficult for the Luftwaffe is beyond question, but the fact still remains that night fighters still left the ground and still destroyed bombers throughout the campaign until at least March 1945. The reasons for the collapse of the German system have been described in some detail and it is clear that 100(SD) Group's fighter squadrons helped this process by the simple if unpalatable expedient of killing German aircrew. In late-war Germany, replacing aircraft was not a problem, replacing men was. Every German crew shot down or forced into making a bad mistake by the thought that a Mosquito was after him was one crew less to attack the bombers the next night.

It is tempting to conclude that there were greater parallels between the Allied day and night bombing offensives than is readily apparent, in that in order for the Eighth Airforce to operate successfully its fighter element had to literally destroy the Luftwaffe's day fighter arm. In the same way, the night fighter arm's successes could only be really stopped by its destruction, which no amount of jamming, however sophisticated in concept or use, could achieve. Perhaps, then, the emphasis of the campaign was wrong and Bomber Command, like its American counterpart, should have striven to destroy the enemy airforce rather than to split its supportive effort between this concept and that of deceiving and blinding him.

Whatever judgements are made in hindsight, 100(SD) Group's motto 'Confound and Destroy' still stands as a good epitaph for the campaign; the men defending Germany from aerial night attack in the mid-war years were certainly confounded by it, and in the ensuing confusion, a fair number were destroyed by it.

Appendix 1

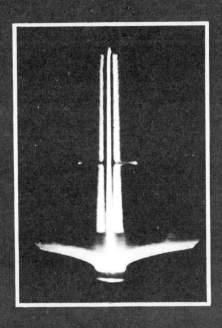

The Electronic Equipment

In this appendix will be found technical details of and notes on the various electronic devices which form the core of the Bomber Support story. For clarity the following categories have been formulated so that the reader may compare the different devices evolved for a similar purpose one with another:

I   Jamming Devices
II Homing and Warning Devices
III Airborne Interception Radar
IV German Ground Radars and Homing Devices
V   Experimental German Electronic Aids
VI Miscellaneous Devices

The last named category covers those equipments which do not readily find a home elsewhere but of necessity are described to complete the picture. The whole is rounded off by a Glossary explaining the more technical terms which will be met in these pages.

I JAMMING DEVICES

This appendix details thirty-two devices which were used for jamming purposes during the course of the Bomber Support campaign.

The British devices fall into two distinct categories: those which generated electronic 'noise' and which were aimed at the enemy's EW, GCI, GL and AI radars; and those which produced an audio interference aimed at disrupting the enemy's R/T communication channels. The distinction is somewhat blurred with devices such as *Dartboard* which generated random bursts of Morse to disrupt W/T links and

Window which was passive, acting like an electronic mirror.

It will be noticed that while the British effort was prodigious (29 of the devices referred to here originate from that country or America), little new ground was broken in that successive device were improvements on predecessors, but aimed at the same target.

German efforts in this direction are something of a grey area. That they did produce jammers is without doubt, but exact details of the equipment is unavailable. Three such devices are detailed here and the author would be most interested to hear from anyone who has more information on this area.

It should be noted that the enemy equipments shown in brackets in the various details are there to give a rough guide to the devices which were affected by a particular jamming measure. Their presence indicates that they came within a certain frequency range and therefore could be affected, rather than that the measure was aimed specifically against them.

BRITISH

Airborne Cigar (RAF designation ARI 5558)
A jamming device developed by the TRE which was designed to disrupt the enemy's R/T control channels

Part of the ABC *installation in a B-17, comprising the wavemeter and the Type 20G visual indicator. The signal to be jammed was displayed as a blip rising out of the base line on the 20G's CRT. (Crown Copyright)*

Above: *The* ABC *transmission mast carried by a B-17. The smaller aerial is probably part of the aircraft's basic radio fit. The* ABC *mast was standard for all aircraft so equipped. (Crown Copyright)*

Right: *The whip aerial associated with* ABC *equipped B-17 aircraft. (See page 237). (Crown Copyright)*

on spot frequencies in the 38.3–42.5, 30–33 or 48–52 MHz bands. *ABC* could also be used to jam *Benito* (the 'Y' navaid) by tone modulation. One aircraft installation comprised three 50 Watt Type 1260B transmitters, one Type 1624A panoramic receiver with a Type 20G visual indicator (developed by Ryle of Mullards), one Type 185 tone modulator, three power units, one switching unit, three transmitting aerials (mast type with interchangeable end sections for frequency matching) and one receiver aerial (whip type).

The receiver, matched to one of the described bands, swept that band, presenting the range as a base line on a CRT. Any signal received, indicated by a blip on the base line, could be checked aurally by throwing a key switch to see if it was of enemy origin. If it was, the operator tuned one of the transmitters to the frequency in question (its exact value being indicated by the position of the blip on the base line) and jam it. He would then continue to search the designated band, investigating signals and jamming them until all three transmitters were in use. The jamming signal itself was an almost musical warbling note.

Airborne Cigar suffered from poor serviceability being sensitive to dampness and prone to aerial breakages due to icing and vibration. The latter problem was solved by filling the hollow sections of the aerial with sand and providing facilities for altering the resonant frequency.

In service, *ABC* proved to have a range of 50 mls (80 km). The first production units were only capable of operating over the 38.3–42 MHz band, later units having the facility to cover all three bands, the particular band being pre-set on the ground. In January 1944, some *ABC* transmitters were modified to act as unmonitored jammers tuned to 31.2 MHz. Such sets could be identified by their longer aerials.

Airborne Grocer

A device designed to jam enemy AI radar in the 480–500 MHz band (FuG 202 and 212). *Airborne Grocer* was available from May 1944 but was not used operationally because the enemy radars it was aimed at were passing out of service and it was considered too vulnerable for being homed on to. The device used four tail-mounted Yagi aerials.

American Mandrel (Service designation RC 183A/T1661)

A device designed to jam enemy EW radar in the 85–135 MHz band (*Freya, Freya Fahrstuhl, Jagdschloss, Mammut* and *Wassermann*). *American Mandrel* consisted of a modulator, a transmitter and power pack built into a single unit and a dipole aerial similar to the standard VHF aerial. The transmitter was pre-tuned to a 10 MHz band within the operating range. The 80 volt power supply provided a 2 Watt output over such a band. The device was used for only a short time and in limited numbers in Main Force aircraft to augment *Mandrel I* (see page 160). In British service, the device was modified (in December 1943) to cover the 138–158 MHz band. When it was decided to use T1661 in the *Mandrel* screen it was further modified in its coverage by the TRE during April 1944. This last modification programme produced three sub-variants:

Opposite top: *Believed to be the transmitters for the* Airborne Grocer *device mounted in a B-17. (Crown Copyright)*

Bottom: *The four Yagi aerials for the* Airborne Grocer *device mounted on a B-17. These aerials are believed to have been used at a latter date for an interim* Dina *installation. (See page 98). The small 'arrow head' aerial below the tail guns is for* Monica. *(Crown Copyright)*

T1661P – covering the 63–103 MHz band;
T1661Q – covering the 92–133 MHz band;
T1661R – covering the 143–203 MHz band.

Aspidistra
The code name for the transmitters used in *Dartboard* (see page 00).

Briar
A ground-based device for jamming the ground receivers (code-named *Hangover*) in the *Egon* system (see page 00).

Briar (R)
A ground-based device for triggering the airborne IFF set (code-named *Raspberry*) in the *Egon* system.

Carpet II (RAF designation ARI 5549)
A device designed to jam enemy *Würzburg* GCI and GL radars in the 300–600 MHz band which was developed by the TRE. An aircraft installation comprised one TR 1621 transmitter/receiver, one Type 210 indicator unit and one Type 315 or 315A $\frac{1}{4}$-wave vertical aerial. A 40 MHz band within the specified range was swept automatically every 1.5 sec. On receipt of a signal, the automatic sweep was stopped and noise modulated jamming was transmitted for a maximum of eight minutes. At the end of such a period of transmission the search sweep started again. In November 1944, the device was modified to prevent the jamming signal slipping off the required frequency. *Carpet II* was used by 8 Group aircraft for protection when flying outside the bomber stream under the code name *Carpet Sweeper*.

Below: *The Type 315A aerial associated with the* Carpet II *device mounted on a Mosquito FB VI. (Crown Copyright)*

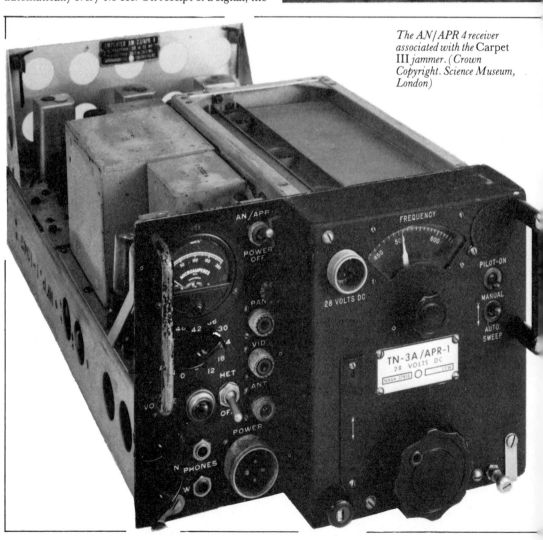

The AN/APR 4 receiver associated with the Carpet III *jammer. (Crown Copyright. Science Museum, London)*

Carpet III (US designation AN/APQ 9 and AN/APR)

A device designed to spot jam enemy *Würzburg* GCI and GL radars in the 475 to 585 MHz band. *Carpet III* was an American development of *Carpet II* with a higher power output. An aircraft installation comprised three AN/APQ 9 transmitters (each with its own power supply), one AN/APR 4 search receiver and four AS-69/APT 'fish-hook' aerials. An operator swept the 300–1,000 MHz band. When the appropriate signal was heard, the sweep was stopped by means of a push button. (The sweep was semi-automatic with the operator acting as a monitor.) One of the transmitters was then tuned to the correct frequency and the signal jammed. The search was then continued and the process repeated with the other transmitters.

Carpet Sweeper

An alternative code-name for *Carpet II* (see page 156).

Corona

A measure designed to disrupt enemy R/T night fighter control links, usually in the 2.5–6 MHz band. The enemy transmissions were monitored at West Kingsdown (later Canterbury) using captured FuG 10

receivers. When the communication channel to be disrupted had been identified, jamming was initiated from four GPO transmitters (three at Rugby and one at Leafield) by an executive order telephoned from the monitoring station. Initially the jamming took the form of misleading instructions broadcast by German speaking personnel and later the transmission of recordings of three or four superimposed German voices.

Dartboard

A measure designed to disrupt enemy night fighter R/T and W/T control channels in the region of 300 kHz. The transmissions were monitored at West Kingsdown and the actual jamming was carried out from three transmitters at Crowborough, Moorside Edge and Droitwich [known under the collective code name *Aspidistra* (see page 156)].

Dina II (US designation AN/APT I)

An American development of the *Mandrel IV* device which was used against radars in the 95–210 MHz band. When used against the FuG 220 AI radar, the device was known as *Piperack* (see page 160).

Drumstick

A measure designed to disrupt enemy high-frequency W/T control channels in the 3–6 MHz band. Up to twenty transmitters were available in the UK within Bomber Command and Number 26 Group for this type of jamming. A listening watch was kept at Cheadle. When this station heard an enemy transmission within the specified band, one of the transmitters

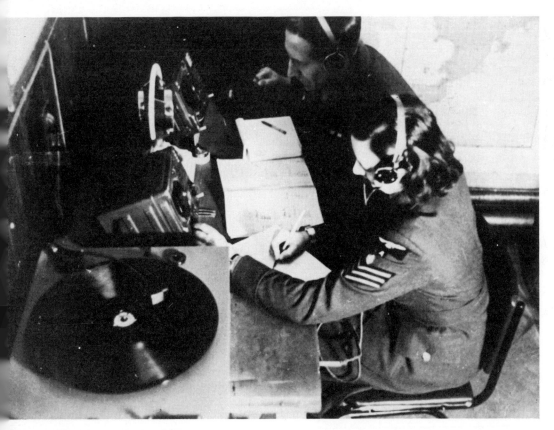

German speaking SOs operating the Corona *measure. Points to note are the log of received signals, the WAAF transcribing the German signals traffic and the gramophone recording of superimposed voices used for jamming. (IWM)*

was tuned to it and the signal was jammed. Cheadle also monitored the jamming transmission to see that the correct frequency was maintained.

Fidget
A measure designed to disrupt enemy night fighter control channels in the medium- and high-frequency bands.

Grocer II
A device designed to barrage jam the enemy's *Würzburg* GCI and GL radars. The BSDU had made a prototype installation of this device in a Halifax aircraft by the war's end.

Ground Cigar
A measure designed to disrupt enemy night fighter control channels in the 38–42 MHz band. The device used fifteen ground-based transmitters in the UK to put up a barrage over the whole band, each transmitter being spot tuned to one part of the band. Amongst the transmitters used were types USP 2, TU 4, SWB 4, AN/GRQ 1 (an American 50 kW television transmitter) and the BBC's sound and vision units at Alexandra Palace.

Ground Grocer
A measure designed to jam enemy AI radar in the 480–500 MHz band (FuG 202 and 212). The device reduced the radar's range to 1,500 ft (461.5 m) when the carrier aircraft was at 12,000 ft (3,692 m), 140 mls

(224 km) from the transmitter and within th transmitted beam.

Ground Mandrel
A measure designed to jam enemy EW radar in th 65–160 MHz band (*Freya, Freya Fahrstahl, Jagdschlos. Mammut* and *Wassermann*). The device comprise twenty-four noise modulated transmitters in groups c six at four sites in the UK. Initially barrage jammin was carried out but later this was superseded by spo jamming. In June 1944, the measure was modified t cover the 90–200 MHz band.

Jostle IV (RAF designation ARI 5289)*
A device designed to provide high power, frequenc

---

*The *Jostle* story remains somewhat mysterious. Previousl the implication has been that *Jostle IV* was a singular devic and not part of a family. This is *not* the case. A device desi nated *Jostle II* was tested in a Mitchell aircraft by the TR during 1943. It would follow from the model numbers tha there was also a *Jostle I* and *III. Jostle II* appears to have serve the same function as *IV* possibly being designed for carriag in a smaller aircraft.

The T1524 transmitter associated with the Jostle IV *device mounted in the bomb bay of a B-17. (Crown Copyright)*

jamming could be undertaken in all six bands while barrage jamming could be produced for the 35–45 and 45–54 MHz bands. The heart of the system was the T1524 transmitter which, together with its power supply, was housed in a pressurised cylindrical casing 51 in (127.5 cm) high and 24.5 in (61.25 cm) in diameter. The device was maintained at a pressure of 35 lb/sq in (2.46 kg/cm²) and was cooled by a heat exchanger with an air scoop fitted to the exterior of the airframe. The unit had an all-up weight of 600 lb (1,320 kg) and was designed primarily for vertical carriage in the bomb bay of a Fortress aircraft. In fact, it proved impossible to fit *Jostle* in any aircraft other than the B-17 and the B-24. (In the latter aircraft, the device was also mounted in the bomb bay.)

The 3–6, 6–12 and 12–18 MHz bands used a trailing aerial whilst the 26–35, 35–45 and 45–54 MHz bands used a mast aerial. *Jostle* was operated by remote control from a CU 286 unit.

The first thirty T1524s built could only operate on the 3–6 MHz band, all other such transmitters being able to cover any of the six bands by means of interchangeable tuning units. In service *Jostle* proved to have a high rate of serviceability, attaining 66.6% in July 1944, 77.4% in August and 90% thereafter.

In the late summer of 1944, a variant of *Jostle* known as *Big Ben Jostle* appeared. This device was aimed at the potential radio control of the enemy's V–2 bombardment rocket and comprised a receiver, modulator, indicator and special oscillator incorporated into the existing hardware. In service, *Jostle* appears to have been known as *Jostle IV* when used for spot jamming and as *VHF Jostle* when used to barrage jam the 38–42 MHz band.

The transmission array for Jostle IV. *The mast aerial covered the 26–35, 35–45 and 45–54 MHz bands while the wire running from the waist window to the top left of the photo covered the 3–6, 6–12 and 12–18 MHz bands. (Crown Copyright)*

modulated, continuous wave jamming of enemy R/T transmissions in the 3–6, 6–12, 12–18, 26–35, 35–45 and 45–54 MHz bands, which was produced by Metropolitan Vickers to TRE specifications. Spot

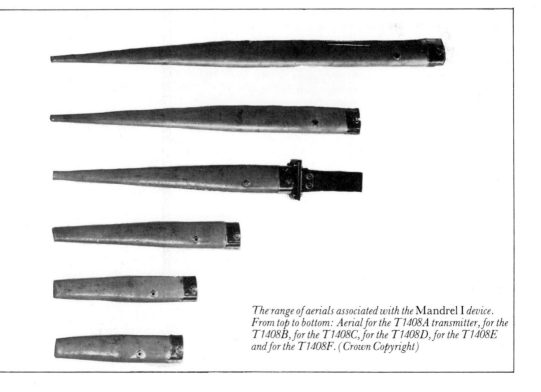

The range of aerials associated with the Mandrel I *device. From top to bottom: Aerial for the T1408A transmitter, for the T1408B, for the T1408C, for the T1408D, for the T1408E and for the T1408F. (Crown Copyright)*

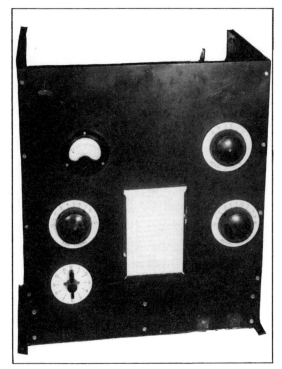

The Type 300 power unit (1.2 Kw, 80 volts AC) associated with the Mandrel I *device. (Crown Copyright)*

Mandrel I

A device designed to jam the enemy's EW radar in 10-MHz bands. (*Freya, Freya Fahrstuhl, Jagdschloss, Mammut* and *Wassermann*). Initially *Mandrel* covered the 118–128 MHz band but this was later broadened to cover the 68–78 and 138–148 MHz bands. An installation consisted of one T1408 transmitter, one Type 68 modulator, one Type 300 power unit (1.2 kW, 80 volts AC) and a Spitfire-type transmission mast.

In June 1943, *Mandrel* was modified to stop transmitting every alternate 60 secs to prevent homing. This transmission gap was lengthened to 120 secs in the following month. During August, the need for additional cover gave rise to a broadening of *Mandrel's* range by taking in the 88 to 142 MHz region of the band. This new range was sub-divided into six bands, each one being covered by an individually tuned transmitter designated T1408A to T1408F [T1408A, 88–98 MHz; T1408B, 98–108 MHz; T1408C, 108–118 MHz; T1408D, 118–128 MHz (the original band covered); T1408E, 128–138 MHz; and T1408F 138–148 MHz ('E' and 'F' used a transmission mast of reduced length)].

At the end of August 1943, eighty T1408D transmitters were converted into 'Es' and 'Fs' (half and half). The 'D', 'E' and 'F' *Mandrels* were used by Main Force (100 Group using 'A' to 'F'); the eighty conversions were for that force. In Main Force, *Mandrel* was installed as single transmitters in an individual aircraft, all the transmitters in a particular squadron being tuned to one frequency.

At the end of 1943, two new ranges were introduced,

'Y' (68–78 MHz) and 'Z' (78–88 MHz), but were never used operationally.

Mandrel III

A device designed to spot jam enemy EW radar in the 148–196 MHz band (*Freya* and *Wassermann*) which was developed by the TRE. An installation comprised a TR1657 transmitter/receiver mounted in the chassis and container of the Mk III IFF set, a modified IFF power unit and a Type 90 aerial (again from the IFF set). *Mandrel III* used the Mk III IFF's standard controls. On hearing the appropriate signal, the operator set the transmitter to DISTRESS to jam the signal.

Eight sub-variants of *Mandrel III* were produced TR1657A 29–39 MHz; TR1657B, 38–50 MHz TR1657C, 48–64 MHz; TR1657D, 62–84 MHz TR1657E, 82–113 MHz; TR1657F, 107–156 MHz TR1657G, 148–196 MHz; and TR1657H, 180–215 MHz. Of those, only 'A' and 'G' were used operationally. TR1657G was the most widely used of the two, 'A' only being introduced in January 1945 This latter type used a three-wire fan aerial mounted between the carrier aircraft's fuselage and starboard tail-unit. (For details of the mode of *Mandrel* operations, see pages 53/54.)

Mandrel IV

A device designed to spot jam enemy EW radar in the 148 to 200 MHz band.

Meerschaum II

A modified *Mandrel III* designed to provide jamming in the 60 to 120 MHz band for use against the FuG 220 A radar. The device was developed by the BSDU late in the war and had not entered service by VE day.

Moonshine

A measure developed by the TRE designed to produce spurious returns on the enemy's *Freya* radar. *Moonshine* worked by re-transmitting the *Freya's* signal and thus increasing the strength of the apparent 'echo'. A similar device was used as part of the D-Day 'spoof' mounted in ASR launches manned by American signals personnel. It must be stressed that this latter device was NOT *Moonshine*, although it followed the same basic method of operation.

Piperack (RAF designation ARI 5699)

An American-developed device designed to jam enemy radars in the 95–210 MHz band. Some units of this type were modified to cover the 69–93 MHz band used by the enemy's FuG 220 AI radar. An aircraft installation comprised between two and six AN/APT-transmitters which used wing-mounted whip aerials *Piperack* was modified in February 1945 by replacing all the American manufactured fittings with British ones The device was also known as *Dina II* (see page 157

Rayon

A ground-based measure used to disrupt *Knickebein* transmissions when these were used for night fighter control.

Shiver

A device designed to jam the enemy's GCI and GL radars in the 53 cm band (*Würzburg*). *Shiver* was essentially the R 3003A Mk II IFF set modified to produce a continuous squittering signal over the 24–27 MHz band. The operator was provided with

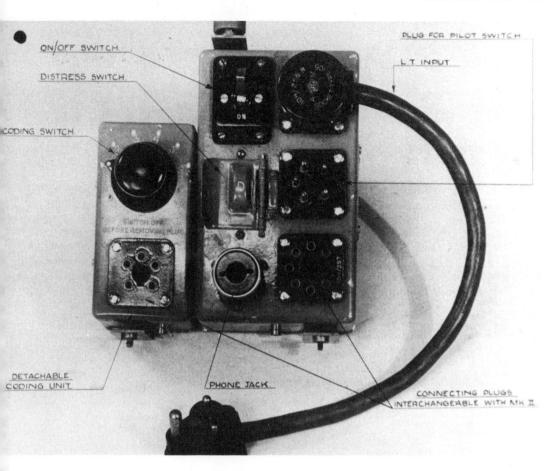

ON/OFF SWITCH.

DISTRESS SWITCH.

CODING SWITCH.

PLUG FOR PILOT SWITCH

L.T INPUT

DETACHABLE
CODING UNIT

PHONE JACK.

CONNECTING PLUGS
INTERCHANGEABLE WITH MK II.

The IFF Mk III control unit used in the Mandrel III device.
(Crown Copyright)

NORMAL and SPECIAL control. The NORMAL setting allowed R 3003A to operate as an IFF set while the SPECIAL setting operated the device as a jammer.

Tinsel

A measure designed to disrupt enemy R/T control channels in the 3–6 MHz band. *Tinsel* comprised a microphone unit from the Type 28 microphone assembly and a Marconi T1154 transmitter. The microphone was mounted in a small metal box in an engine nacelle and was connected to the transmitter through the normal microphone socket. A German speaking operator would use the carrier aircraft's communications receiver to search for the enemy's control transmissions. When such a transmission was found, the T1154 would be tuned to its frequency and switched on, flooding it with engine noise.

The original microphone installation proved to be unsatisfactory as the engine vibration broke up the carbon elements in the unit. In May 1943, the microphone was re-located on the port side fuselage skin in line with the propellor arc. By June of 1944, the installation of the *Tinsel* microphone was further improved by bringing it inside the airframe and

housing it in the power unit for the transmitter. This modification was at first unofficial but was given official approval in March 1944.

In May 1944, the T1154 was made compatible with the standard bomber communications equipment so that it could be used for R/T in emergencies. This was done by adding a CARBON-ELECTROMAGNETIC switch so that the standard electromagnetic microphone could be used with the set.

In the summer of 1943, the measure was redesignated *Special Tinsel*. From this point on, Kingsdown monitored the enemy's control transmissions. Once the frequency being used was established, instructions were sent out to the bombers and all *Tinsel* jammers were tuned to the frequency and switched on. This had the advantages of doing away with the need for German speaking operators and concentrated the jamming effort.

Tuba

A device designed to jam enemy EW radars in the 70–200 MHz band (*Freya, Freya Fahrstuhl, Jagdschloss, Mammut* and *Wassermann*).

Window

A measure developed by the TRE designed to disrupt the enemy's EW, GCI, GL and AI radars (*Freya, Seetakt, Würzburg*, FuG 202, 212, 216, 217, 218 and 220) by generating spurious responses therein. *Window* was produced in the following sub-variants:

Type	Enemy equipment at which directed	Frequency range over which one bundle gave a 'heavy bomber' echo	Dimensions of strips and number of strips per bundle	Weight of bundle	Size of bundle	Remarks
A	Würzburg and FuG 202. Also covered FuG 212	450 to 500 MHz	27 cm by 1.5 cm; 2,000. (Initially 30 cm by 1.5 cm; 2,000)	27 oz (900 gm)	10.5 in by 2.5 in by 2.5 in (26.25 cm by 6.25 cm)	The original 30 cm long strip was replaced by the 27 cm lighter type.
C	Würzburg and FuG 202. Also covered FuG 212	450 to 500 MHz	25 cm by 0.4 cm; 800. 30 cm by 0.4 cm; 800.	6 oz (200 gm)	12 in by 2 in (30 cm by 5 cm)	Produced on a rotary cutter. The strips had longitudinal creases.
E	Würzburg and FuG 202. Also covered FuG 212	450 to 500 MHz	26 cm by 0.5 cm; 2,000. 31 cm by 0.05 cm; 2,000.	2.6 oz (86.7 gm)	12.5 in by 0.7 in (31.25 cm by 1.75 cm)	Cellophane-coated foil.
F	Würzburg and FuG 202. Also covered FuG 212	450 to 500 MHz	25 cm by 0.55 cm; 500. 30 cm by 0.55 cm; 500.	8 oz (266.7 gm)	12 in by 0.7 in (30 cm by 1.75 cm)	Heavy paper backing to permit cutting by guillotine.
F3	Würzburg and FuG 202. Also covered FuG 212	450 to 500 MHz	25 cm by 0.3 cm; 500. 30 cm by 0.3 cm; 500.	4.5 oz (150 gm)	12 in by 1.3 in (30 cm by 3.25 cm)	Heavy paper backing to permit cutting by guillotine.
N	Würzburg, Seetakt and FuG 202. Also covered FuG 212	350 to 600 MHz	25 cm by 0.55 cm; 800. 35 cm by 0.55 cm; 400.	9.5 oz (316.7 gm)	13.5 in by 2 in (33.75 cm by 5 cm)	Originally designed for use by 'spoof' forces when Seetakt had to be covered. Late it was put into general use to cover the frequency spread of Würzburg.
N3	Würzburg, Seetakt and FuG 202. Also covered FuG 212	350 to 600 MHz	25 cm by 0.3 cm 600. 30 cm by 0.3 cm	5.7 oz (190 gm)	13.5 in by 1.5 in (33.75 cm by 3.75 cm)	Originally designed for use by 'spoof' forces when Seetakt had to be covered. Later it was put into general use to cover the frequency spread of Würzburg.
MB	Designed to cover Freya and FuG 220. Also covered FuG 216, 217 and 218	70 to 200 MHz with two bundles released together	180 cm by 5 cm; 605. Folded concertina fashion into six in four sets of 15	29 oz (966.7 gm)	12.5 in by 3 in by 2 in (31.25 cm by 7.5 cm by 5 cm)	Designed for 'spoof' operations to cover Freya (75 to 200 MHz by releasing two bundles together. Later used as an interim measure against FuG 220.

Type	Enemy equipment at which directed	Frequency range over which one bundle gave a 'heavy bomber' echo	Dimensions of strips and number of strips per bundle	Weight of bundle	Size of bundle	Remarks
MC	Designed to cover FuG 220. Also covered FuG 216, 217, and 218	85 to 100 MHz and 140 to 200 MHz	160 cm by 3.5 cm 60. Folded into six in four sets of 15	18 oz (600 gm)	11 in by 2 in (27.5 cm by 5 cm)	A replacement for 'MB' for use against FuG 200.
MC2	Designed to cover FuG 220. Also covered FuG 216, 217, and 218	85 to 100 MHz and 140 to 200 MHz	157 cm by 2 cm; 120. Folded into six in eight sets of 15	12 oz (400 gm)	11 in by 2 in (27.5 cm by 5 cm)	A replacement for 'MC' for use against FuG 200.
MD2	Designed to cover FuG 220. Also covered FuG 216, 217, and 218	65 to 100 MHz and 140 to 200 MHz	157 cm by 2 cm; 60. Folded into six in four sets of 15. 210 cm by 2 cm in 60. Folded into eight in four sets of 15.	14 oz (466.7 gm)	11 in by 2 in by 1.5 in (27.5 cm by 5 cm by 3.7 cm)	A replacement for 'MC2' to cover the extension of FuG 220 frequencies.
MM	Designed to cover *Freya* and FuG 220. Also covered FuG 216, 217, and 218	65 to 200 MHz	190 cm by 3.5 cm 45. Folded into six. 150 cm by 3.5 cm in 45. Folded into five. 110 cm by 3.5 cm in 45. Folded into four.	22 oz (733.3 gm)	12.5 in by 2.25 in by 2 in (31.25 cm by 5.6 cm by 5 cm)	A replacement for 'MB'.

Note: Type 'C' was produced on a rotary cutter, all the other sub-variants being cut by guillotine. In 100 Group service, *Window* was dispensed automatically (see *Window Research Section,* page 208) and was used in mixed packings when a number of radars needed to be disrupted.

GERMAN

Heinrich
A device designed to disrupt the *Gee* navigational system.

Postklystron
A device designed to jam the H2S navigational radar.

Roderich
Another device designed to jam the H2S navigational radar.

II HOMING AND WARNING DEVICES

The proliferation of airborne radar and other transmitting devices made it inevitable that both sides would develop 'homing', that is, receivers designed to give a bearing on a transmission source, and 'warning' devices to alert crews to the presence of other aircraft in their vicinity. Twelve electronic devices are described in this appendix, all but one of which, *Monica*, were 'passive', that is they did not produce any signal themselves. *Monica* was really a small radar but it is included here because in its original form it was not related to any AI, the usual starting point for tail warning radars during the Second World War. Details of the German equivalents of *Monica* (*Neptun* R-1, R-2 and R-3) will be found in the **Airborne Intercept Radars** appendix grouped with the families of AI radars to which they belong.

It is interesting to note the different philosophies behind 'homer' design in Britain and Germany. The British devices were mostly intended to counter the enemy's interceptors while their German counterparts, with the exception of *Naxos*, which had a secondary 'warning' role, were all designed to bring the interceptor into contact with the bomber or jamming aircraft, never to bring the interceptor into contact with 100 Group's intruders and escort fighters.

The Germans also differed from their English counterparts in pursuing infra-red detection methods long after developments in this field had been abandoned. Details of such devices that saw service, the *Spanner* family and FuG 280 *Kiel Z* appear at the end of this appendix.

BRITISH

Abdullah
The 'homing' group at the Telecommunications Research Establishment (TRE) under Russel, developed a homing device which, by means of interchangeable heads, could be used for a variety of purposes as and when the need arose. The only operational use made of this device was as *Abdullah*, to home on to *Würzburg* transmissions to allow the target radar to be marked for attack by fighter bombers. Its use was short lived as it had to be spot tuned to the target's frequency on the ground and the Germans tended to suddenly go off the air or switch on another radar of the same frequency in another location, thus totally negating the homer's value.

Benito
Developed by the TRE and tested by the Bomber

Support Development Unit (BSDU) during September 1944, *Benito* was a homer for the 'Y-system' navigational aid (operating in the 38 to 42 MHz band). The BSDU report on it was adverse due to its poor direction-finding qualities and its weak aerials, and the device was abandoned.

Boozer

This was a warning device which entered service in the Spring of 1943 developed by the TRE to give bomber crews notice when their aircraft were being 'painted' by *Würzburg* or FuG 202/212 transmissions. Three sub-variants were developed as follows:

Boozer I (RAF designation AR 5538)
A Type 164 receiver and associated aerial giving warning of a FuG 202/212 'paint'.
Boozer II (AR 5538)
As *Boozer I* but with the addition of a Type 165 receiver

Below: *The indicator unit for the* Boozer II *device mounted in the cockpit of a B-24. (Crown Copyright)*

Bottom: *The Type 338 rearward looking aerial associated with the* Boozer III *device mounted on a Halifax bomber. (Crown Copyright)*

The Type 315 aerial associated with the Boozer III *device.*
(Crown Copyright)

(Type 314 aerial) to cover *Würzburg* 'paints'.
Boozer III (AR 5557)
This unit comprised an R 1625 receiver, made up of a Type 170 receiver (490 MHz) and a Type 165 (530 to 600 MHz) receiver, a Type 565 power unit (24 Volt DC), a Type 177 or 181 indicator, a Type 338 rearward-looking dipole aerial with reflector (490 MHz) (Type 338A on the Mosquito) and a Type 315A downward-looking quarter-wave aerial (530 to 600 MHz).

Boozer III worked visually. One yellow and one red lamp were provided. When the red lamp was illuminated dimly, the operator was warned of the presence of *Würzburg* GCI transmissions. (There was a 30 to 180 sec delay between the reception of the signal and the illumination of the bulb, depending on pre-setting.) When the red light shone brightly, the operator was warned of the presence of *Würzburg* GL transmissions (with a 2 to 15 sec delay). When the yellow lamp came on, the operator was warned of the presence of FuG 202/212 transmissions. During its life *Boozer's* detection range for FuG 202/212 was increased by 70% to 6,000 ft (1,846 m) and further increased by the use of the Type 338/338A aerial in the 'III' model. Crew reaction to this device was adverse because there were so many transmissions of the right frequency over Germany that it give continual warnings. Naturally not all such transmissions were directed at a particular aircraft and the crews consequently found it more nerve racking than valuable!

Hookah
A homing device, whose origin is uncertain, for pinpointing the transmission sources of a wide variety of enemy airborne radars. Development was begun in 1944 and had not been completed before the end of the war.

The wing mounted aerials associated with the Hookah *device.*
(Crown Copyright)

Monica

This was an active tail warning device developed by the Royal Aircraft Establishment (RAE) during 1942 for use against interceptors and which was first used operationally on 19th/20th June 1943. The device was produced in a large number of sub-variants. Those for which details are available being as follows:

Monica I

The original device developed by the RAE during 1942.

Monica III

Comprised a *Monica I* transmitter and aerial, modified *Monica I* and ASV II receivers and an ASV Mk II indicator. The device had a minimum range of 1,000 ft (308 m) and a maximum range of from 2 to 4 mls (3,200 to 6,400 m).

5 Group Monica IIIC

Number 5 Group, Bomber Command, developed this sub-variant of *Monica IIIC* to have automatic frequency changing to prevent it being homed on to. A trial installation by the BSDU in a Fortress aircraft of 214 Squadron proved unsuccessful.

Monica IIIE

One hundred sets of this unit were produced by the BSDU workshops for use by 100(SD) Group.

Monica IV

This sub-variant was used as a tail-warner for 100(SD) Group aircraft fitted with AI Mk VIII and AI Mk X.

Monica VI

Ninety-six sets of this sub-variant, which acted as a tail-warner for AI Mk X aircraft (giving azimuth and range readings), were produced by the BSDU work-

The receiver from the ASV Mk II set used in the Monica III *installation. (Crown Copyright. Science Museum, London)*

Monica IIIA

A *Monica III* with the modified *Monica I* receiver deleted. This sub-variant proved to be superior to the standard 'III' model.

Monica IIIC/Eureke Racon

A BSDU modification to the *Monica IIIC* to allow it to home on to the *Eureke Racon* which proved to be unsuccessful.

shops for use by 100(SD) Group. An anti-jamming prototype of this model was also produced.

Monica VIII

A modified AI Mk IV, *Monica VIII* probably originated from the TRE and was a tail-warner for aircraft fitted with AI Mk X. The azimuth and range readings from the device were displayed on a 3 in (7.5 cm) CRT.

Monica IX

The display from this model was used in the *Perfectos 1B* device.

Monica was withdrawn from general main force use in 1944 after the discovery of its compromise by FuG 227 *Flensburg*. After this, the device continued in use with 100(SD) Group and certain squadrons of Fighter Command, (or Air Defence of Great Britain as it was then known).

The *Monica VIII CRT mounted below the AI Mk X display unit in a Mosquito 30. (Crown Copyright)*

Perfectos

This was a device developed by the BSDU during the summer of 1944, designed to trigger the enemy's FuG 25a *Erstling* IFF set and then to provide a bearing on the transmission. Three sub-variants were produced as follows:

Perfectos I

Displayed on the AI Mk VIII CRT. The direction-finding ability of the model proved to be unsatisfactory, but it was nevertheless used operationally (by 169 Squadron). The BSDU produced forty sets of this model for 100(SD) Group. (This total probably includes the 'IB'.)

Perfectos IB

Similar to the 'I', but used a *Monica IX* display. The device was used in aircraft fitted with AI Mk XV from December 1944.

Perfectos II

This used a special display built into the AI Mk X unit. The device appeared in November 1944 and was operational in January 1945. The BSDU produced forty-eight sets of this model for 100(SD) Group.

Serrate

This was a homing device developed by the TRE which was designed to give a bearing on the transmissions from the enemy's FuG 202, 212 and 220 AI radars. One source quotes the device as having a range of 50 mls (80.5 km) when used against FuG 202/212, when the source was pointing towards it and 10 mls (16.1 km) when it was pointing away from the receiver. The device was first used in June 1943 (by 141 Squadron) and was produced in a number of sub-variants. Those for which details are available being as follows:

Serrate II

An adaption of the original device for installation in the Mosquito.

Serrate IV

The BSDU produced twenty-four sets of this type for 100(SD) Group. A further modification (of an unknown nature) designated 'IVA' was also produced from the 'IV' by the BSDU, who built twenty-one such sets.

Serrate V

An experimental sub-variant produced by the BSDU (one set only).

Serrate VI

A homer aimed at the enemy's FuG 220 radar. This model gave a 'dot-dash' aural indication rather than the visual one of those models aimed at FuG 202/212. (A small CRT display.) 'VI' became operational in January 1945.

FuG 221 Freya-Halbe

A homing device developed by Siemens and aimed at *Mandrel* jamming aircraft. [The *Mandrels* covered were – *Mandrel I* (models D and E), *Mandrel III* (models F to H) and *American Mandrel* (model R)]. The device could receive signals in the 115 to 135 MHz band, had a range of 62.5 mls (100 km) and used two rod aerials above and below each wing (eight in all). *Freya-Halbe* was used on an extremely limited scale.

FuG 221a Rosendaal-Halbe

A homing device developed by Siemens and aimed at a range of Allied radar including *Monica* and decimetric

The Serrate *installation (the two rectangular boxes) in a Mosquito II. It is believed that the device used the AI Mk IV receiving aerials to pick up the FuG 202/212 transmissions. (Crown Copyright)*

ASV. The device could receive signals in the 190 to 230 MHz band and had a range of 62.5 mls (100 km). FuG 221a was only used on a small scale. It should be noted that *Rosendaal* was a German code name for an, as yet, unidentified British radar.

A Bf110G-4 of Stab I/NJG 4 displaying the FuG 227 reception aerials on its wing tips. The nose array is for the FuG 220 SN-2d AI radar. (E J Creek)

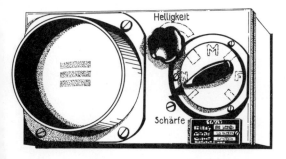

The indicator unit for the FuG 227 Flensburg *homing device.*
(Author's collection)

FuG 227 Flensburg

A homing device developed by Siemens and aimed at
Monica (Model 'I') and various jamming devices
including *Mandrel I* (all models), *Mandrel III* (models
D to H), *American Mandrel* (models Q and R) and
Piperack/Dina II (Models 'II' and 'III'). The device
could receive signals in the 80 to 230 MHz band and
had a range of 62.5 mls (100 km). FuG 227 used wing-
mounted dipole and support aerials and a total of 250
such sets was built.

FuG 350 Naxos Z

A homing device developed by Telefunken and aimed
at the H2S navigation radar and Allied centimetric AI
sets. The device could receive signals in the 2,500 to
3,750 MHz band and had a range of 31.25 mls (50 km).
FuG 350 used a horizontally aligned U-shaped aerial
in a dorsal mounting and could only give a bearing on

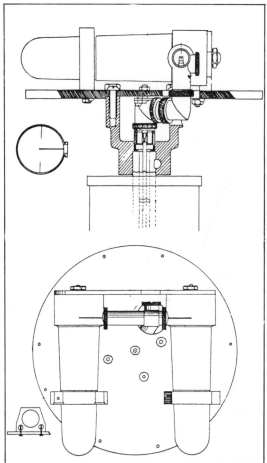

Two views of the FuG 350 dialectric aerial. (Crown Copyright)

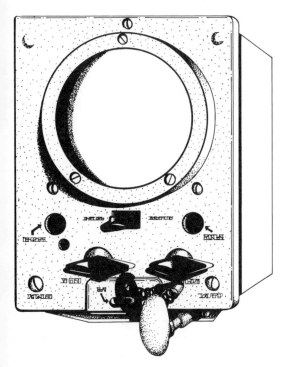

The display unit for one of the FuG 350 Naxos *family of
homing devices. (Author's collection)*

the transmission, rather than its altitude and range.
Altogether, twenty-five variants of *Naxos* were evolved,
the most important being:
Naxos Zc
Featured an artificially intensified blip on the display
CRT (CRT presentation common to all models of
Naxos).
Naxos ZR
Naxos Z combined with a tail warning capacity. Used
only in Ju88 aircraft with an antenna in the fuselage
tail.
Naxos ZX
Featured an enlargement of the receivable band width
to enable 3 and 9 cm wavelength radars to be tracked.
Naxos RX
As *Naxos ZX* but with a tail warning capacity.
Naxos ZD
A combination of *Naxos Z* and *ZX*. In prototype form
only.
   A total of at least 700 *Naxos Z* and *Naxos ZR* sets saw
operational service. It should be noted that *Naxos* was
also used by the German Navy to give warning of the
presence of centimetric ASV equipped aircraft to that
services' submarines.

FuG 351 Korfu Z

A homing device aimed at 3 and 9 cm wavelength radars. The device had considerably higher sensitivity than *Naxos* and a range of 62.5 mls (100 km). FuG 351 was used in extremely limited numbers.

Spanner I to IV

A family of infra-red search devices developed by AEG. *Spanner I* was the only active device and comprised an infra-red searchlight, lens and sighting screen. The remainder of the family were all passive homers and comprised a lens system and sighting screen. *Spanner* was produced in limited numbers for service use.

FuG 280 Kiel Z

This was a passive infra-red detector developed by Zeiss. The heart of the system was a lead-sulphide selenium cell, the output from which was fed to a CRT display via an amplifier. FuG 280 had a range of 2.5 mls (4 km), a weight of 92.4 lb (42 kg) and was produced in limited numbers for trials.

III AIRBORNE INTERCEPTION RADAR

The twelve devices covered in this appendix represent all the operational AI radars used during the Bomber Support campaign.

Clear differences will be noted in the philosophies of AI design between the combatants. Immediately noticeable is the greater number of German sets detailed (eight as against four used by the RAF). This was in part due to the prompt and mostly effective action taken by the various jamming agencies. in Britain against new enemy equipments. This meant that the Luftwaffe was constantly forced to develop new radars which operated on as yet unaffected frequencies.

The change over from *Himmelbett* to *Zahme Sau* meant that the older short-range sets had to be replaced by longer range ones more suited to the running battles now being fought. This proliferation was further enhanced by the German de-centralised system of research; the electronics industry was busy duplicating effort to meet individual requirements and following blind alleys which a more open dissemination of research data would have avoided.

Britain, on the other hand, had a much tighter relationship between operational need, service research and industry, with all three working in close harmony bringing about a consequential concentration of effort in one direction. This methodology was carried through to a multi-national level between Britain and America where individual interests were overridden by the common war effort, a case in point being the abandonment of the indigenous AI Mk IX when the American SCR 720 proved to be superior.

Finally, it will be noted that the Allies had an immeasurable lead in centimetric radar with its superiority over decimetric sets in range, accuracy and resistance to jamming.

ALLIED

Airborne Interception Radar Mk IV

An AI radar developed by the Air Ministry Research Establishment and built by Pye and EMI from the Autumn of 1940. AI Mk IV had a wavelength of 1.5 m and a frequency in the 190 to 195 MHz band. At 5,000 ft (1,519 m) and 21,000 ft (6,379 m), this set had a maximum range of 1 ml (1,600 m) and 4 mls (6,400 m) respectively, while its minimum range was in the region of 800 to 1,000 ft (243 to 304 m). Two display CRTs gave azimuth and elevation readings. Because the transmitter 'floodlit' the area around the aircraft, AI Mk IV had a degree of rear cover. In September 1944, the sets of this type used in bomber support aircraft had their frequency modified to 188 MHz in an attempt to overcome enemy jamming. The BSDU produced a prototype AI Mk IV with anti-jamming circuitry sometime in 1944 (?).

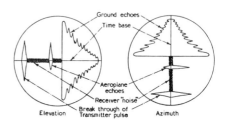

Diagrams of the indications which would be seen on the azimuth and elevation CRTs of the AI Mk IV radar. (Crown Copyright)

Airborne Interception Radar Mk VIII (RAF designation ARI 15093)

An AI radar developed by the Telecommunications Research Establishment (TRE) and built by Ekco and GEC, which entered service during 1942. AI Mk VIII had a wavelength of 10 cm and a frequency in the region of 3 GHz. At most altitudes, the set had a maximum range of 6.5 mls (10,400 m) straight ahead, decaying to 2 mls (3,200 m) when the target was at a 45° angle to the transmitter. A fixed transmitter aerial was used, around which a parabolic reflector was driven in successively increasing and decreasing spirals out to a maximum angle of 30°. Apart from the range limitation already described (due to a reduction in power when the parabolic reflector neared the 30° angle in relationship to the aerial), the set had difficulty in following small movements of a target when it was at a 20° plus angle to the transmitter, (straight ahead, AI Mk VIII could follow movement in the order of 2° to 3°). A single radial CRT gave both range and bearing readings. Two types of AI Mk VIII were produced: the 'A' (ARI 15093A); and the 'B' (ARI 15093B), differing solely in that the 'B' model had a *Lucero* position-fixing facility (using 1.5 m ground beacons) in addition to the 'A' models IFF and *Racon* (radar beacon) facilities.

Airborne Interception Radar Mk X (US designation SCR 720)

An AI radar developed by the Radiation Laboratory, Massachusetts Institute of Technology and built by the Western Electric Company which entered service with the RAF in 1943. AI Mk X had a wavelength of 10 cm and a frequency in the region of 3 GHz. At most altitudes, the set had a range of 8 to 10 mls (12,800 to 16,000 m) in an arc terminating in an 80 to 100° angle to the transmitter. In the vertical plane, the set could

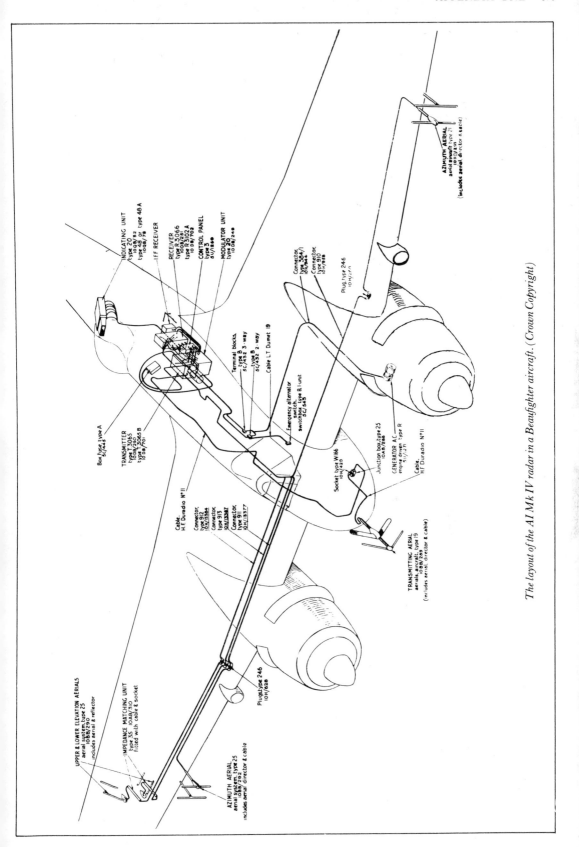

INDICATING UNIT
type 20
10QB/82
type 48 or type 48 A
10 DB/78

IFF RECEIVER

RECEIVER
type R.3066
10DB/231
type R.3102 A
10 DB/702

CONTROL PANEL
type 3
8U/1800

MODULATOR UNIT
type 20
10 DB/248

AZIMUTH AERIAL
aerial aircraft type 21
(013/231
(includes aerial, director & cable)

Connector,
type 38A/1
10H/44
Connector,
type 910
10H/988

Plug, type 246
10H/621

Box fuse type A
5U/443

TRANSMITTER
type T.3065
10AY/262
type T.3065 B
(013/701

Cable,
H.F. Duradio No 11

Connector,
type 912
10H/3564
Connector,
type 913
92H/2387
Connector,
type 911
92H/1377

Plug, type 246
10H/621

Terminal blocks

type B
5C/432 3-way

type B
5C/432 2-way

Cable LT Dumet 19

Emergency alternator
switch,
switchbox type B unit
5C/545

Socket, type W166
10H/420

Junction box, type 25
10AS/268

GENERATOR A.C.
engine driven type R
5U/271

Cable,
Hf Duradio No 11

TRANSMITTING AERIAL
aerial, aircraft, type 19
10SB/268
(includes aerial, director & cable)

UPPER & LOWER ELEVATION AERIALS
aerial system, type 25
10BB/290
includes aerial & reflector

IMPEDANCE MATCHING UNIT
type 35   10AB/310
fitted with cable & socket

AZIMUTH AERIAL
aerial system, type 25
10BB/282
includes aerial, director & cable

The layout of the AI Mk IV radar in a Beaufighter aircraft. (Crown Copyright)

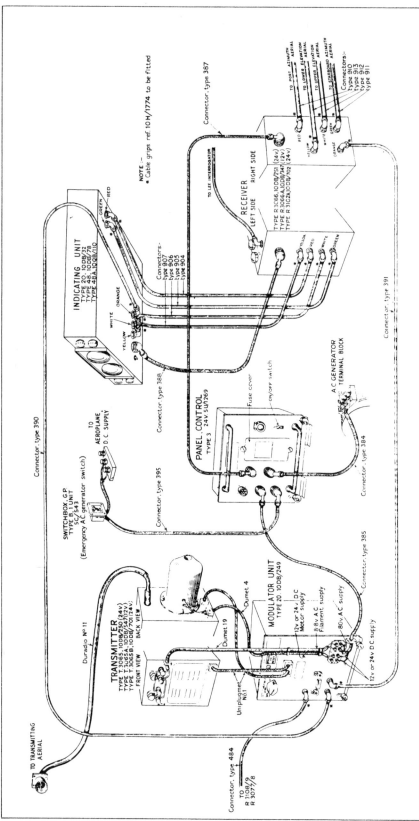

INTERCONNEXION OF UNITS

A further view of the components which went to make up AI Mk IV. (Crown Copyright)

Above: *The indicator unit associated with AI Mk IV mounted in a Mosquito II. (Crown Copyright)*

Below: *The indicator and receiver units associated with AI Mk VIII mounted in a Mosquito aircraft. (IWM)*

A detail shot of the AI Mk VIII indicator without the CRT visor. (Crown Copyright. Science Museum, London)

see up to 50° above the aircraft's centre-line and between 15 and 30° below it. AI Mk X's transmitting aerial was mounted in a frame facing a parabolic reflector, the whole revolving at 350 rpm. A second drive caused the frame to 'nod' at the same time between angles of +50 and −20° from the rest position. Three types of CRT display could be used with the set (any two in combination) as follows:

(1) An azimuth and range display Calibrated 60° left and right and from 1 to 8 mls (1,600 to 12,800 m) range.

(2) An azimuth and elevation display Azimuth, 60° left and right and elevation, −10 to +60°.

(3) A radial elevation display Calibrated in 20, 40 and 60° arcs, right and left.

Initial supplies of AI Mk X could not use British *Racons* having instead to utilise the American AN/CPN-6 beacon.

Airborne Interception Radar Mk XV (US designation AN/APS-4 ASH [Air-Surface H])

An ASV/AI radar developed by the Radiation Laboratory, Massachusetts Institute of Technology which entered service with the RAF in 1944. AI Mk XV had a wavelength of 3 cm and a frequency in the region of 10 GHz. At most altitudes, the set had a maximum and minimum range of 4 mls (6,400 m) and 250 ft (76 m) respectively and it weighed 180 lb (80 kg)

The parabolic reflector and aerial drive associated with AI Mk VIII. This example lacks the transmit/receive dipole. (Crown Copyright. Science Museum, London)

complete. In azimuth, AI Mk XV could 'see' to 7½ right and left of the centre line and in elevation 30 above and below it. The set used a single CRT displa

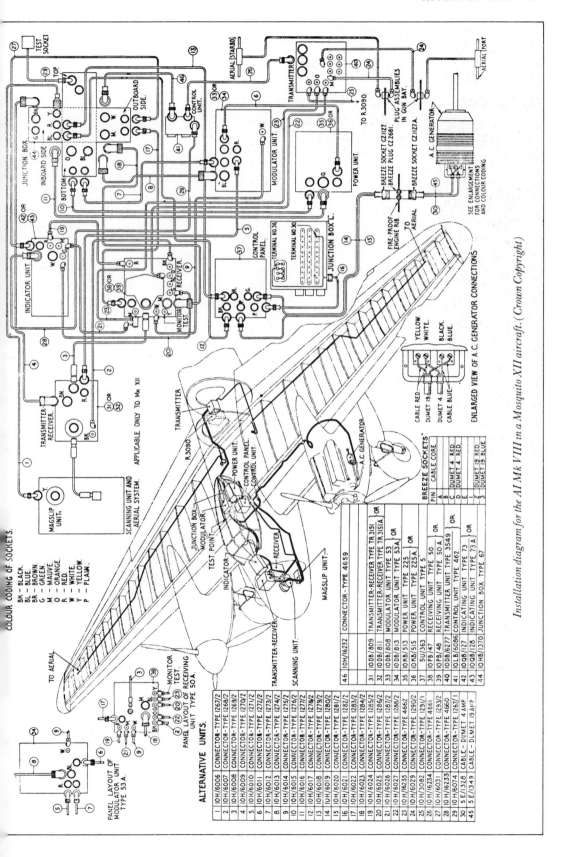

Installation diagram for the AI Mk VIII in a Mosquito XII aircraft. (Crown Copyright)

One of the two azimuth/elevation displays associated with the AI Mk X radar. The purpose of the small CRT below the AI Mk X indicator is uncertain but may well be for Perfectos. (Crown Copyright)

The receiver unit for the AI Mk X radar, sharing a common chassis with the transmitter. (Author's collection)

The transmitter unit for the AI Mk X radar. The cylindrical unit nearest the camera is the Klystron valve. (Author's collection)

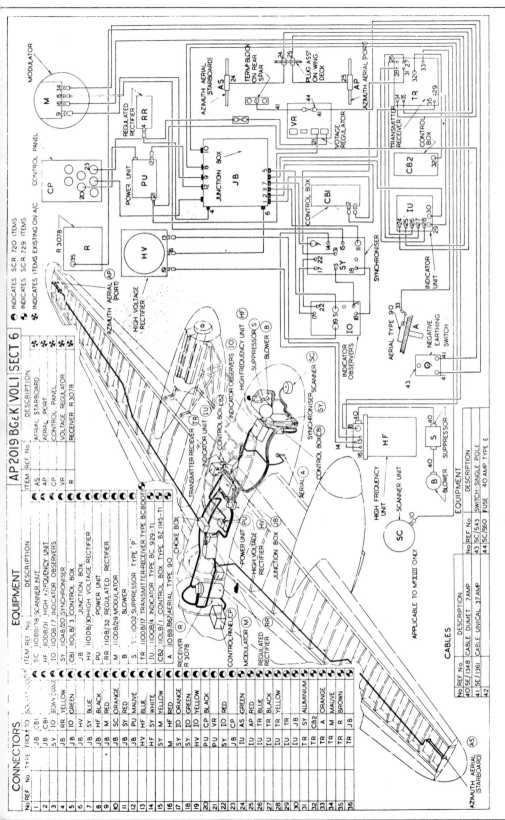

The installation diagram for the AI Mk X radar in a Mosquito XVII aircraft. (Crown Copyright)

A sketch of the mounting of the RT-5 transmitter/receiver of the AN/APS-4 radar. It should be noted that this installation is the naval pod mounting and not 100 Group's nose one. (USAF)

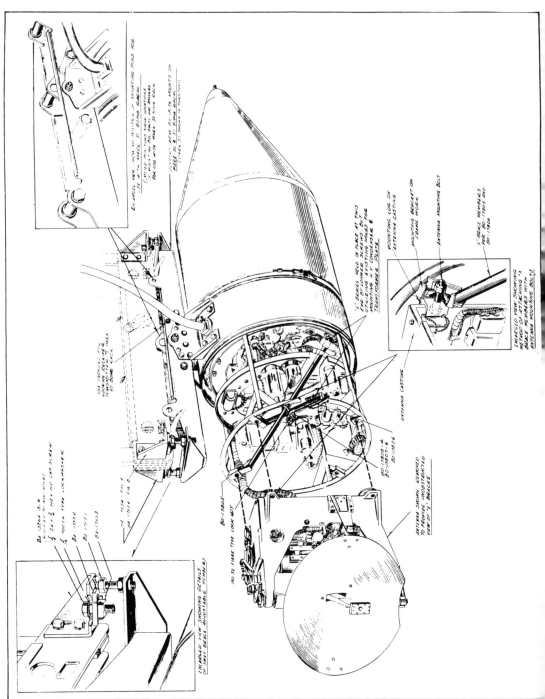

using a 'double blip' presentation. The left hand 'blip' was the target while the right hand one was 'manufactured' and represented the interceptor. The relative movement of the two 'blips' gave the operator his position vis à vis the target.

GERMAN

FuG 202 Lichtenstein BC
An AI radar developed and manufactured by Telefunken which entered service in 1942–43. FuG 202 had a frequency of 490 MHz, a power output of 1.5 kW, a maximum and minimum range of 2.1 mls (3,500 m) and 650 ft (200 m) respectively, a search angle of 70° and a weight of 52.8 lb (24 kg). The set used four nose-mounted antennae, each with four dipoles and four reflectors, used jointly for transmission and reception. Three CRT display, one each for azimuth, elevation and range. FuG 202 was developed from the 1939 *Lichtenstein B* high-altitude radio altimeter.

FuG 212 Lichtenstein C-1
An AI radar developed and manufactured by Telefunken which was in series production between June and November 1943. FuG 212 had the same basic performance as *Lichtenstein BC* but was re-designed

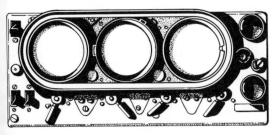

The indicator unit for the FuG 212 AI radar viewed from above. (Author's collection)

internally (its components were now grouped together in a so-called *Gërat Block*) and had an overall weight of 132 lb (60 kg). In August 1943, the frequency of the set was changed to within the 420 to 480 MHz band in an attempt to overcome jamming. Three CRT display. The device used the same aerial array as the *Lichtenstein BC*.

FuG 212 Lichtenstein C-1 Weitwinkel (Wide-angle)
An AI radar developed and manufactured by Telefunken for use in conjunction with FuG 220 *Lichtenstein SN-2b* to overcome the latter's minimum range limitations. The set used a single-pole antenna (with four dipoles and four reflectors), had a search angle of 120°, a maximum range of 1.25 mls (2,000 m) and had a two CRT display.

FuG 216 Neptun
A family of radars developed by the Flugfunk Forschungsanstalt (FFO) which appeared in two sub-variants as follows:
FuG 216 *Neptun R-1* A tail-warning set with a frequency of 182 MHz and power output of 1 kW. 'R-1' used four receiving and four transmitting rod aerials mounted above and below the carrier aircraft's wings. Its display gave a range reading only.
FuG 216 *Neptun V* An AI set for single-seat, single-

engined aircraft. 'V' had a frequency of 125 MHz, a power output of 1.2 kW, a maximum and minimum range of 2.2 mls (3,500 m) and 1,625 ft (500 m) respectively and a search angle of 100° (?). The set used fuselage rod aerials, or on the Fw190, wing mounted aerials (port and starboard). Only a small series of this type of radar was produced.

FuG 217 Neptun
A family of radars developed by the FFO which appeared in three sub-variants as follows:
FuG 217 *Neptun R-2* A tail-warning set with a weight of 59.4 lb (27 kg).
FuG 217 *Neptun J-2* An AI set for single-seat, single-engined aircraft with a weight of 59.4 lb (27 kg).

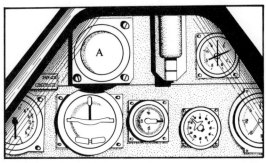

A sketch showing the position of the Neptun *CRT (marked A) in a Fw190. (Author's collection)*

Two views of the wing aerials associated with the FuG 216 Neptun V *AI radar mounted on a Fw190 aircraft. (E J Creek)*

FuG 217 *Neptun VR* A combined AI and tail-warning set for multi-engined aircraft. 'VR' had two frequencies, 158 or 187 MHz, a search angle of 120°, a maximum and minimum range of 2.5 mls (4,000 m) and 1,300 ft (400 m) respectively and weighed 77 lb (35 kg). The set could use rod or dipole and support aerial arrays.

FuG 218 Neptun
A family of radars developed jointly by Siemens and the FFO and manufactured by Siemens which appeared in four sub-variants as follows:
FuG 218 *Neptun R-3* A tail-warning set which used rod antenna.
FuG 218 *Neptun J-3* An AI set for single-seat, single-engined aircraft which used rod antenna.

Part of the aerial array associated with the FuG 218 Neptun J-3 AI radar mounted on a Fw190 aircraft. (E J Creek)

FuG 218 *Neptun VR* A combined AI and tail-warning set for multi-engined aircraft which used a dipole and support aerial array.
FuG 218 *Neptun GR* A combined AI and tail-warning set for multi-engined aircraft which used a dipole and support aerial array. 'GR' could use any one of six frequencies within the 158 to 187 MHz band, had a power output of 30 kW (later to be boosted to 100 kW), a search angle of 120°, a maximum and minimum range of 3.1 mls (5,000 m) and 390 ft (120 m) respectively, and a weight of 110 lb (50 kg).
All four sub-variants of FuG 218 were in series production.

FuG 220 Lichtenstein SN-2
An AI set developed and manufactured by Telefunken which was in series production from September 1943 and appeared in three sub-variants. 'Basic' FuG 220 had a frequency range of 73, 82 or 91 MHz (later enlarged to fall within the 37.5 to 118 MHz band), a power output of 2.5 kW, a maximum and minimum range of 2.5 mls (4,000 m) and between 975 and 1,625 ft (300 and 500 m) respectively, a search angle in azimuth and elevation of 120° and 100° respectively and a weight of 154 lb (70 kg). The set was developed from FuG 213 *Lichtenstein S* ASV radar with which it shared a number of common components. Two CRT display. The three sub-variants differed as follows:
FuG 220 *Lichtenstein SN-2b* Incorporated wide-angle *Lichtenstein C-1*.

The indicator unit for an early model of the FuG 220 A radar. (Author's collection)

FuG 220 *Lichtenstein SN-2c* *Lichtenstein C-1* deleted.
FuG 220 *Lichtenstein SN-2d* Antenna dipoles mounted at a 45° angle. Incorporated a tail warning capacity.

FuG 240/1 Berlin N-1a
An AI set developed and manufactured by Telefunken which entered service in 1945. (Ten sets of this type produced.) FuG 240/1 had a wavelength of 9 to 9.3 cm a frequency in the region of 3 GHz, a maximum and

The aerial array associated with the FuG 220 SN-2d AI radar (IWM)

The aerial array associated with the FuG 220 SN-2b AI radar mounted on a Bf110G-4. The central array is for the Lichtenstein C-1 Weitwinkel *set. (IWM)*

minimum range of 3.1 mls (5,000 m) and 975 ft (300 m) respectively, a search angle of 55° and a weight of 396 lb (180 kg). Two CRT display.

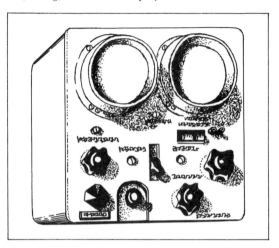

The indicator unit for the FuG 240/1 AI radar. (Author's collection)

The aerial array for the FuMG 80 Freya early warning radar. (via D Wood)

IV GERMAN GROUND RADARS AND HOMING DEVICES

At the beginning of the war, Germany was as well advanced in ground radar technology as the Allies. In fact, the quality of components used in the former country's devices was far superior to that of comparable British equipment.

The seven radars detailed in this appendix formed the cornerstone of Germany's night defence against the RAF's bomber offensive. As will be seen, the individual radars were under constant development to meet the rapidly changing tactical situation. The main data for each 'family' may be regarded as being general for the whole with the changes incorporated in sub-variants being noted where known.

The growth of electronic warfare led to the development of receiving devices to track the multiplicity of signals from the bomber streams as a substitute for vulnerable radars. Two of these 'homers', *Korfu* and *Naxburg* are detailed here.

FuMG 80 Freya

Role and Builder:	An air-search and EW radar built by Gema.
Search radius:	360°
Range:	Dependent on target and site altitude

Target altitude	Range
163 ft (50 m)	15.7 mls (25 km)
325 ft (100 m)	18.7 mls (30 km)
3,250 ft (1,000 m)	37.5 mls (60 km)
9,750 ft (3,000 m)	62.5 mls (100 km)
26,000 ft (8,000 m)	75.0 mls (120 km)

Maximum range:	125 mls (200 km) [Under ideal operating conditions]
Range accuracy:	±487.5 ft (150 m)
DF accuracy:	Azimuth, ± 0.5°; no elevation measurement
Weight:	6 to 6.4 tons (6.2 to 6.5 tonnes)
Dimensions:	Height, 26 to 32.5 ft (8 to 10 m); width 19.5 ft (6 m)
Wavelength/ Frequency:	2.40 m, 125 MHz [Average values]
Anti-jamming provision:	*Freya-Laus*
IFF capability:	Late Model *Freyas* had a FuG 25a *Erstling* capability. Earlier production sets were retrofitted with this capability.
Crew:	Three
Remarks:	FuMG 80 gained its accuracy in azimuth by lobe switching (6° right, 6° left) which gave a double blip display. However, this method had the disadvantage that, at extreme range, the target could be lost during the switch. This was overcome to an extent by limiting the device's range by one third of its theoretical maximum.

The initial production FuMG 80 used both a transmitter and reciever antenna. In later models a dual-purpose aerial was introduced which operated by means of a switching unit.

Sub-variants:

AI Gerat: Prototype *Freya* produced by Gema with a wavelength of 2.4 m, a frequency of 125 MHz and a range of 40.6 mls (65 km).

FuMG ?: *Freya Detector I* produced by Gema with a wavelength in the 1.9 to 2.5 m band, a frequency in the 120 to 158 MHz band and a range of 40.6 mls (65 km). This was the first *Freya* to go into series production and had the alternative designation FMG 39G-fB.

FuMG ?: *Freya Detector II* produced by Gema with a wavelength in the 1.2 to 1.9 m band, a frequency in the 158–250 MHz band and a range of 50 mls (80 km). This was an improved *Detector I* and had the alternative designation FMG 40G-fB.

FuMG 80: *Freya Detector III* produced by Gema. See main data for details of this device which had the alternative designation FMG 41G-fB.

FuMG 401: *Freya LZ* produced by Gema. This was an air-transportable model with a modified antenna

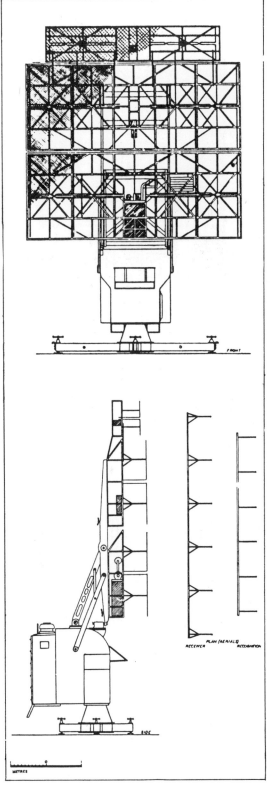

Two elevations of the aerial array for the FMG 39G-fb Freya early warning radar. (Crown Copyright)

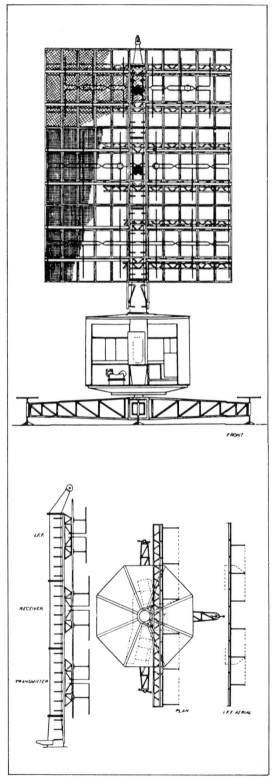

The range measuring delay unit from the FMG 39G-fb.
(Crown Copyright. Science Museum, London)

Two elevations of the aerial array for the FMG 40G-fb Freya
early warning radar. (Crown Copyright)

The presentation CRTs from the FMG 39G-fb. (Crown
Copyright. Science Museum, London)

and four sub-variants ('A'; wavelength in the 2.32 to 2.48 m band and frequency in the 121 to 138 MHz band, 'B'; wavelength in the 2 to 2.4 m band and frequency in the 134 to 144 MHz band, 'C'; wavelength in the 3 to 3.3 m band and frequency in the 91 to 100 MHz band and 'D'; wavelength in the 1.5 to 1.85 m band and frequency in the 162 to 200 MHz band.) All the variants of this set had a range in the region of 93.75 mls (150 km) and the alternative designation FMG 42G.

FuMG ?: *Freya Simultan* (*Joint Freya*) developed jointly by Gema and the Luftwaffe's Experimental Signals Regiment (Ln-Vers-Rgt) on an experimental basis. The device had a wavelength of 2.4 m, a frequency of 125 MHz and a range of 93.75 mls (150 km).

FuMG ?: *Freya Fahrstuhl* (*Freya Lift*) developed jointly by Gema and the Ln-Vers-Rgt in three versions.

FuMG ?: *Freya Hochbahn* (*Freya High Road*) developed jointly by Gema and the Ln-Vers-Rgt for the detection of high altitude aircraft.

FuMG ?: *Freya Kothen* developed jointly by AEG and FASV. This device was based on the FMG 40G with a frequency changing capability and a Yagi antenna. *Kothen* operated on three frequencies: 95, 88, and 75 MHz with wavelengths of 3.1, 3.4 and 4 m respectively.

FuSAn 730: *Freya Egon I* developed jointly by the E-Stella Rechlin, Fritze and Lorenz as part of the *Egon* system (see page 194). This device was based on the *Freya LZ* with FuG 25a and FuG 226 capacities. *Egon I* both received and transmitted signals, the transmitter having a frequency and wavelength of 110 to 125 MHz and 2.4 to 2.7 m respectively while the receiver operated on a frequency and wavelength of 143 to 158 MHz and 1.9 to 2 m respectively. The device had a range of 125 mls (200 km). 150 such sets were built.

FuSAn 730: *Freya Egon II* developed jointly by Rechlin and Fritze. This was an experimental development of *Egon I* of which two were built.

FuMG ?: *Dreh Freya* (*Rotating Freya*) developed by Lorenz. This was a development of *Freya LZ* for DF and so called 'panoramic' EW, that is, providing a complete picture of the air situation in a 360° arc around the radar. *Dreh Freya* had a wavelength and frequency of 1.9 to 2.5 m and 120 to 158 MHz respectively, and a range of 125 mls (200 km).

FuMG ?: *Freya lange Latte* (*Lanky Freya*) developed by Lorenz. This was a development of *Dreh Freya* with a new aerial and worked on a wavelength and frequency in the 1.2 to 2.5 m, 158 to 250 MHz band.

FuMG? Freya Fahrstuhl (Freya Lift)

Role and Builder:	An air-search and EW radar developed jointly by Gema and the Ln-Vers-Rgt.
Search radius:	Azimuth, 360°; elevation (for ranges between 12.5 and 62.5 mls (20 and 100 km), 3 to 20°.
Range:	Dependent on target and site altitude

Target altitude	Range
6,500 ft (2,000 m)	40.6 mls (65 km)
19,500 ft (6,000 m)	100 mls (160 km)
25,000 ft (8,000 m)	115.6 mls (185 km)
32,500 ft (10,000 m)	143.75 mls (230 km)

Range accuracy:	±650 ft (200 m).
DF accuracy:	Azimuth, ±1.5 to 2°; elevation, ±10% (3° angle) or ±5% (3 to 25° angle) [see table 1]
Weight:	16.7 tons (17 tonnes)
Dimensions:	Height 66.7 ft (25.5 m)
Wavelength/ Frequency:	2.40 m, 125 MHz
Anti-jamming provision:	The device had two alternative frequencies: 107 MHz (2.8 m wavelength) and 167 MHz (1.8 m wavelength)
IFF capability:	None
Remarks:	Late production *Freya Fahrstuhl* were mounted on a 16.25 ft (5 m) concrete base with a turntable. To overcome 'dead zones', the reflector could be raised or lowered mechanically.

FuMG 404 Jagdschloss (Hunting Castle)

Role and Builder:	'Panoramic' EW radar built jointly by Gema, Siemens and Lorenz
Search radius:	360°. Automatic rotation of aerial at 5 to 10 rpm.
Range:	Depending on the altitude of the target

Target altitude	Range
325 ft (100 m)	9.4 mls (15 km)
3,250 ft (1,000 m)	25 mls (40 km)
16,250 ft (5,000 m)	40.6 mls (65 km)
19,500 ft (6,000 m)	56.25 mls (90 km)
26,000 ft (8,000 m)	75 mls (120 km)

Maximum range:	50 to 93.75 mls (80 to 150 km); 50 mls (80 km) was the more usual figure.
Display:	175 in (70 cm) diameter CRT which was sealed to 1:750,000. A circular scan with image retention.
Weight:	24.5 to 29.5 tons (25 to 30 tonnes).

TABLE 1

Target altitude	Range where it was possible to measure altitude	Accuracy
6,250 ft	{Up to 11.9 mls (19 km) 11.9 to 18.75 mls (7 to 52 km)	± 162.5 ft (50 m) ± 325 ft (100 m)
9,750 ft (3,000 m)	{4.4 to 32.5 mls (7 to 52 km) 32.5 to 56.25 mls (52 to 90 km)	± 487.5 ft (150 m) ± 975 ft (300 m)
19,500 ft (6,000 m)	{9.4 to 71.9 mls (15 to 115 km) 71.9 to 103.1 mls (115 to 165 km)	± 975 ft (300 m) ± 1,950 ft (600 m)
26,000 ft (8,000 m)	{11.9 to 93.75 mls (19 to 150 km) 93.75 to 115.6 mls (150 to 185 km)	± 1,300 ft (400 m) ± 2,600 ft (800 m)
32,500 ft (10,000 m)	{15.6 to 118.75 mls (25 to 190 km) 118.75 to 143.75 mls (190 to 230 km)	± 1,625 ft (500 m) ± 3,250 ft (1,000 m)

Dimensions: Antenna height 78 ft (24 m);
                antenna width 1.6.25 ft (5 m).
Wavelength/
Frequency: 2.4 m, 125 MHz
Anti-jamming
provision: Some facility of an unknown nature.
IFF capability: Not known.
Remarks: *Jagdschloss* needed skilled operators
                due to 'dead zones' which created
                gaps in the cover at altitudes over
                16,250 ft (5,000 m) and difficulties
                in reading the display due to the
                presence of 'solid' echoes in the centre
                of the CRT. One source quotes there
                being 50 such sets in service by the end
                of the war.

Sub-variants

FuMG 404:   *Jagdschloss* (Hunting Castle) developed
jointly by Gema, Siemens and Lorenz. See main data
for details of this device.

FuMG ?:   *Jagdschloss Michael* (Hunting Castle
Michael) developed jointly by Siemens and
Telefunken. This device seems to have been a combination of the *Jagdschloss* and *Würzburg* sets with a new
antenna code-named *Michael*. Three frequencies were
used: 120 MHz (1.9 m wavelength); 158 MHz (2.5 m
wavelength); and 560 MHz (5.3 m wavelength) and
the set had a range of 50 to 93.75 mls (80 to 150 km).

FuMG ?:   *Jagdschloss Umstellung* (Hunting Castle
Conversion) developed by Siemens. This was a
development of *Jagdschloss* with a double aerial and
had a frequency/wavelength in the 120 to 158 MHz,
1.9 to 2.5 m band.

FuMG ?:   *Jagdschloss MA* (Hunting Castle MA)
developed by Siemens. This was another
Jagdschloss/Würzburg combination with the *Michael*
antenna and had a frequency/wavelength of 560 MHz,
5.3 m.

FuMG ?:   *Jagdschloss Z* (Hunting Castle Z)
developed by Siemens. A combination of *Berlin*

components into *Jagdschloss* producing a centimetric
variant of the latter. Under development at the end of
the war.

FuMo 51 Mammut (Mammoth)
Role and   Long-range EW radar developed
Builder: jointly by Telefunken and the
                Experimental Signals Kommando.
Search radius: 100° (the device 'swung' its signal
                through this arc electrically).
Range: Dependent on target and site altitude)

Target altitude	Range
162.5 ft (50 m)	21.9 mls (35 km)
325 ft (100 m)	31.25 mls (50 km)
3,250 ft (1,000 m)	62.5 mls (100 km)
9,750 ft (3,000 m)	106.25 mls (170 km)
19,500 ft (6,000 m)	156.25 mls (250 km)
26,000 ft (8,000 m)	187.5 mls (300 km)

Range
accuracy: ±975 ft (300 m).
DF accuracy: Azimuth, ±0.5°; no elevation
                measurement.
Weight: 24.5 tons (25 tonnes)
Dimensions: Height 32.5 ft (10 m); width 97.5 ft
                (30 m).
Wavelength/
Frequency: 2.1 to 2.5 m, 120 to 138 MHz.
Anti-jamming
provision: Some facility of an unknown nature.
IFF capability: None.
Remarks: *Mammut* was a development of *Freya*
                with a greater range and accuracy.
Sub-variants: None known.

The aerial array for the FuMo 51 Mammut *early warning
radar. (via D Wood)*

FuMG 402 Wassermann (Aquarian)

Role and Builder:	Long-range EW radar developed by Siemens.
Range:	Dependent on target and site altitude.

Target altitude	Range
163 ft (50 m)	21.9 mls (35 km)
325 ft (100 m)	31.25 mls (50 km)
2,600 ft (800 m)	131.25 mls (210 km)
3,250 ft (1,000 m)	50 mls (80 km)
9,750 ft (3,000 m)	81.25 mls (130 km)
19,500 ft (6,000 m)	118.75 mls (190 km)

Range accuracy: ±975 ft (300 m)

DF accuracy: Azimuth ±¼°; elevation ±¾° within a 3 to 18° arc above the horizon.

Weight: 29.5 to 59 tons (30 to 60 tonnes) dependent on the antenna used.

Dimensions: Antenna height 117 to 195 ft (36 to 60 m) dependent on the antenna used; antenna width 19.5 to 40.3 ft (6 to 12.4 m) dependent on the antenna used.

Anti-jamming provision: Some facility of an unknown nature.

IFF capability: FuG 25a *Erstling* facility.

Crew: Seven.

Sub-variants

FuMG ?: *Wassermann L* (Aquarian L) developed by Gema. 'L' had a frequency of 125 MHz, a wavelength of 2.4 m, an aerial height of 117 ft (36 m) and a range of 125 mls (200 km). Replaced FuMG 402 from 1942.

The aerial array for the FuMG 404 Jagdschloss early warning radar. (via D Wood)

FuMG ?: *Wassermann S* (Aquarian S) developed jointly by Gema and Siemens. 'S' had a frequency of 125 MHz, a wavelength of 2.4 m, an aerial height of 195 ft (60 m) and a range of 187.5 mls (300 km). Replaced FuMG 402 from 1942.

FuMG 402: Developed by Siemens and produced in five versions as follows:

Wassermann MI (Aquarian MI) Frequency 120–158 MHz; Wavelength 1.9–2.5 m; Range 175 mls (280 km); and Aerial Height 117 ft (36 m)

The aerial array for the Jagdschloss Michael early warning radar. (via D Wood)

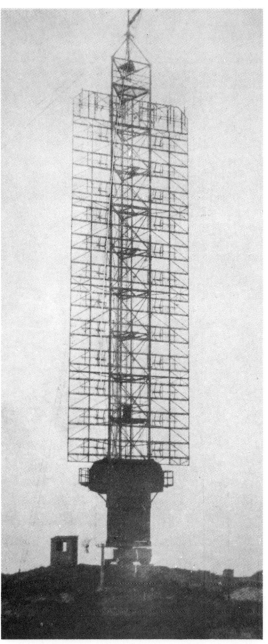

Wassermann MII (Aquarian MII) Frequency 120–158 MHz; Wavelength 1.9–2.5 m; Range 175 mls (280 km); and Aerial Height 130 ft (40 m)

Wassermann MIII (Aquarian MIII) Frequency 158–250 MHz; Wavelength 1.3–1.9 m; Range 175 mls (280 km); and Aerial Height 165.75 ft (51 m)

Wassermann MIV (Aquarian MIV) Frequency 120–158 MHz; Wavelength 1.9–2.5 m; Range 175 mls (280 km); and Aerial Height 165.75 ft (51 m)

Wassermann MV (Aquarian MV) Frequency 75–125 MHz; Wavelength 2.4–4.0 m; Range 175 mls (280 km); and Aerial Height 195 ft (60 m)

FuMG ?: *Wassermann Panorama* (Panoramic Aquarian) developed by the research station at Werneuchen. An experimental development of *Wassermann* with a 'Panoramic' display and a frequency wavelength of 125 MHz, 2.4 m.

FuMG 62D Wurzburg

Role and
Builder: A GCI and GL radar developed by Telefunken.
Search radius: Azimuth 360°; elevation −8° to +96°.
Range: In the search mode 18.75 to 25 mls (30 to 40 km); in the direction finding mode 11.25 mls (18 km).
Range
accuracy: ±162.5 ft (50 m)
DF accuracy: Azimuth ±0.45°; elevation ±10°.
Weight: Initially 3,520 lbs (1,600 kg) rising in later production sets to 3,960 lbs (1,800 kg).

A view of the FuMG 62C Würzburg *GCI radar. (via J Scutts)*

Dimensions: Height 13.8 ft (4.25 m); width 17.9 ft (5.50 m).
Wavelength/
Frequency: 5.3 m, 560 MHz.
Anti-jamming   Late production models had different
provision: frequencies and wavelengths (5.3 to 6.7 m).
IFF capability: None except on an experimental basis.
Crew: Four.

A view of one of the types of presentation CRT used in the Würzburg *GCI radar. (Crown Copyright. Science Museum, London)*

A view of one of the types of presentation CRT used in the Würzburg *GCI radar. (Crown Copyright. Science Museum, London)*

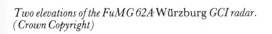

Two elevations of the FuMG 62A Würzburg *GCI radar. (Crown Copyright)*

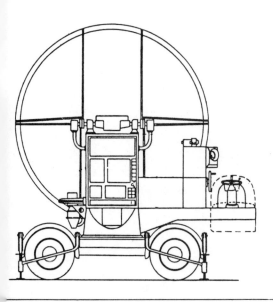

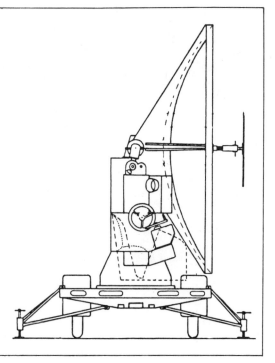

Remarks: Approximately 4,000 FuMG 62 sets were delivered for service use. Although designed and used as a GL radar, *Würzburg* saw large-scale service in the GCI role and was even occasionally used for EW.

Sub-variants

FuMG 62A: *Würzburg A*   Frequency 560 MHz; Wavelength 5.3 m; and Range 25 mls (40 km)

FuMG 62B: *Würzburg B* An experimental development of *Würzburg A* with an additional infra-red detection as a possible counter to *Window* (see page 000). This infra-red detector was probably the *B-Gerät* which had a range of 8 to 10 mls (12–15 km) and proved to be extremely sensitive being quite capable of responding to 'Flak' bursts.

FuMG 62C: *Würzburg C* Similar to the *Würzburg A* but with an approved capacity for determining height and a slight increase in range.

FuMG 62D: *Würzburg D* See main data. Many *Würzburg C* sets were converted to 'Ds'.

FuMG 65 Wurzburg-Riese (Giant *Würzburg*)

Role and
Builder: GCI radar developed by Telefunken.
Range: In the search mode, 37.5 to 50 mls (60–80 km) [50 ms (80 m) was only achieved under exceptional circumstances]. In the direction finding mode, 31.25 to 37.5 mls (50–60 km).

The FuMG 65 Würzburg-Riese *GCI radar. (Crown Copyright)*

A view of the rail mounting for the FuMG 65E Würzburg-Riese *mobile GCI radar. (Crown Copyright)*

The Korfu *tracking receiver for use against* H2S *transmissions. (Crown Copyright. Science Museum, London)*

Range
accuracy: ±325 ft (100 m).
DF accuracy: Azimuth ±0.2°; elevation ±0.25°.
                    These figures gave the following
                    altitude errors for given ranges on a
                    target at 9,750 ft (3,000 m):

Range	Altitude errors
3.2 mls (5 km)	±260 ft (80 m)
6.25 mls (10 km)	±325 ft (100 m)
12.5 mls (20 km)	±390 ft (120 m)
31.25 mls (50 km)	±520 ft (160 m)
43.75 mls (70 km)	±812.5 ft (250 m)

Weight: 14.7 tons (15 tonnes).
Dimensions: Height 25.7 ft (7.9 m); width 24.4 ft
                    (7.5 m).
Wavelength/
Frequency: 5.3 m, 560 MHz.
Anti-jamming
provision: As for the *Würzburg D*.
IFF capability: None.
Crew: Six.
Remarks: A replacement for *Würzburg D* from
                    1942. At least 1,500 such devices were
                    produced during the war.

Sub-variants
At least eight variants of FuMG 65 are known to have
existed of which three have been identified as follows:
Würzburg-Riese B (Giant Würzburg B) Fitted with
an IFF capability
Würzburg-Riese E (Giant Würzburg E)   Railway
mounted
Würzburg-Riese-Gigant (Giant Giant Würzburg)
A replacement for FuMG 71 *Koburg IG* [itself a combination of FuMG 65G and *Freya*] With a fre-
quency/wavelength of 560 MHz, 5.3 m.

GROUND BASED HOMING DEVICES

Korfu
A device designed to track and give a bearing on the
transmissions from the H2S navigational radar with a
range of about 100 mls (160 km). An airborne version
of *Korfu* was also developed (see page 170).

Naxburg
A device designed to track and give a bearing on the
transmissions from the H2S navigational radar.
Naxburg was an adaptation of the *Würzburg* aerial dish
to accommodate the FuG 350 *Naxos* homer (see page
169), the combination having a range of between 100
mls (160 km) and 160 mls (256 km).

V EXPERIMENTAL GERMAN
ELECTRONIC AIDS

During the last two years of the war, Germany put an
enormous effort into bridging the technological gap
which had opened with the Allied introduction of
centimetric radars and advanced electronic
navigational and bombing aids. This appendix is
included to give some idea of the extent of this work.
    The Luftwaffe only managed to introduce one
centimetric radar into service, *Berlin N-la*, before May
1945, and then only on a limited scale, but was
developing no less than five others. It is interesting to
note that the *Berlin* family was based on the British *H2S*
navigational radar (known in Germany as *Rotterdam*).

Indeed, so impressed were the German scientific com-
munity that the first models (not detailed here) were
almost straight copies designed for the navigation of
bombers.
    Perhaps more interesting than the centimetric AI
work were the automatic gun laying devices, six of
which are detailed here. For their day they were
extremely sophisticated, presaging in many ways
today's semi-automatic modes of interception.
    Finally, details are given of the FuG 226, the
Luftwaffe's last IFF set, designed to replace the com-
promised FuG 25a if the war had continued.

AI AND TAIL-WARNING RADARS

FuG 202 Lichtenstein BC/S
An experimental AI development of *Lichtenstein BC*
which featured additional wing-mounted aerials to
increase the search angle to 120°. The type was not
proceeded with.

FuG 212 Lichtenstein C22
An experimental development of *Lichtenstein C-1* in
which the minimum range was reduced to 487.5 ft (150
m). Development of the device was discontinued in
favour of *Lichtenstein SN-2*.

FuG 214 Lichtenstein BC/R
A tail-warning derivative of *Lichtenstein BC* which was
superseded by FuG 216 *Neptun*. There is some evidence
to suggest that FuG 214 saw limited service.

FuG 219 Weilheim
An AI outgrowth from the *Neptun* family developed by
Siemens. FuG 219 had a frequency in the 172 to 188
MHz band, a power output of 100 kW and a maximum
range of about 9.4 mls (15 km). *Weilheim* was still in the
development stage when the war ended.

FuG 228 Lichtenstein SN-3
An AI radar developed by Telefunken. FuG 228 had a
frequency in the 115 to 148 MHz band, a power output
of 20 kW, a maximum and minimum range of 5 mls (8
km) and 812.5 ft (250 m) respectively, a search angle in
azimuth and elevation of 120 and 100° respectively and
a weight of 209 lbs (95 kg). Initially, *SN-3* used the
same antenna as the *SN-2c* but with thicker forward
dipoles. A *Morgenstern* array with $\frac{1}{4}$- and $\frac{1}{2}$-wave dipoles
was later used experimentally. It is thought that about
ten sets of this type were produced, but it is not known
whether any were used operationally.

FuG 240/2 Berlin N-2
An AI radar with a wavelength of 9 to 9.3 cm, a
maximum range of 3.75 to 5 mls (6 to 8 km), a search
angle of 55° and a PPI display, which was still under
development at the war's end.

FuG 240/3 Berlin N-3
An AI radar with a similar wavelength and range to the
previous *Berlin* sets, a search angle in azimuth and
elevation of 90° and 20° respectively and with a
parabolic reflector/antenna installation which
followed a spiral search pattern. FuG 240/3 was later
developed into FuG 244.

FuG 240/4 Berlin N-4
Perhaps the most interesting of the *Berlin* family, N-4
was a project for an airborne early warning radar. FuG

240/4 was to have had a similar wavelength and range to the other members of the family and was designed to give coverage to a 180° arc above the carrier aircraft.

FuG 244 Bremen O
An AI radar developed by Telefunken out of the *Berlin N-3*. FuG 244 had a wavelength of 9 to 9.3 cm, a power output of 20 kW a maximum and minimum range of 3.1 mls (5 km) and 650 ft (200 m) respectively, a search angle in azimuth and elevation of 100° and 20° respectively, a measuring accuracy of ±1° and a weight of 220 lbs (100 kg). One set of this type was produced before the war's end.

FuG 245 Bremen
An AI radar developed by Telefunken to supersede FuG 244. One set of this type was bench tested before the end of the war.

GUN LAYING AND BLIND FIRING DEVICES

FuG ? Lichtenstein O
A radar device for firing the *Schräge Musik* weapons mounted in night-fighter aircraft with a possible frequency of 490 MHz. The antenna used was that of the *Lichtenstein BC*, mounted parallel to the gun barrels of the oblique armament. One set was produced during 1943 and trials were undertaken with a Do17Z-10 carrier aircraft.

FuG 215 Pauka A
A radar device developed by Telefunken for automatic gun laying (ranging). *Pauka A* had a frequency in the 410 to 490 MHz band and six range settings. Initially, the device used the antenna from the *Wide-Angle Lichtenstein C-1* with thickened dipoles, but this was replaced by a 28 in (70 cm) parabolic reflector mounted under a plywood nose radome. Ten FuG 215 sets were produced for concept proving trials.

FuG 222 Pauka S
A radar device developed by Telefunken for automatic gun ranging and blind firing in night fighter aircraft. *Pauka S* had a wavelength of 9 to 9.3 cm, a maximum

and minimum range of 6.25 mls (10 km) and 975 ft (300 m) respectively, a search angle in azimuth and elevation of 100° and 20° respectively, a measuring accuracy of ±1° and a weight of 484 lbs (22 kg). FuG 222 featured an azimuth, elevation and gun sight CRT display. The gun sight display had a target selection facility. Three sets of this kind were produced for concept proving trials.

FuG 247 Bremerhaven (Formerly Pauka SD)
A radar project probably developed by Telefunken for automatic gun ranging and blind firing in night fighter aircraft. *Bremerhaven* was to have had a wavelength of 3 cm, a maximum range of 6.25 mls (10 km), a search angle of 120°, a measuring accuracy of ±1° and a weight of 264 lbs (120 kg). FuG 247 was to have featured a rotating parabolic reflector and a form of manufactured pictorial display containing all the information needed by the operator.

FuG 248 Eule (Owl)
A radar blind firing device for night fighter aircraft developed by Telefunken. *Eule* had a frequency of 10,000 MHz and a maximum range of 1.25 mls (2 km). The device used funnel-shaped aerials built into the wings of the carrier aircraft and the range data it provided was automatically fed into an EZ 42 gyrogunsight.

EG 3 Elfe 3 (Fairy or Goblin 3)
An automatic firing device developed by the FFO for use in combination with FuG 216, 217, 218, 219 and 248. *Elfe 3* generated a firing circuit when a received radar echo indicated that the target was at a predetermined distance. The device had a number of range settings.

The Bagful *device used to produce permanent recordings of enemy signals traffic on paper tape.* (*Crown Copyright*)

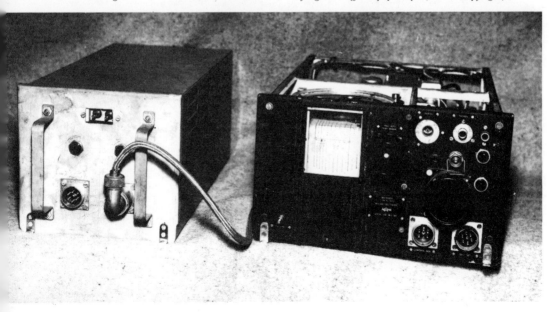

IDENTIFICATION FRIEND OR FOE (IFF) DEVICES

FuG 226 Neuling (Novice or Beginner)

An IFF set developed by Lorenz. FuG 226 was tied in with the carrier aircraft's radio equipment and could give an air-to-air or air-to-ground response as well as a ground-to-air 'command' facility. *Neuling* appeared as test sets only but was going into mass production at the war's end.

VI MISCELLANEOUS DEVICES

This appendix gives the reader a view of the Allied and German navigational aids and the German communications sets which were so vital to the successful prosecution of the night fighter war by both sides.

Also included are details of various British devices which can not readily be included in other categories.

Bagful

A paper-tape-type recording device developed by the TRE designed to detail the wavelength, time and duration of a received enemy signal. (A wire-type device was used to provide an audio record of such signals.)

Blonde

An automatic receiving device developed by the TRE which was designed to provide a photographic record of all signals received within a pre-set band. *Blonde* could be used both in the air and on the ground.

Egon

A German blind-bombing system introduced into service during the latter part of 1943. There is some evidence to indicate that the system was utilised on a limited scale as a navigational aid by the Luftwaffe's night fighter arm.

Egon used two specially modified *Freya* sets (FuSAn 730 *Freya Egon I*, see page 185), each with a FuG 25a IFF capacity, situated about 100 miles apart. In the blind-bombing mode, one of these radars was used to track the aircraft (identified by its FuG 25a signal) and to keep it on an arc which was at a constant distance from it. The second set also tracked the aircraft (on a different frequency) and gave the release order when the correct point on the arc, the target, had been reached.

The *Freya* signals were received by the aircraft, amplified and re-transmitted in order to extend the range of the system.

FuG 10

Radio communications equipment developed and manufactured by Lorenz. The device could be used for both R/T and W/T, had a frequency in the 3 to 6 MHz band and weighed 220 lb (100 kg). A number of sub variants of this equipment were developed as follows

FuG 10K series: A variant of the basic set for different frequency coverage to the standard 3 to 6 MHz which appeared in three sub-variants: K1, 5.3 to 10 MHz; K2, 6 to 12 MHz; and K3, 6 to 18 MHz. Types K1 and 2 were mainly used in four-engined aircraft such as the Fw200 and the He177.

FuG 10P: A variant which combined FuG 10 with the *Peilgerät 6* D/F set. In this equipment, the standard E10L receiver was replaced by the EZ6 unit from the *Peilgerät 6*.

The S 10 K short-wave transmitter from the FuG 10 unit. (Crown Copyright. Science Museum, London)

The FuG 16ZY radio/DF installation. (Crown Copyright. Science Museum, London)

The E 16 receiver from the FuG 16Z unit. (Crown Copyright. Science Museum, London)

FuG 16

Radio communications equipment developed and manufactured by Lorenz. The device could be used for both R/T and W/T and operated in the 38.5 to 42.3 MHz band. A number of sub-variants of the equipment were developed as follows:

FuG 16Z: An amplified version of the basic set for use in single-engined fighters and which was replaced by FuG 16ZY.

FuG 16ZE: A variant similar to the ZY model but with modified operating controls.

FuG 16ZS: A variant similar to the Z model but operating in the 40 to 45 MHz band.

FuG 16ZY: A variant which was developed from the Z model but which incorporated D/F capacity. FuG 16ZY was the major production model of the series.

FuG 25a Erstling (First born)

An IFF set developed and manufactured by Gema which comprised a control unit (BG 25) a junction box (VK 25), a resistance box (WK 25), a transmitter-receiver (SE 25a), a rotary invertor and an aerial matching unit (AAG 25a). The device was able to receive signals in the 123 to 128 MHz band and transmitted in the 150 to 160 MHz band. *Erstling* was used in conjunction with the *Freya* family of radars and had a range of 166.7 mls (268 km).

FuG 120 Bernadine

A teleprinter-type device designed to give the operator

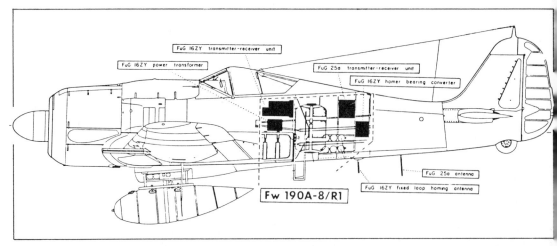

Installation diagram for the FuG 16ZY and FuG 25a units in the Fw190A-8/R1. (Author's collection)

The Bernhard transmission aerial used in conjunction with the airborne FuG 120 unit. (IWM)

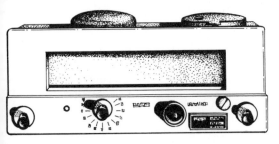

Above: *The printer unit from the FuG 120 installation.* (*Author's collection*)

Below: *The* Gee *installation in a 100 Group Mosquito II aircraft.* (*Crown Copyright*)

a continuous bearing on a given transmitter (*Bernhard*) and information relating to the air situation. The device consisted of an EBL 3F or H receiver (part of the FuBl 2 blind-approach set), a writing amplifier (SV 120), a filter unit (SG 120), a switch unit (UG 120), a power unit (U 120) and printer unit. FuG 120 operated in the 30 to 33.3 MHz frequency band.

Gee

A navigational and blind-bombing device introduced into RAF service during August 1941. The *Gee* system consisted of the reception by equipment in the aircraft of transmissions from three ground stations situated on a base line approximately 200 mls (322 km) long. One of these transmitters was known as the 'A' or 'Master' station and the other two were called the 'B' and 'C' or 'Slave' stations. Each 'Slave' transmission was locked

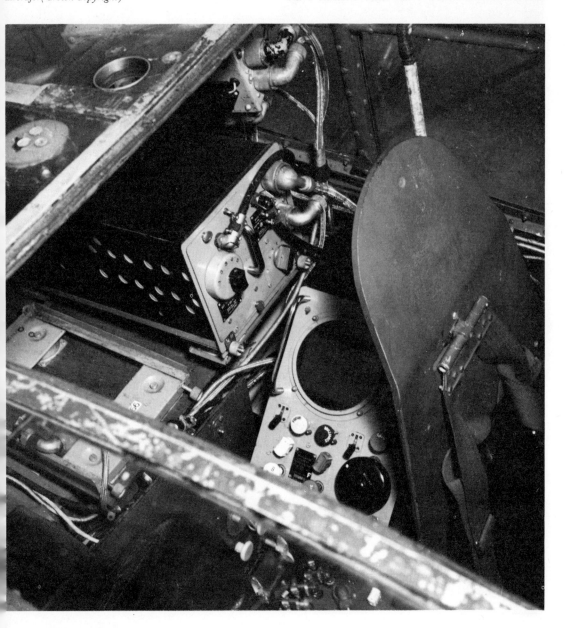

to the 'Master' transmission and the difference in the time taken by the 'A' and 'B' and the 'A' and 'C' signals to reach the aircraft were measured and displayed on a CRT on the navigator's table in the aircraft. From them, the aircraft could be located on two position lines known as 'Gee co-ordinates' and the ground position of the aircraft coincided with the point at which these co-ordinates, which were printed as a grid on special Gee charts, intersected. The co-ordinates could be obtained by a competent navigator in less than a minute.

360° arc of the ground below the equipped aircraft. The operator was able to differentiate between water and land and between built-up areas and open countryside. The device had four ranges (100, 50, 30 and 10 mile radius 160, 80, 48 and 16 km) and incorporated a radio altimeter and in many instances *Fishpond*. This was a tail warning device which used

The Type 184 indicator and the Type 207 switch unit used in the H2S Mk IIB installation. (Crown Copyright)

The accuracy of a *Gee* fix varied from less than half a mile to about five miles, depending upon the skill of the navigator, upon whether the aircraft was in an area where the *Gee* grid intersected acutely or obtusely and upon the range of the aircraft from the transmitters. The range of *Gee* itself varied with conditions from three to four hundred miles, but in general, the rule was that the greater the range, the less was the accuracy.

H2S
A navigational radar developed by Dr Lovell at the TRE which produced a 'map' on a CRT display of a

The plastic radome used to protect the H2S scanner on a B-17. (Crown Copyright)

that part of the signal not used for mapping which radiated between the ground and the aircraft. A separate CRT display was provided for this capacity. *H2S* was developed in a number of versions, known details of which are as follows:

Mk I: First production model with a 9 cm wavelength.

Mk IIA: Featured an improved aerial and mounting system.

Mk IIB: Type 184 scan-corrected indicator.

Mk IIC: Barrel shaped scanner.

Mk III: Featured a 3 cm wavelength.

Mk IIIB: Type 184 scan-corrected indicator.

Mk IIIF: Featured a 6-foot scanner code-named *Whirligig*.

Mk IV: Incorporated a bomb computing facility.

Mk VI: Featured a 1.25 cm wavelength and codenamed *Lion Tamer*.

Infra-red Identification Equipment

As the numbers of bomber and bomber support aircraft increased, the fighter elements of 100(SD) Group began to find that more often than not that they were chasing friendly aircraft. There was an obvious need for some form of identification system. A number of solutions to this problem were tried including the use of infra-red equipment of Types F or Z. (Other solutions which saw service were a modified Mk IIIF IFF set and an ID capacity built into the *Monica* device.) Infra-red equipped aircraft had a source positioned in the extreme rear fuselage which could be recognised by a suitably equipped pursuing aircraft.

Loran

An American hyperbolic navigational aid similar in operation to the British 'Gee' device. 'Loran' was primarily designed for use over water, having a maximum range in the region of 700 mls (1127 km). In RAF service, use was made of 'Loran's' ability to operate over much longer ranges at night (in the region of 12000 mls [19320 km]) under the code name 'Skywave Synchronized' or 'SS Loran'. In the last six months of the war, Bomber command used 'SS Loran' during 22000 sorties.

Window Dispensers

The *Window* Research Section developed five dispensers for use by 100(SD) Group, the details of which are at the bottom of the page.

The Y-System

A fighter control system introduced by the Luftwaffe in mid-1943. Using the FuG 16ZY communications gear, a 'Y' aircraft would be continuously in receipt of a running commentary on the position, course and altitude of enemy formations. This information could be passed to non-'Y' aircraft by the equipped aeroplane using a different frequency. Four pilot's controls were associated with the system as follows:

Position one: Y FUHRUNGSFREQUENZ Voice communication between the flight leader and the fighter controller on the ground.

Position two: GRUPPENBEFEHLSFREQUENZ Voice communication between individual aircraft in formation.

Position triangle: NAH-FLUGSICHERUNGS-FREQUENZ Voice communication between the pilot and the ground.

Position square: REICHSJAGERFREQUENZ The running commentary.

Designation	Length	Width	Depth	Weight (loaded)	Weight (unloaded)	Number of bundles carried	Remarks
Mk I	14 ft 6 in (4.5 m)	1 ft 4 in (0.4 m)	1 ft 6 in [less chute] (0.46 m)	700 lb (318 kg)	260 lb (118 kg)	552	Designed to fit into the bomb bays of heavy bomber types and to carry MM and N3 *Window*.
Mk IA	14 ft 6 in (4.5 m)	1 ft 4 in (0.4 m)	1 ft 6 in [less chute] (0.46 m)	1,000 lb (454.5 kg)	300 lb (136 kg)	850	A replacement for the Mk I.
Mk II	8 ft 0 in (2.5 m)	2 ft 8 in (0.8 m)	1 ft 8 in [less chute] (0.5 m)	1,400 lb (636 kg)	350 lb (159 kg)	1200	Designed to take up less space than previous models.
Mk III				345 lb (157 kg)	160 lb (73 kg)	160	Designed to be carried in the 100 gal (471 litre) Mosquito drop tank.
Mk IIIA				345 lb (157 kg)	160 lb (73 kg)	160	As the Mk III but made of plastic.

Glossary

AI:	Airborne Interception (radar).
AN/XXX-X:	US radar designation. The first two letters indicate that the device is a joint Army/Navy venture, the next three the exact nature of the equipment (AI, ASV, etc) and the last numeral the model number.
ARI:	RAF designation meaning Airborne Radio Installation.
ASV:	Air-to-surface-vessel (radar).
Blip:	Bright spot generated on a radar screen representing a target.
Carrier wave:	A wave with the necessary properties to enable it to be transmitted through a physical system after it has been modulated.
Centimetric:	Family name for radars with wavelengths betweeen 1 and 10 centimetres.
CRT:	Cathode-ray tube (Brauntube).
CW:	Continuous wave. Radio or radar waves which maintain a constant amplitude (the maximum departure on the value of the wave from the average value) and a constant frequency.
Decimetric:	Family name for radars with wavelengths of 1 metre or above (usually expressed in centimetres).
Dipole aerial:	A straight radiator/receiver, usually half a wavelength long and fed at the centre to produce the maximum radiation in the plane normal to its axis.
ELINT:	ELectronic INTelligence. The gathering of information about the operation and performance of the enemy's electronic equipment by electronic means.
EW:	Early warning (radar).
FFO:	The *Flugfunk FOrschungsanstalt* – Electrical Research Institute for High Frequency. A German research establishment at Oberpfaffenhofen which conducted work on electronic measurement, radio control for aircraft and missiles, infra-red detectors for night fighters, radar and related subjects.
Frequency:	The number of cycles produced in radio energy by an oscillator (a cycle being the transition between positive and negative values). Expressed in Hz, that is the number of cycles which occur in a second.
Frequency, spot:	A particular and precisely defined frequency.
FuG:	German airborne radio prefix (*Funkgerät*).
FuMG:	German ground radar prefix (*Funkmessgerät*). Also abbreviated to FMG.
GCI:	Ground control of interception (radar)
GHz:	Gigaherz. Thousands of millions of cycles per second.
GL:	Gun-laying (radar)
IFF:	Identification friend or foe. An automatic radar transponder giving a coded reply if friendly.
Jamming:	Signals or a screen of reflective material designed to deny an enemy a radar picture of the aerial situation or intelligible R/T and W/T communications.
Jamming, barrage:	Jamming conducted against a frequency range.
Jamming, CW:	Jamming by means of a continuous wave signal.
Jamming, noise Modulated:	Jamming by means of 'noise' introduced into a carrier wave to change its characteristics in an undesirable manner.
Jamming, spot:	Jamming conducted against a particular and precise frequency.
Jamming, tone modulated	Jamming by means of an audio tone introduced into a speech transmission to change its characteristics in an undesirable manner.
Lobe switching:	In radar, a form of scanning in which the direction of maximum radiation or reception is switched in turn to each of a number of preferred directions, eg. first to one side and then to the other of a target.
MF:	Medium frequency. A family name for frequencies with a value between 300 and 3000-thousand cycles per second and a wavelength of between 1000 and 100m.
MHz:	Megaherz. The number of millions of cycles which occur in one second.
Modulation:	The modification of radio energy from one set of characteristics to another.
Navaid:	An electronic NAvigational AID.
Noise:	An undesired electrical disturbance within a useful frequency band.
Paint:	The illumination of a target with radio energy generated by a radar transmission.
Parabolic reflector (aerial):	A concave reflector of radio energy so shaped that all the rays from the transmitter or receiving dipole at its focus are concentrated in a direction parallel to the former's axis.
PPI:	Plan-Position Indicator. A radar display painting a map-like picture.
$\frac{1}{4}$ wave, $\frac{1}{2}$ wave etc:	A reference to aerial size. Aerial size in the indicated proportion of the wavelength of the signal to be received.
Radar:	RAdio Detection And Ranging (American term). A method of detecting and determining the range of an object by means of the transmission of a beam of radio-frequency energy in the general direction of the object and the measurement of the time taken for the reflected part of the energy (the echo) to return to the source of the transmission.
R/T:	Radio Telegraphy. Voice communication by radio.
SCR:	US signals equipment designation (Signal Corps Radio)
Search angle:	The area which can be 'seen' by a particular radar in an arc with the source at its centre.
TRE:	Telecommunications Research Establishment. A British research establishment stationed at Worth Matravers and then Malvern which worked in all aspects of radio and radar. Previously known as the Air Ministry Research Establishment and now the Royal Radar Establishment.
UHF:	Ultra high frequency. Family name for a group of frequencies with a value of between 300 and 3000 MHz and a wavelength of between ten and one cm. Covers the 'S', 'C', 'X' and 'Ku'-bands now known as the 'F-' through 'J'-bands.
VHF:	Very High Frequency. Family name for a group of frequencies with a value of between 30 and 300 MHz and a wavelength of between 10 and one metre. Now known as the 'VHF' and 'A'-bands.
Volt:	The practical unit of electromotive force. It is that force applied steadily to a conductor of resistance one ohm produces a current of one ampere. (Ampere; unit of electric current corresponding to the flow of 6×10^{18} electrons per second.)
Watt:	The unit of electrical power calculated by multiplying the voltage by the ampage.
Wavelength:	A measurement of the disturbance caused by the frequency of radio energy in the medium through which it is travelling. Calculated by dividing the speed of the radio energy by its frequency. Expressed in metric units of measurement.
W/T:	Wireless telegraphy. Non-voice communication by radio telegraphy, ie. Morse code.
Yagi:	A type of aerial array developed in Japan and exemplified by the present British TV aerial used for the reception of UHF transmissions.

Appendix 2

The Bomber Support Units

Number 23(SD) Squadron (Coded 'YP')
History

Became non-operational in Malta during April 1944, returning to the UK in May of that year. Transferred to 100(SD) Group for bomber support duties. (First sortie in this role on 5/6 July 1944.) Disbanded at Little Snoring on 25 September 1945. Reformed in Fighter Command on 11 September 1946.

Bases

Little Snoring   June 1944 to September 1945

Commanding Officers

Wing Commander A M Murphy   December 1943 to December 1944

Wing Commander S P Russell   December 1944 to September 1945

Representative Aircraft

Mosquito VI   (May 1943 to September 1945)
HR201 'YP-K', HR216 '-T', PZ172 '-C', PZ176 '-B', PZ315 '-Y', PZ437'-O', RS507 '-C', RS548 '-V'

Number 25(F) Squadron (Coded 'ZK')
History

In September 1943, AI Mk IV was installed in the aircraft of 'A' Flight for *Mahmoud* trials. This type of operation was continued until December 1943 when the squadron began to re-equip with Mosquito XVII aircraft.

Bases

Church Fenton   May 1942 to December 1943 (Detachment to Predannack)

Commanding Officers

Wing Commander S N L Maude   April 1943 to October 1943

Wing Commander C M Wight-Boycott   October 1943 to September 1944

Representative Aircraft

Mosquito II   (October 1942 to March 1944)
DD733, DD746, DD756, DD782, DZ238, DZ655, DZ685, DZ759, HJ645, HJ653, HJ713, HJ914

Mosquito VI   (August/September 1943 to January/February 1945)
HJ743, HJ757, HP853, HX827, HX866, PZ200 'ZK-A'

Number 85(SD) Squadron (Coded 'VY')
History

Transferred to 100(SD) Group from 11 Group on 1 April 1944 for bomber support duties. Suspended these in favour of anti-*Diver* patrols on 25 June 1944 which continued until 29 August 1944, when the squadron returned to its original role. After the end of the European war, the squadron reverted to Fighter Command.

Bases

Swannington   May 1944 to July 1944 and August 1944 to 1945 (for bomber support operations)

West Maling   July 1944 to August 1944 (for anti-*Diver* operations)

Commanding Officers

Wing Commander C M Miller   March to October 1944

Wing Commander F S Gonsalves   October 1944 to January 1945

Wing Commander W K Davison   January 1945 to ?

Representative Aircraft

Mosquito XII   (March 1943 to ?1944)
HK111 'VY-T', HK119 '-S', HK120 '-P', HK218 '-U'

Mosquito XVII   (November 1943 to ?1944)
HK245 '-X', HK282 '-D', HK299 '-C'

Mosquito 30   (November 1944 to 1947)
MV533 '-G', MV546 '-P', NT252 '-Y'

Number 101(B) Squadron (Coded 'SR')
History

The squadron operated as a heavy bomber unit within 1 Group until October 1943 when this role was combined with that of *Airborne Cigar* jamming. Such operations were continued until the end of the war in Europe.

Bases

Ludford Magna   June 1943 to October 1945

Commanding Officers

Unknown

Representative Aircraft

Lancaster BI (All used during the European war and all equipped with *ABC*)

DV299 'SR-K2'   Delivered 11.43, lost 17.12.43 with 41 hrs flying time. Built by Metro. – Vickers (MV)

DV300 '-W'   Delivered 11.43, lost 17.12.43 with 68 hrs flying time. Built by MV

LL756 '-Q'   Lost 25/26.2.44 (raid on Augsburg) with 261 hrs flying time. Served with 467 and 101 Squadrons

LL757 '-W'   Delivered from 32 Maintenance Unit 4.44, lost 30.8.44 with 214 hrs flying time. Built by Armstrong-Whitworth (AW) and flown by Pilot Officer R R Waughmann and crew 5/6.44. Named 'Oor Wullie'

LL758 '-A'   Delivered from 32 Maintenance Unit 4.44, lost 5.10.44 with 311 hrs flying time

ME558 '-Q'   Delivered from 32 Maintenance Unit 4.1.44, lost 16.3.44. Built by MV

ME616 '-B'   Delivered 31.1.44, lost 1.7.44, with 242 hrs flying time. Built by MV

NF983 '-D'   Delivered 9.44. To 46 Maintenance Unit 4.45, struck off charge 1.47. Built by AW (Babington). Flown by Flight Lieutenant M C C Haycroft

NG128 '-B'   Delivered 9.44. To 46 Maintenance Unit 5.45, struck off charge 1.47. Built by AW (Babington)

NG131 '-M2'   Damaged 14.10.44, lost 17.12.44. Built by AW (Babington)

NN705 '-O'   Delivered from 32 Maintenance Unit, lost 26.8.44 (raid on Russelheim) with 22 hrs flying time. Built by Austin (Longbridge)

Lancaster BIII   (All used during the European War and all equipped with *ABC*)

LM395 '-Q'   At the Royal Aircraft Establishment 12.43 To 101 1.44, lost 23.5.44. Built by Avro (Yeadon)

LM457 '-A'   Delivered 16.2.44, struck off charge 2.1.45. Built by Avro (Yeadon). May have been coded 'V2'

ND983 '-B'   Wrecked 7.9.44. Built by Avro (Chaderton)

Number 141(F) Squadron (Coded 'TW')

History

In June 1943, the squadron began *Serrate* operations, which continued until September. In the following month, the unit began to re-equip with Mosquito aircraft and in December, 141 was transferred to 100(SD) Group.

Bases

Wittering   April to December 1943 (Detachment at Drem)

Commanding Officers

Wing Commander J R D Braham   December 1942 to October 1943

Representative Aircraft

Beaufighter VIf   (June 1943 to January 1944)
V8402, V8515, V8673 'TW-K', V8744, V8799, EL185

Number 141(SD) Squadron (Coded 'TW')

History

Transferred to 100(SD) Group from 12 Group on 3 December 1943 for bomber support duties. The squadron was disbanded at West Raynham on 7 September 1945, reforming as part of Fighter Command on 17 June 1946.

Bases

West Raynham   December 1943 to July 1945 (with a detachment at Fiskerton)

Commanding Officers

Wing Commander K C Roberts   October 1943 to February 1944

Wing Commander F P Davies   February 1944 to June 1944

Wing Commander C V Winn   June 1944 to September 1945

Representative Aircraft

Beaufighter VIf   (June 1943 to January 1944)
V8673 'TW-K'

Mosquito II   (November 1943 to August 1944)
W4089 '-W', DD672 '-P', DD712 '-E', DD758 '-N', DZ240 '-H', DZ203 '-E', DZ761 '-C', HJ659 '-B', HJ701 '-U', HJ911 '-A'

Mosquito VI   (August 1944 to April 1945)
HR180 '-B', HR203 '-C', HR250 '-Y', NS961 '-H', NT234 '-W', PZ165 '-S', PZ171 '-R', PZ244 '-M', PZ252 '-Z'

Mosquito 30   (April 1945 to September 1945)
NT371 '-D', NT472 '-H', NT500 '-K', NT507 '-F', NT554 '-R'

Number 151(F) Squadron (Coded 'DZ')

History

At the end of 1944, 151 Squadron's aircraft were fitted with *Monica* tail warners in preparation for bomber support duties. These began on 21 February 1945 and took the form of low-level intruder sorties and freelance patrols. Such operations continued until the end of the European war.

Bases

Hunsdson   November 1944 to March 1945

Bradwell Bay   March to May 1945

Commanding Officers

Wing Commander G H Goodman   October 1943 to December 1944

Wing Commander W R L Beaumont   December 1944 to ?

Representative Aircraft

Mosquito VI   (Used for bomber support intruder sorties)
HR190, HR240, NS982, NS983, PZ191, PZ201, PZ224

Mosquito 30   (September 1944 to October 1946)
MM726, MM800 'DZ-V', MM802 '-C', MM814, MV559, NT304 '-T'

Number 157(SD) Squadron (Coded 'RS')

History

Transferred to 100(SD) Group from 11 Group in May 1944, for bomber support duties. Suspended these in favour of anti-*Diver* patrols on 27 June 1944, which continued until 20 August 1944 when the squadron returned to its original role. On 16 August 1945, the squadron was disbanded at Swannington.

Bases

Swannington   May 1944 to July 1944 and August 1944 to August 1945. (For bomber support duties)

West Malling   May 1944 to July 1944 (detachment) and July to August 1944 (squadron). (For anti-*Diver* duties)

Commanding Officers

Wing Commander H D U Denison   March to June 1944

Wing Commander W K Davison   June to September 1944

Wing Commander Beauchamp   September 1944 to August 1945

Representative Aircraft

Mosquito XIX   (May 1944 to May 1945)
MM630 'RS-E', MM643 '-F', MM652 '-S', MM671 '-C', MM677 '-U', TA391 '-N', TA392 '-K', TA404 '-M', TA446 '-Q'

Mosquito 30   (March to August 1945)
MV551 '-W', MV534 '-F', NT242 '-F', NT319 '-V', NT364 '-K', NT382 '-T', NT487 '-M', NT493 '-H'

Number 169(SD) Squadron (Coded 'VI')

History

Transferred to 100(SD) Group from 13 Group on 7 December 1943 for bomber support duties. The squadron was disbanded at Great Massingham on 10 August 1945.

Bases

Little Snoring   December 1943 to June 1944

Great Massingham   June 1944 to August 1945

Commanding Officers

Wing Commander E J Gracie   October 1943 to February 1944

Wing Commander R G Slade   February to April 1944

Wing Commander N B R Bromley   April to September 1944

Wing Commander T A Heath   September 1944 to January 1945

Wing Commander N E Reeves   January to August 1945

Representative Aircraft

Mosquito II   (October 1943 to July 1945)
W4076 'VI-F', DD631 '-G', DZ310 '-B', HJ707 '-B', HJ711 '-C', HJ917 '-N', HJ944 '-C'

Mosquito VI   (June 1944 to April 1945)
PZ247 '-M', NS997 '-C', NT110 '-T', NT169 '-T'

Mosquito XIX   (January to August 1945)

MM644 '-G', MM670 '-G'

Number 171(SD) Squadron (Coded '6Y')
History
Formed on 7 September 1944 for jamming duties from a Flight of 199(SD) Squadron. The unit was disbanded on 27 July 1945 at North Creake.
Bases
North Creake   September 1944 to July 1945
Commanding Officers
Wing Commander Renaun   September 1944 to ?
Representative Aircraft
Stirling BII   (September to November 1944)
    No serials known
Halifax BIII   (October 1944 to July 1945)
    MZ971 '6Y-E' NA694 '-H'

Number 192(SD) Squadron (Coded 'DT')
History
The Squadron was formed on 4 January 1943 from 1474 Flight for ELINT duties. In November 1943, control of the unit passed from 3 to 100(SD) Group. In February 1944, 1473 Flight was amalgamated with the squadron. 192 Squadron was disbanded on 22 August 1945 at Foulsham.
Bases
Gransden Lodge   January to November 1943
Foulsham   November 1943 to August 1945
Commanding Officers
Unknown
Representative Aircraft
Mosquito BIV   (November 1943 to ?)
    DK327, DZ375, DZ376, DZ410, DZ491, DZ590, DZ617
Mosquito BXVI   (April 1945 to ?)
    No serial numbers available
Wellington BX   (November 1943 to late 1944)
    No serial numbers available
Halifax BIII   (November 1943 to ?)
    MZ817 'DT-Q'
[Halifax BII and BV also used. No serials known]
Other aircraft
DZ292 Mosquito II fitted out for radar/radio investigation.
W4071 Mosquito PRI. Used from November 1944 to the end of the war for jamming operations.

Number 199(SD) Squadron (Coded 'EX')
History
Transferred to 100(SD) Group from 1 Group on 1 May 1944 for jamming duties. The squadron was disbanded on 29 July 1945 at North Creake.
Bases
North Creake   May 1944 to July 1945
Commanding Officers
Unknown
Representative Aircraft
Stirling BIII   (July 1943 to March 1945)
    BK762 'EX-C', EE946 '-P', EE953 '-L', EF450 '-N', EH934 '-K', LJ480 '-S', LJ531 '-N', LJ569 '-C', LJ578 '-S', LJ614 '-S', LJ649 '-P', LK397 '-P'
Halifax BIII   (February 1945 to July 1945)
    LK868 '-J', NA275 '-W', NR243 '-D', PN375 '-F', RG375 '-R'

Number 214(SD) Squadron (Coded 'BU')
History
Transferred to 100(SD) Group from 3 Group in January 1944 for jamming duties. The squadron was disbanded on 27 July 1945 at Oulton. On the same day, 614 Squadron was re-numbered and the new 214 resumed the normal bombing role in the Middle East.
Bases
Sculthorpe   January to May 1944
Oulton   May 1944 to July 1945
Commanding Officers
Wing Commander D J McGlinn   January to August 1944
Wing Commander D D Rogers   August 1944 to April 1945
Wing Commander R L Bowes   April to July 1945
Representative Aircraft
Fortress BII   (January 1944 to July 1945)
    SR377 'BU-M', SR382 '-B', SR388 '-H'
Fortress BIII   (January 1944 to July 1945)
    HB788 '-B', HB800 '-V', HB818 '-H', KJ101 '-M', KJ110 '-B'

Number 223(SD) Squadron (Coded '6G')
History
Formed on 23 August 1944 as part of 100(SD) Group for jamming duties. [The previous 223 was redesignated 30(SAAF) Squadron in Italy on 12 August 1944]. The squadron was disbanded on 29 July 1945 at Oulton.
Bases
Oulton   August 1944 to July 1945
Commanding Officers
Wing Commander D J McGlinn   August to September 1944
Wing Commander H H Burnell   September 1944 to July 1945 (?)
Representative Aircraft
Liberator BVI   (August 1944 to July 1945)
    TS520 '6G-J', TS526 '-T', TS528 '-R', TS532 '-N', TT336, VD245. Squadron mainly operational on Liberators
Fortress BII   (April to July 1945)
    SR383 '-X'
Fortress BIII   (April to July 1945)
    KH998 '-C', KJ109 '-F', KJ118 '-H', KJ121 '-B', KL836 '-Z'

Number 239(SD) Squadron (Coded 'HB')
History
Transferred to 100(SD) Group from 13 Group on 9 December 1943 for bomber support duties. The squadron was disbanded on 1 July 1945 at West Raynham.
Bases
West Raynham   December 1943 to July 1945
Commanding Officers
Wing Commander P M J Evans   September 1943 to September 1944
Wing Commander W F Gibb   September 1944 to July 1945
Representative Aircraft
Mosquito II   (December 1943 to September 1944)
    W4084, W4097, DD722, DD759, DD789, DZ247,

DZ263, DZ297, DZ654, DZ749, HJ644, HJ709, HJ394, HJ937

Mosquito VI   (December 1943 to February 1945)
PZ170, PZ228, PZ245, PZ340, PZ356, PZ498

Mosquito 30   (January to July 1945)
NT271, NT278, NT330, NT352, NT362 'HB-S', NT385, NT437, NT480

Number 264(F) Squadron (Coded 'PS')

History

In September 1943, the squadron began *Flower* sorties. These operations were short lived, being replaced by *Mahmouds* in October. Bomber support sorties continued spasmodically until the squadron joined the Second Tactical Air Force in December 1943.

Bases

Firwood Common   July to November 1943

Coleby Grange   November to December 1943

Commanding Officers

Wing Commander W J Alington   March 1943 to April 1944

Representative Aircraft

Mosquito VI   (August to October 1943)
HX834, HX852

Mosquito XII   (December 1943 to August 1945)
HK418 'PS-R', HK471 '-D', HK477 '-C', HK479 '-F', HK481 '-O', HK506 '-G', HK515 '-S', MM455 '-Q', MM 467 '-J', MM493 '-T', MM559, MM623

Number 307(F) Squadron (Coded 'EW') [Polish Air Force]

History

In December 1944, the squadron's aircraft were fitted with *Monica* tail warners in preparation for the bomber support role. Such operations, taking the form of both high- and low-level patrols, were continued until the end of the European war.

Bases

Church Fenton   May 1944 to January 1945 (with a detachment at Coltishall)

Castle Camps   January to May 1945

Commanding Officers

Wing Commander G K Ranoszek   May 1944 to March 1945

Wing Commander S Andzejewski   March to ? 1945

Representative Aircraft

Mosquito 30   (October 1944 to January 1947)
MT497/G 'EW-O', MV539 '-M', MV542 '-Y', NT259/G '-W', NT267/G '-J', NT333/G '-G', NT482 '-L', NT565 '-A', RK951 '-N'

Number 406(F) Squadron (Coded 'HU')

History

In August 1944, the squadron was re-equipped with the Mosquito 30 and operated from this time in the bomber support role. Such operations consisted of intruder sorties and freelance patrols and were continued until the end of the European war.

Bases

Manston   November 1944 to July 1945

Commanding Officers

Wing Commander R Bannock   November 1944 to May 1945

Wing Commander R G Gray   May to September 1945

Representative Aircraft

Mosquito 30   (July 1944 to September 1945)
MM751 'HU-S', NT283 '-V', NT312 '-M', NT433 '-P'

Number 410(F) Squadron (Coded 'RA')

History

In August 1943, the squadron began *Mahmoud* sorties, followed by *Flowers* in September. Such bomber support operations were short lived, ceasing in mid-September.

Bases

Coleby Grange   February to October 1943 (with detachments at Predannack and Hudson)

Commanding Officers

Wing Commander G H Elms   May 1943 to February 1944

Representative Aircraft

Mosquito II   (October 1942 to December 1943)
DD608, DD720 'RA-G', DD753, DD786, DZ256, DZ304, DZ661, DZ757, HJ913, HJ928 '-R', HJ936, HJ944

Mosquito VI   (July to September 1943)
HJ824, HJ827, HP848, HP849

Number 456(F) Squadron (Coded 'RX')

History

At the end of March 1945, the squadron began full-time bomber support sorties which were continued until the end of the European war. The squadron was disbanded on 15 June 1945 at Bradwell Bay.

Bases

Bradwell Bay   March to June 1945

Commanding Officers

Wing Commander B Howard   November 1944 to May 1945

Squadron Leader R B Cowper   May to June 1945

Representative Aircraft

Mosquito 30   (December 1944 to June 1945)
MM687, NT241 'RX-W', NT269, NT282, NT296, NT328, NT363, NT387

Number 462(SD) Squadron (Coded 'Z5' [Royal Australian Air Force]

History

Transferred to 100(SD) Group from 4 Group on 22 December 1944 for jamming duties. The squadron was disbanded on 24 September 1945 at Foulsham.

Bases

Foulsham   December 1944 to September 1945

Commanding Officers

Unknown

Representative Aircraft

Halifax BIII (fitted with jamming equipment)   (March 1945 to September 1945)
PN168/G 'Z5-T', PN433/G '-R', PN451/G

The Defiant Flight (Code unknown, if any)

History

The Flight was formed in April 1942 for *Moonshine* jamming operations. On 1 October 1942 the unit was redesignated 515 Squadron (see page 207).

Bases

Possibly Northolt

Commanding Officers

Unknown

Representative Aircraft
Defiant II   (April to October 1942)
  No serials known

Number 515(SD) Squadron (No code)
History
Formed on 1 October 1942 from the Defiant Flight for general jamming duties (see page 206 for details). In May 1943, the squadron began to convert to Beaufighter aircraft. At the end of July, the unit became non-operational until its transfer to 100(SD) Group in December 1943 (see page 36).
Bases
Northolt   October 1942
Heston   October 1942 to June 1943
Hunsdson   June to December 1943
Commanding Officers
Squadron Leader S R Thomas   October 1942 to July 1943
Wing Commander J F Inkster   July 1943 to January 1944
Representative Aircraft
Defiant II   (October 1942 to December 1943)
  AA381, AA383, AA405, AA420 'O', AA438, AA542 'N', AA566 'E', AA575 'P', AA578 'K', AA629, AA652 'B'
Beaufighter II   (June 1943 to January 1944)
  T3368, T3374, T3417, V8155, V8191 'N', V8203, V8205
Note: 515 Squadron carried no codes until it joined 100 Group in December 1943

Number 515(SD) Squadron (Coded '3P')
History
Transferred to 100(SD) Group from 11 Group on 15 December 1943 for bomber support duties. The squadron was disbanded on 10 June 1945 at Little Snoring.
Bases
Little Snoring   December 1943 to June 1945
Commanding Officers
Wing Commander F F Lambert   January 1944 to December 1944
Wing Commander H C Kelsey   December 1944 to June 1945
Representative Aircraft
Mosquito II   (February 1944 to ?1944)
  DD666, DD756, HJ654
Mosquito VI   (March 1944 to June 1945)
  NS933 '3P-G', NS957 '-V', NS961 '-H', NS992 '-S', PZ188 '-J', PZ203 '-X', PZ217 '-K', PZ337 '-D', PZ338 '-A', PZ457 '-P', PZ459 '-D', RS518 '-L', RS548 '-H', RS566 '-F'

Number 605(F) Squadron (Coded 'UP')
History
In June 1943, the squadron began *Flower* sorties. These bomber support operations were extended in August when escort patrols for the bomber streams were begun. Such operations were continued until June 1944 when the squadron became involved in protecting the Normandy beach-head from night attack. In September of the same year the unit joined the Second Tactical Air Force as a fighter-bomber squadron.
Bases
Castle Camps   March to October 1943

Bradwell Bay   October 1943 to April 1944
Manston   April to November 1944
Commanding Officers
Wing Commander C D Tomalin   May to September 1943
Wing Commander B R O'B Hoare   September 1943 to April 1944
Wing Commander N J Storr   April to September 1944
Representative Aircraft
Mosquito II   (February to July 1943)
  DZ684, DZ714, DZ717 'UP-O', DZ724.'-S', DZ760 '-K'
Mosquito VI   (July 1943 to November 1944)
  HJ761 '-P', HJ775 '-U', HJ778 '-A', HJ784 '-F', HJ790 '-R', HJ809 '-D', HX823 '-B'

803rd Bombardment Squadron (P) (Coded 'R4')
[Later the 36th Bombardment Squadron (H) with the same code]
History
Formed from an electronic counter measures detachment (itself formed on 19 January 1944) in March 1944 for *Carpet* and *Mandrel* jamming duties. In August 1944, the squadron was redesignated the 36th Bombardment Squadron (H) and continued its jamming operations in support of both the 8th Air Force and RAF Bomber Command until the end of the war in Europe.
Bases
Sculthorpe   January to May 1944
Oulton   May to August 1944
Cheddington   August 1944 to March 1945
Alconbury   March to June 1945
Commanding Officers
Captain G E Paris   9 January 1944 to 25 April 1944
Major C A Scott   25 April 1944 to   ?
Major R F Hambaugh   ?   to June 1949
Representative Aircraft
B-17F and G   (January to September 1944)
  See page 78
B-24H and J   (June 1944 to May 1945)
  See pages 78 to 82
P-51   (Late 1944)
  No known serials

858th Bombardment Squadron (H) (No code)
History
Originally part of the 801st Bombardment Group (P), the squadron became part of the 492nd Bombardment Group (H) in August 1944. During the winter of 1944, the squadron, along with the 857th Bombardment Squadron (H) until its disbandment in March 1945, began operating as part of the 'Special Window Force' in the bombing role. Such operations were continued until the end of the war in Europe.
Bases
Harrington   March 1944 to July 1945
Commanding Officers
Unknown
Representative Aircraft
B-24H and J   (Dates of service unknown)
  No serial numbers known

Number 1692 Flight (Code unknown, it any)
History
The Flight was formed in late 1942 as the Radar Development Flight. In June 1943, the unit was redesignated 1692 Flight for *Serrate* training. On 7 December 1943, the Flight was transferred to 100(SD) Group. In June 1944, the Flight was upgraded to the status of a Bomber Command Training unit, now being known as 1692 Bomber Support Training Unit. 1692 was presumably disbanded at the end of the war in Europe.
Bases
Drem   late 1942 to December 1943
Little Snoring   December 1943 to April 1944
Great Massingham   April 1944 to ?
Commanding Officers
Wing Commander J Benson   January 1944 to ?1945.
Aircraft Used
Defiant (Mk unknown), Beaufighter (Mk unknown*), Anson (Mk unknown), Mosquito VI, XIX and TIII, Wellington TXVIII
No serials known

Number 1694 Flight (Code unknown, if any)
History
The Flight was formed in April 1944 for target towing within 100(SD) Group and was known as 1694 Bomber Defence Training Flight. The unit was disbanded on 30 July 1945 at Great Massingham.
Bases
Great Massingham   April 1944 to July 1945
Commanding Officers
Unknown
Aircraft Used
Unknown

Number 1699 Flight (Code unknown, if any)
History
The Flight was formed in June 1944 to train Fortress and later Liberator crews for 100(SD) Group. The unit was presumably disbanded at the end of the war in Europe.
Bases
Oulton   June 1944 to ?
Commanding Officers
Flight Lieutenant Henderson   June to September 1944
Squadron Leader D J Bollingham   September 1944 to ?
Representative Aircraft
Fortress II and III   (June 1944 to ?)
    HB793 and HB818
Liberator ?   (September 1944 to ?)
    TS538 'B'

The Bomber Support Development Unit (Code unknown, if any)
This unit was formed at Foulsham in April 1944 as a development and trials unit for 100(SD) Group. At the time of its formation, the unit took control of 80 Wing's workshop facilities at Radlett. In December 1944, the unit moved to Swanton Morley being followed shortly afterwards by the Radlett facility which now became known as the Radio Engineering Section. A Flight of nine Mosquito aircraft was established to carry out flight and operational trials of equipment pertaining to the Group's fighter arm. In June 1945, the Window Research Section came under its control and on 21 July 1945, the unit was disbanded. Details of the work undertaken by the Bomber Support Development unit will be found in the main text.

The Window Research Section
This unit was formed in February 1945 to regularise the development of automatic *Window* dispensers within 100(SD) Group and was based at Swanton Morley. Work of this nature had begun within 199(SD) squadron under the direction of F/Lt Merryfull who now commanded the section. The unit co-operated with the Bomber Support Development Unit, with whom it amalgamated in June 1945, and comprised a design office, a drawing office and workshop facilities. The section also supervised flight testing of its dispensers, details of which will be found on page 199.

---

*One source quotes Mk I, II and VIs.

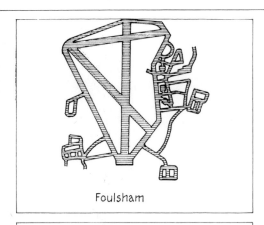

Foulsham

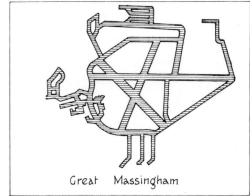

Great Massingham

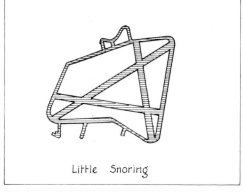

Little Snoring

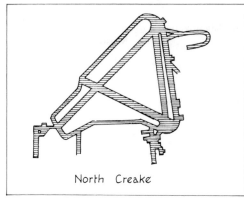

North Creake

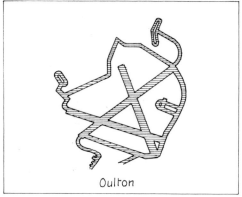

Oulton

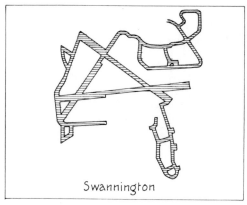

Swannington

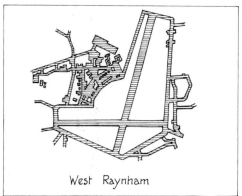

West Raynham

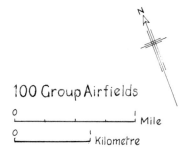

100 Group Airfields

0 _____ Mile

0 _____ Kilometre

Appendix 3

The Luftwaffe
Night Fighter Arm

At the beginning of the Second World War, contrary to popular belief, the Luftwaffe possessed a reasonably adequate night defence organisation in terms of the current state of the air force of Germany's most likely Continental enemy, France. That country's air force was in a state of chaos, trying as it was to re-equip wholesale in a very short space of time and in consequence able to field only a modest bomber force which was even less able to bomb by night than by day. Great Britain was not seriously considered as an enemy in view of the political weakness shown by her Government during the period of 'appeasement', and even if hostilities did break out, the RAF was wholly wedded to the idea of daylight bombing with turret-armed aircraft in close defensive formations. The only other possible rivals, Russia and Poland, could be discounted as neither possessed large heavy bomber elements within their airforces and both were essentially tactical rather than strategic in nature.

Thus, in 1939, Germany was reasonably well prepared to meet any night bombing threat that her High Command could envisage.

Throughout Germany elements of some 31 Luftwaffe Flak regiments were positioned armed to a large extent with the FLAK 36/37 family of 88 mm guns, one of the best anti-aircraft weapons to see service during the war. These were backed by an efficient searchlight organisation and the first tentative experiments were being carried out with radar as a means of early warning against air attack.

In the air, the Luftwaffe fielded the following night fighter units on 1 September 1939:

11/(N)LG2 with 10 Bf109 aircraft based at Garz;
10/(N)JG2 with 9 Bf109 aircraft based at Furstenwalde;
10/(N)JG26 with 9 Bf109 aircraft based at Düsseldorf;
10/(N)JG72 with 16 Ar 68 aircraft based at Mannheim-Sandhofen;
11/(N)JG72 with 12 Ar 68 aircraft based at Stuttgart-Echterdingen.

This force was backed by a considerable body of experience gained in aerial night fighting during the First World War and a high degree of training and professionalism amongst the air crews.

The inability of RAF Bomber Command to pursue a daylight offensive in the face of the Luftwaffe's fighter defences was to radically upset the German High

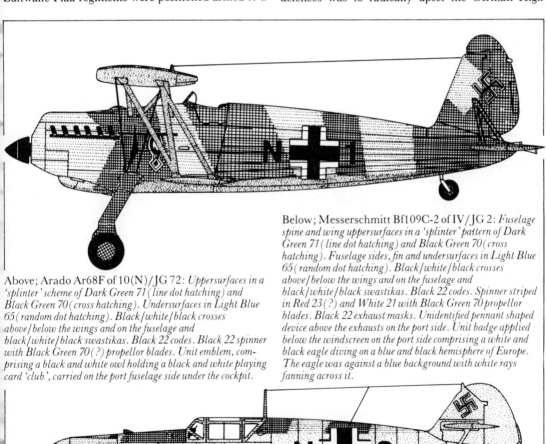

Above; Arado Ar68F of 10(N)/JG 72: *Uppersurfaces in a 'splinter' scheme of Dark Green 71 (line dot hatching) and Black Green 70 (cross hatching). Undersurfaces in Light Blue 65 (random dot hatching). Black/white/black crosses above/below the wings and on the fuselage and black/white/black swastikas. Black 22 codes. Black 22 spinner with Black Green 70 (?) propellor blades. Unit emblem, comprising a black and white owl holding a black and white playing card 'club', carried on the port fuselage side under the cockpit.*

Below; Messerschmitt Bf109C-2 of IV/JG 2: *Fuselage spine and wing uppersurfaces in a 'splinter' pattern of Dark Green 71 (line dot hatching) and Black Green 70 (cross hatching). Fuselage sides, fin and undersurfaces in Light Blue 65 (random dot hatching). Black/white/black crosses above/below the wings and on the fuselage and black/white/black swastikas. Black 22 codes. Spinner striped in Red 23 (?) and White 21 with Black Green 70 propellor blades. Black 22 exhaust masks. Unidentified pennant shaped device above the exhausts on the port side. Unit badge applied below the windscreen on the port side comprising a white and black eagle diving on a blue and black hemisphere of Europe. The eagle was against a blue background with white rays fanning across it.*

Command's postulations; from early 1940 until the summer of 1944, Bomber Command operated, with very few exceptions, by night. To begin with, the RAF's night raids were almost farcical; each night a few bombers would set course for Germany and be extremely lucky if they came within ten miles of the designated target. Unsuitable aircraft, non-existent navigational aids, poor bombsights and bombs conspired to make a mockery of the aircrews' courage as they battled against cold and appalling weather conditions to strike at the German homeland.

Obviously such attacks caused Germany very little damage, but the fact that they occurred and more importantly kept on occurring sowed the first seeds of disquiet in the minds of the Luftwaffe's High Command. These doubts crystallised when it became clear that even a light industrial haze, not uncommon over such places as the Ruhr, denied accuracy to the Flak arm and that the night fighter aircraft were unable to find the bombers; the relatively fast RAF monoplane bombers were rather more difficult to counter than the sort of obsolete machine the Luftwaffe had expected to be faced with.

A pointer to what was possible was contained in a report submitted by Oberleutnant Wolfgang Falk, Kommander I/ZG 1 at the end of the campaigns in Denmark and Norway.

Falk's Gruppe was based at Aalborg near the Danish border and was subjected to frequent dawn attacks by RAF bombers. The unit was fortunate in that one of the early *Freya* radars was stationed nearby and received adequate warning of the approach of the raiders to allow the Gruppe's personnel to take cover. Quite unofficially, Falk took this warning a stage further and tried to intercept the bombers with the help of the radar unit. Although I/ZG 1 did not claim any victories during these engagements, both Falk and another pilot, Werner Streib, came close enough to the enemy to exchange fire with him.

All this was contained in the report. Nothing happened until early June 1940 when the Gruppe, along with part of IV/ZG 26, was pulled out of the French campaign and, redesignated the *Nacht und Versuchs Staffel* – the Night and Experimental Staffel, was ordered to begin tactical night fighter trials at Düsseldorf.

On 17 July 1940, General Kammuhuber, newly liberated from a French prisoner-of-war camp, was entrusted with the organisation of a modern night fighter force. Kammhuber had little upon which to build other than his own energies. Personally he had no knowledge of radar, his staff, mostly drawn from the Flak arm, had no knowledge of how to apply radar to interception by aircraft and the flying formations available to him were modest – the already mentioned *Nacht und Versuchs Staffel* and IV/JG 2, into which the remains of the pre-war night-fighter units had been concentrated.

Nothing daunted, Kammhuber set to work. On 20 July 1940, the *Nacht und Versuchs Staffel* was designated I/NJG 1 with a strength of 23 Bf110 aircraft. IV/JG 2 with its Bf 109s became II/NJG 2 shortly afterwards.

By July 1940, a new Second Gruppe was formed Zerstorer Staffel/KG 30 with an establishment of two Staffeln with 20 JU88C-0 and C-2 aircraft and a number of Do17Z aircraft. The original second Gruppe became III/NJG 1, still flying the Bf 109. The Geschwader was initially under the control of Luftflotte 2, the night-fighter organisation having Divisional status with its headquarters at Zeist in Holland.

Throughout the late summer and autumn, the night-fighter units continued to expand. In early September, II/NJG 1 became the first Gruppe of *Nachtjagdgeschwader* 2, its role being defined as that of a *Fernnachtjagd Gruppe* – a long range night fighter Gruppe, to undertake intruder sorties against RAF bomber bases. By October, a third *Nachtjagdgeschwader* had been formed when V/(Z)LG 1 was redesignated I/NJG 3.

As well as expanding the number of aircraft at his control, Kammhuber completely revitalised the technique of night fighting. He abandoned the existing point defence system and repositioned the searchlights and sound detectors from that system in three blocks across the main routes into Germany used by RAF bombers – the Zuider Zee, the Rhine estuary and in front of the Ruhr conurbation. These zones were forbidden to friendly aircraft, other than night fighters, during the hours of darkness so that any aircraft approaching from the west could be safely assumed to be hostile.

Each zone was divided into boxes 27 miles (45 km) long by 13.2 miles (22 km) wide. Along the long side facing the enemy, sound locators were positioned to give early warning of the direction of flight of the enemy. Behind these and filling the rectangle were searchlight batteries and behind the searchlights a light and a radio beacon. A night fighter would be allocated to the zone and would orbit the beacons until a bomber crossed into the rectangle of searchlights. On seeing the enemy illuminated, the fighter would close in for the kill. Once the bomber had been downed or contact with it lost, the fighter would return to orbit the beacons to await the next customer.

This *Helle Nachtjagd* – illuminated night fighting, was infinitely superior to any previous technique but was still far from being a total solution. Its main weaknesses were its reliance on searchlights and sound locators. In the first instance, the searchlights could only operate effectively in clear weather and even then with little hope of success, due to the lack of a suitable method of accurately pinpointing the area of sky in which the bomber would appear relative to its forward speed and track. The sound locators which were supposed to provide such information, very quickly proved to be at best unreliable and at worst useless.

Added to these difficulties in finding the enemy there were problems with the intercepting aircraft. The art of night flying has never been easy and even though Germany was in advance of most of her enemies in the provision of blind flying radio aids, she had much to learn and accidents were alarmingly frequent. Air-to-air identification was another problem and there were instances of night fighters firing on one another. Finally, and perhaps most important of all, there was a steady fall in the morale of the aircrews. Successes were few and far between, accidents and failure were the norm, whereas their day fighter colleagues, despite the reverses of the summer campaign over Britain, could be seen to be eminently successful in the numbers of enemy aircraft being destroyed. On top of this, the Wehrmacht was still geared to an offensive war and defending the Reich was looked upon with scorn. Why bother when the war was so nearly won?

It was obvious that the problems with the aircrew and night flying could be overcome and from the autumn of 1940 a solution was at hand to the tracking difficulties in the form of the *Würzburg* radar (see page 188). In radar was the means of locating the enemy with the greatest accuracy in any weather conditions. Previously only the *Freya* radar (see page 183) had been available and then only in limited numbers. *Freya* was essentially an early-warning radar and lacked the precision to give more than a general picture of the air situation. *Würzburg* on the other hand, was a gun-laying radar which would give the searchlight batteries the precise date on speed and track to cone a bomber and keep it illuminated long enough for the interceptor to position itself for an attack.

The fact that *Würzburg* was a gun-laying radar meant that there was keen competition between the Flak and night fighter arms for such sets as were available. General Martini, the Luftwaffe's Director General of Signals, allocated Kammhuber six companies equipped with the device during October and the latter rapidly integrated them into the *Helle Nachtjagd* system.

The searchlight boxes remained as before but a *Würzburg* was inserted into the forward field of sound locators, which were retained as a standby. The light and radio beacons were moved from behind the searchlights to in amongst them. The method of operations was much as before, with the fighter orbiting the beacons until directed on to the bomber, but with three important exceptions. Firstly, the fighter could be positioned near the bomber *before* it was illuminated by the searchlights and, perhaps most importantly for the future, the instructions as to course etc passed to the interceptor were vastly more detailed and accurate than before, thus allowing the pilot to concentrate fully on the interception rather than trying to get into a position to intercept. Secondly, because the searchlight crews were in receipt of accurate and timely information, they were able to keep the bomber illuminated for far longer thus increasing the time available for an interception. Lastly, the increased efficiency of the system greatly enhanced crew morale as they were no longer groping in the dark for a rarely seen enemy but were now part of a system which increasingly placed them exactly in the right place to carry out their prime objective, the destruction of the enemy.

The only problem remaining was that of the adverse relationship between searchlight illuminated interception and the weather. *Helle Nachtjagd* was almost entirely dependent on searchlights, even in its modified form, and as such was obviously outmoded by radar, largely impervious as it was to meteorological conditions. Kammhuber grasped this fundamental fully and channelled his energies into creating a fully radar dependent system which was to see fruition in the *Himmelbett* ('Heavenly' or 'Four-poster bed') system.

Before examining the *Himmelbett* technique in detail, it would be appropriate to review the other side of the night fighter arm's activities; the intruder force.

As has been recounted, I/NJG 2, upon its formation in September 1940, was designated a *Fernnachtjagd Gruppe*, a long range night fighter Gruppe, for attacking the RAF's bomber bases. Working in close co-operation with the Luftwaffe's Radio Interception Service, who provided clues from received test traffic as to which bases were likely to be active, the Gruppe was soon making almost nightly forays over England. Attempts were made not only to attack landing circuits but also to affect route interceptions and attacks on airfields in the process of getting their squadrons airborne.

These intruder sorties had a measure of success, in fact, at times, they proved to be more effective than the home defence units. In the first four months of its existence, I/NJG 2 claimed 18 kills over England and by October 1941, when the Gruppe transferred to the Mediterranean, it had destroyed a total of 143 aircraft.

Coincidental with this move was the famous ban on intruder operations by Hitler which Kammhuber has since described as 'one of the Luftwaffe's biggest mistakes'.

In the light of present evidence however, this does not seem to be quite the case. First and foremost, intruder operations *did not cease*, as shown by the activities of I/KG 51 (see page 227) and such operations as *Unternehmen Gisela* on the 3/4 March 1945, but continued on a small scale where and when possible. Further, there seems to be good reason to believe that intruder operations were not as profitable as was generally believed. Out of I/NJG 2s total bag of 143 victories claimed while operating over England between September 1940 and October 1941, no less than 54 were destroyed over the North Sea, that is during route interceptions. This point of profitability is reinforced by *Gisela* when 100 aircraft could only claim 14 victories.

It is the author's contention that I/NJG 2s intruder operations were of value not because of the 'panic and confusion' they caused over England but rather because of the experience they gave of interception over the North Sea and of using the potential of the Radio Intercept Service for intelligence gathering. Overwater interception was an integral part of the later *Zahme Sau* technique both during the bomber's outward and return journeys. The thought of being intercepted before even crossing the enemy coast and not being safe from attack when nearing friendly shores was just as nerve wracking for the late 1943 bomber crew as had been the possibility of an intruder in the circuit for the 1940 crew; indeed the 1943 pilot was occasionally confronted with both route and base attacks.

While NJG 2 had been pursuing its activities over England, the development of the *Himmelbett* radar interception system had been going on apace. *Himmelbett* retained the box concept from *Helle Nachtjagd* but totally replaced searchlights with radar. Each box now contained two *Würzburg* radars, a *Freya*, light and radio beacons and a control room. A night fighter would be allocated to the box and would orbit the beacons until needed. The *Freya* was used to gain a long-range picture of the air situation and to sight the shorter *Würzburgs*. The two *Würzburgs*, coded Red and

Airfield	Unit	Operational Area	Gruppe Kommandeur/ Staffel Kapitan
Schleswig	5/NJG3	Helle Nachtjagd Area 1, Wolf and Kiebitz	—
Stade	II/NJG1	Helle Nachtjagd Area 2	Ehle
Luneburg	7/NJG3	Hummel	—
Wittmund-haven	5/NJG2	Languste	Shonert
Vechta	I/NJG3	Helle Nachtjagd Area 3	Knoetzsch
Leeuwarden	II/NJG2	Tiger, Lowe and Languste	Lent
Deelen/ Twente	Stab and III/NJG1	Helle Nachtjagd Area 4	Schon
Menlo/ Hangela	Stab and I/NJG1	Helle Nachtjagd Area 5, Drossel, Kolibri	Streib
Gilze-Rigen	Erganzs/ NJG2	Hampster	—
St Trond	1/NJG1	Helle Nachtjagd Areas 6 and 13	—
Mainz-Finthen	II/NJG3	Kranich and Dachs	Radusch
Werneuchen	3/NJG3	Bar	—

Blue, were used to track the interceptor (Blue) and the chosen target (Red). Red and Blue were linked by land line to the control post where their pilots were transcribed on to a Seeburg table. This was a large, two-storeyed wooden structure, the focus of which was a frosted glass screen gridded to correspond to the standard Luftwaffe map of the area covered by the particular box.

Beneath the screen sat two operators equipped with pencil light sources. The Red operator plotted the position of the interceptor on the screen above him while the Blue operator did the same for the target. Grouped around the screen on the second storey were a plotter, who marked the traces in with a wax crayon, a plotting supervisor, who made sure that the transcription of the plots was accurate; he was able to cut in on any of the land lines from the radar posts in order to do this, a controller, who directed the night fighter into position for the interception by radio, a Flak liaison officer, who passed information to the local batteries on the whereabouts of friendly aircraft so that they would not be fired on by mistake, and an observer corps liaison officer, who fed information from his posts in the area into the system.

By the last day of December 1941, six such boxes,

code named Hampster, Hering, Lowe, Tiger, Languste, and Wolf had been set up along the coast between the Danish border and the mouth of the Rhine estuary. Each of these boxes overlapped so that an enemy could be passed down the line if necessary. In addition to this radar barrier a system of Helle Nachtjagd zones were positioned to form a second line of defence. This second barrier stretched from Kiel in the north almost to Wiesbaden in the south. Particularly important targets were further defended by Combined Night Fighter Areas which combined Himmelbett, Helle Nachtjagd and Flak defences into an integrated whole. These areas were code named Kiebitz (around Kiel), Hummel (Hamburg), Roland (Bremen), Drossel (running north from Düsseldorf), Kolibri (around Cologne and overlapping Drossel) and Bar (Berlin). Finally there was a further Himmelbett box covering the southern end of the Ruhr code-named Kranich which also contained a combined area code-named Dachs centred upon Wiesbaden in the north and Mannheim in the south. The above table shows the disposition of aircraft in relation to this ground organisation.

The Himmelbett system as part of the greater whole already described came close to being a perfect solution to the problem of defending German territory from night attack. During 1940, Bomber Command lost 342 aircraft over Germany from all causes. By the end of 1941, this figure had risen to 1,043, almost twice as many aircraft as in the previous year. An ever-increasing part of this toll was directly attributable to the actions of night fighter aircraft.

The new year saw the continuing expansion of the system. In May 1942, the XII Fliegerkorps, as the night fighter arm had been designated in August 1941, had the order of battle shown on page 218.

By the end of the year, the number of Himmelbett boxes along the coast had increased from six to eleven. The Helle Nachtjagd zones had been extended as far as Luxemburg in the south and were now backed by Dunkelnachtjagd zones – Dark Night Fighting Zones. The new system placed powerful radar-directed searchlights in front of and behind each Helle Nachtjagd box, so that in adverse weather the precise position of an enemy bomber could be indicated to the interceptor, if only by a glow on the cloud base. A new Helle-/Dunkelnachtjagd barrier had been set up in front of Berlin which reached down to Leipzig and new combined areas had been created around Frankfurt and Darmstadt. The Himmelbett coastal boxes had also been increased to (60 km) in diameter with the introduction of the longer range Würzburg-Riese radar (see page 190).

The most important innovation of the period was without doubt the introduction of FuG 202AI (see page 179) during the early months of 1942. Kammhuber had long seen airborne radar as an essential part of the defensive system he was building and had issued a specification for such a device to industry during 1940. The firm of Telefunken had sets ready for service trials in August 1941 but the general introduction of FuG 202 was hampered by slow production and aircrew resistence. The aerials festooning AI equipped aircraft were regarded as drag producers, degrading performance for little or no purpose, as the close ground control of the Himmelbett system was more than

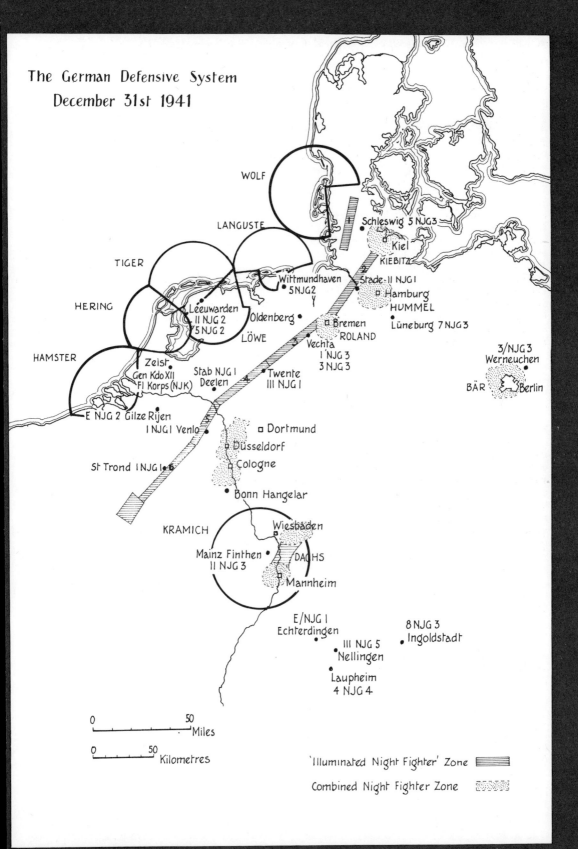

The German Defensive System
December 31st 1941

WOLF

LANGUSTE

Schleswig 5 NJG3

Kiel

KIEBITZ

TIGER

Wittmundhaven
5 NJG2

Stade II NJG1

Hamburg

HUMMEL

HERING

Leeuwarden
II NJG 2
5 NJG 2

Oldenberg

Bremen

ROLAND

Lüneburg 7 NJG3

LÖWE

Vechta
I NJG 3
3 NJG 3

HAMSTER

Zeist

Gen Kdo XII
Fl Korps (NJK)

Stab NJG I
Deelen

Twente
III NJG I

3/NJG 3
Werneuchen

BÄR

Berlin

E NJG 2 Gilze Rijen

I NJGI Venlo

Dortmund

Düsseldorf

Cologne

St Trond I NJG I

Bonn Hangelar

KRAMICH

Wiesbaden

Mainz Finthen
II NJG 3

DACHS

Mannheim

E/NJG I
Echterdingen

8 NJG 3
Ingoldstadt

III NJG 5
Nellingen

Laupheim
4 NJG 4

0   50
|————————| Miles

0   50
|————————| Kilometres

'Illuminated Night Fighter' Zone

Combined Night Fighter Zone

XII Fliegerkorps (Commanded by Gen. Lt. Kammhuber) HQ: Zeist May 1942		
1st Jagddivision (Commanded by Gen. M v. Doring *HQ:* Deelen *Operational area:* Holland, North Belgium and the Ruhr *Operational units:* NJG 1 and Signal Regiments 201 and 211	**2nd Jagddivision** (Commanded by Gen. M Schwabedissen) *HQ:* Stade *Operational area:* NW Germany and Berlin *Operational units:* NJG 3 and Signal Regiments 202, 212 and 222	**3rd Jagddivision** (Commanded by Oberst. Junck) *HQ:* Metz *Operational area:* North France, South Belgium, and SW Germany *Operational units:* II/NJG 2, III/NJG 4 and Signals Regiments 203 and 213

adequate for the pilot to affect an interception. Few crews perservered with the device long enough to cope with its temperamental penchant for stopping working at the vital moment or its ability to 'squint' when the aerials became damp with the consequential false readings. Successful pilots such as Helmut Lent and Paul Gildner would have nothing to do with the device and it was only after another pilot, Ludwig Becker, had made an increasing number of claims directly attributable to radar, that a slow acceptance of the advantages AI could offer began.

Unfortunately, airborne radar had come just too late for the Luftwaffe to reap the full benefits of it. The RAF had been watching the development of Germany's night defences all too closely and had realised the system's two-fold vulnerability. Firstly, the whole system was geared to the interception of a single bomber in each box, and secondly that the whole organisation was dependent on radio and radar. The introduction of the bomber Stream in May 1942, the massed passage of bombers through one part of the system in a short space of time, sounded the death knell of the *Kammhuber Line* as the German organisation was known to the RAF. Tampering with the radar and radio elements of the system would hasten its end, but, as has been said, streaming was the fundamental cause.

The downfall of Kammhuber's carefully constructed system came with incredible swiftness; in fact what had taken three years to build was destroyed in one night – that of 24 July 1943. On that date, the RAF used *Window* for the first time. This measure made the GCI *Würzburgs* unusable and had an equally devastating effect on the FuG 202 212 AI sets.

In retrospect, it seems strange that the Luftwaffe was so unprepared for *Window*, having themselves experimented with the measure under the code name *Duppel*. The attitude of their forces High Command

goes some way to explaining this lapse while Kammhuber's personality contributed materially to the situation.

Even in 1943, night fighting was an unpalatable concept to many of the Luftwaffe's policy makers. That Germany had a night fighter force at all was almost entirely due to Kammhuber's drive and, latterly, to the obvious success of the *Himmelbett* system. Bearing this in mind, it becomes obvious why Kammhuber was reluctant to change tactics to suit the new conditions under which the night bombing offensive was being carried out. Change meant the possibility of a temporary drop in victory claims which would put the whole arm at risk in the battle of priorities and supplies which Kammhuber had fought for so long. He was not prepared to take that risk in the political conditions which prevailed in the early part of the year.

More subtly, Kammhuber's forte was organisation and it was anathema to him to replace his disciplined neat system with a freer approach even though the tactical conditions warranted such a change.

The Hamburg disaster of the 24th galvanised the Luftwaffe into action. Kammhuber presented Goring with his proposals (to massively increase the numbers of fighters and *Himmelbett* zones and to inject *Window*-proof hardware into the system with all despatch), which the latter passed on to Hitler. His response was a total rejection. Kammhuber's political enemies jumped at this opportunity and he was relieved of the command of XII Fliegerkorps and posted to Norway, in November 1943, as AOC Luftflotte 5. Prior to his departure, the night fighter arm was disposed as per the table below:

Into the void left by the destruction of the *Himmelbett* system appeared two new tactical doctrines, *Wilde Sau* and *Zahme Sau*.

The first of these was *Wilde Sau*, the brain child of an ex-bomber pilot, Hajo Herrmann. He reasoned that the

Lw. BEFH. MITTE (Commanded by Gen. Oberst Weise) HQ: Berlin-Wannsee

XII Fliegerkorps (Commanded by Gen. D Flieger Kammhuber) HQ: Zeist August 1943				
1 Jagddivision (Commanded by Maj. v. Doring) *HQ:* Deelen I to IV/NJG 1	**2 Jagddivision** (Commanded by Gen. Lt. Schwabedissen) *HQ:* Stade I to IV/NJG 3 NJkdo 190	**3 Jagddivision** (Commanded by Gen. Maj. Junck) *HQ:* Metz II/NJG 4	**4 Jagddivision** (Commanded by Gen. Maj. Huth) *HQ:* Doberitz I and III/NJG 4 I and II/NJG 2 I and III/NJG 5	**5 Jagddivision** (Commanded by Oberst v. Bulow) *HQ:* Schliessheim I/NJG 6 Einsatzschwarme/NJG 101 (under the control of I/NJG 6)

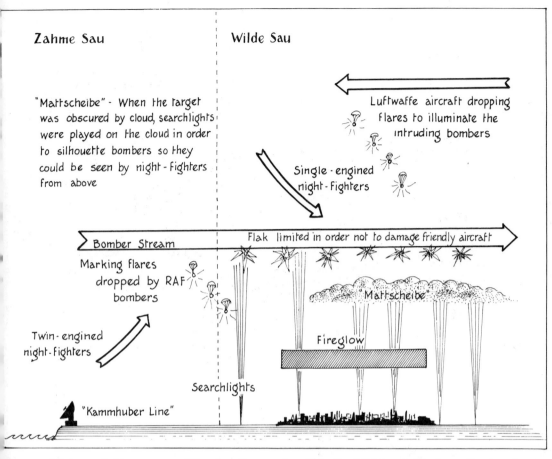

Zahme Sau

Wilde Sau

"Mattscheibe" - When the target was obscured by cloud, searchlights were played on the cloud in order to silhouette bombers so they could be seen by night-fighters from above

Luftwaffe aircraft dropping flares to illuminate the intruding bombers

Single-engined night-fighters

Flak limited in order not to damage friendly aircraft

Bomber Stream

Marking flares dropped by RAF bombers

"Mattscheibe"

Twin-engined night-fighters

Fireglow

Searchlights

"Kammhuber Line"

amount of light available over one of Bomber Command's targets (from the ground fires, target markers, searchlights, etc) should be enough to enable an experienced pilot to affect an interception visually without the aid of radar. Further, he intended this type of attack as an adjunct to the activities of the specialised night fighters using single-engined day fighters and the daytime fighter control system to direct the *Wild Boars* to the target under attack by means of a Running Commentary on the enemy's course, altitude, strength and likely destination.

Herrmann approached Kammhuber with this plan *before* Hamburg but the Kammhuber turned it down. Undaunted, Herrmann went over his head to Weisse who gave his approval for a trial. Arrangements were made with the Ruhr Flak defences to limit their fire to a specified ceiling above which the fighters could operate, aircraft were found and volunteers gathered to await the first suitable RAF raid.

The *Wild Boars*, baptism of fire came on 3/4 July 1943 during an attack on Cologne. At the end of the raid, Herrmann's Kommando had claimed 12 bombers destroyed. This success, led to the immediate formation of a full Geschwader, JG 300, to undertake such operations with Herrmann as Kommodore.

The debacle of the 24th, left *Wilde Sau* as the only tactical option immediately open to the Luftwaffe and the whole of the night fighter force was over to this mode of attack. Herrmann himself was ordered to form

the 30th Jagddivision with three Geschwader to increase the number of single-engined fighters available.

Wilde Sau could only be regarded as a stop-gap and indeed it was soon replaced by *Zahme Sau*. The 30th Jagddivision fought on through the summer and autumn and suffered increasing losses as the weather deteriorated with the approach of winter. Latterly, elements of the Division were equipped with radar, thus taking them back into the true night fighter fold and in March 1944 the organisation was dissolved. However, single-seat night fighters remained a part of the night fighter arm's front-line strength for the remainder of the war.

If nothing else, the *Wilde Sau* technique provoked thought about the whole question of night fighter tactics. Oberst von Lossberg of the Luftwaffe's Staff College in Berlin produced the *Zahme Sau* concept which when adopted brought the night fighter arm its greatest victories.

The core of *Zahme Sau* was to place night fighters in the bomber stream as early as possible and to keep them there for as long as possible. The *Himmelbett* system was retained but its radar components were now used for early warning rather than pure interception. Control was now centred upon the Jagddivision control centres at Doberitz, Stade, Arnhem/Deelan, Metz and Schleisshim. Perhaps the best way to describe the system is to follow through a typical

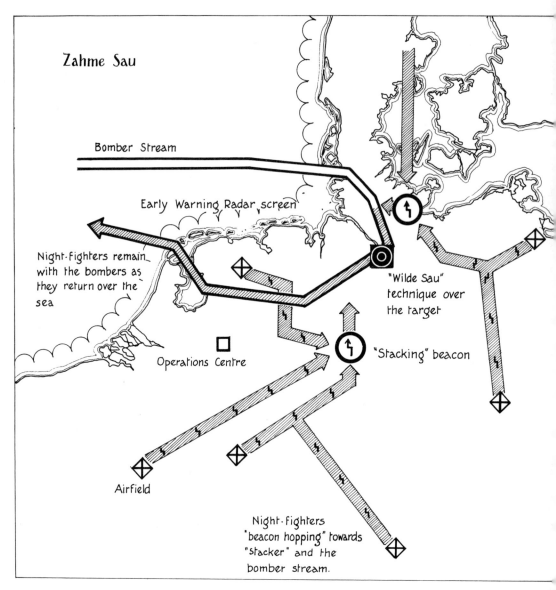

operation.

During the daylight hours, the stations of the Luftwaffe's listening service watched for radio and radar test transmissions coming from the other side of the channel. If these were heard, a raid was indicated. This information plus weather conditions, etc., allowed a projection of where the enemy were likely to penetrate friendly airspace. The various night fighter Geschwader would be informed of the likelihood of a raid and would begin preparations for the night's work. In the late afternoon, the early-warning radars and the German observer corps, (which had achieved greater prominence with the use of the *Zahme Sau* technique), would be activated along with the various control centres. Those radars and observer posts in the likeliest area of penetration would become operational earlier than those elsewhere.

As soon as the raiders were picked up by a radar station, the nearest control centre would take control and direct operations. One of its first orders would be to the reconnaissance unit under its control to fly out over the sea to try to pick up the bomber stream and having found it to report its composition, course and altitude. Having done this, the reconnaissance aircraft would attempt to stay with the stream.

The controller would now attempt to establish the target and marshal his forces accordingly. This was never easy and became progressively harder as the bomber support operations increased.

Three types of interception were available Himmelbett, Zahme Sau and Wilde Sau and aircraft were allocated according to suitability.

The *Himmelbett* and *Wilde Sau* aircraft operated in the manner already described. *Zahme Sau* aircraft were controlled by means of a running commentary broadcast over the Y-system; giving the night fighter details of the bomber stream's composition, altitude and heading.

Aircraft were scrambled from all over Europe and navigated via radio beacons to a designated stacking beacon where the fighters were concentrated ready to meet the oncoming bomber stream. When the order came to leave the stacker, round which as many as 50 aircraft might be now flying, the fighters received the latest information on the bombers and made-off in their direction.

When the fighters made visual or radar contact with the enemy, they reported the exact position of the stream back to the operations centre and then went into the attack. In this way, the Germans could feed all available night fighters into the bomber stream with which they would stay until forced down by lack of fuel.

If the bomber stream changed course and passed out of the area of one control centre, another would take over, and so on as the bombers proceeded across Reich territory.

The *Zahme Sau* technique served the Luftwaffe until the end of the war and brought it its greatest victories but also saw it fall into a decline from which it never recovered. The loss of the coast of France in the autumn of 1944 deprived the Luftwaffe of its early-warning radar chain, a difficulty compounded by an increasing lack of fuel and a growing shortage of aircrew. The general decline of the night fighter arm due to these three factors was steady and unremitting so that by the spring of 1945 it was all but impotent.

The last months of the war saw a limited introduction of jet-propelled aircraft which were extremely successful against the RAF's Mosquitos, which until this time had been almost immune from interception. The inevitability of defeat led to an increasing use of the remaining piston-engined aircraft in the night ground attack role, a role which cost the night fighter dear in its remaining crews. A view of the Nachtjagdverbande in its decline can be gained from the following order of battle for November 1944:

ORGANISATION
The following notes give brief outline histories of the Nachtjagdgeschwader and other night fighter units which saw service against RAF Bomber Command in

the West 1940 and 1945. Nachtjagdgeschwader 100 is included because, although it saw most of its service in Russia, elements of the unit flew in the defence of Berlin during the early months of 1945.

In *Aircraft Used*, the round brackets indicate the user unit and where possible the date of usage of a particular aircraft type while the square brackets indicate the sub-variants of a basic airframe used by a particular unit.

In *Known Bases*, the round bracket indicates the particular sub unit and its date of tenure, i.e. Malacki (II – 11.44) indicates that II/NJG 100 was based at Malacki in November 1944.

Nachtjagdgeschwader 1 (Coded G9)

NJG 1 was formed in June 1940 and by May 1945 had claimed 2,209 victories by night and day. The Geschwader was commanded by the following:
W Falk (26.6.40–30.6.43), W Streib (1.7.43–3.44) and H J Jabs (3.44–5.45).

I Gruppe
Formed 22.6.40 from elements of I/ZG 1 and IV/ZG 26. The Gruppe was commanded by the following:
G Radusch (1.7.40–6.10.40), W Streib (18.10.40–1.7.43), H D Frank (1.7.43–27.9.43), M Meurer (28.9.43–21.1.44), ? Förster (1.44–1.10.44) and W Baake (2.10.44–5.45).

II Gruppe
Formed 22.6.40 from IV/(N) JG 2. The Gruppe was redesignated III/NJG 1 on 1.7.40. On the same day, a new II/NJG 1 was formed from Z/KG 30. This in turn was redesignated I/NJG 2 on 7.9.40 and a third Second Gruppe was formed, on the same date, from I/ZG 26. The Gruppe was commanded by the following:
? Stillfried (2.10.40–6.10.40), W Ehle (6.10.40–17.11.43) E W v. Bonin (18.11.43–25.10.44) and ? Breves (26.10.44–5.45).

III Gruppe
Formed 7.9.40 from II/NJG 1. The Gruppe was commanded by the following:
? v. Bothmer (1.7.40–1.11.40), ? Schön (1.11.40–1.2.41), ? v. Graeve (8.2.41–5.6.42), ? Thimmig (6.6.42–31.5.43), Prinz Lippe-Weissenfeld

LUFTFLOTTE REICH (Commanded by Gen. Oberst Stumpff) HQ: Berlin-Wannsee

1 Jagdkorps (Commanded by Gen. Ltd Schmid) HQ: Treuenbrietzen November 1944

1 Jagddivision (Commanded by Lt. Heinrath) HQ: Doberitz	2 Jagddivision (Commanded by Gen. Maj. Ibel) HQ: Stade	3 Jagddivision (Commanded by Oberst Grabmann) HQ: Wiedenbruck	7 Jagddivision (Commanded by Gen. Maj. Huth) HQ: Pfaffenhofen	8 Jagddivision (Commanded by Oberst Handrick) HQ: Wien-Kobenzl
NJGr 10	Stab, I-IV/NJG 3	Stab, I-IV/NJG 1	Stab, I, II,	III/NJG 6
3/NJG 11	1/NJG 5	Stab, I, II/NJG 2	IV/NJG 6	II/NJG 100
	1/NJG 11	I/NJGr 10	Stab, I/NJG 101	(without 4 Staffel)
Fighter Leader East Prussia:		2/NJG 11		II/NJG 101
Oberst Nordmann	*Fighter Leader Denmark:*			
HQ: Insterburg	Oberst Vieck	*Fighter Leader*		*Day and Night Fighter*
Stab, I, IV/NJG 5	HQ: Grove	Middle Rhine:		Leader Hungary
III/NJG 102	IV/NJG 2	Oberst Trubenbach		HQ: Budapest
	Kdo III/NJG 3	HQ: Darmstadt		4/NJG 100
Fighter Leader Schlesien:		I-III/NJG 4		Hungarian NJ St 5/1
Oberst Witt				
HQ: Cosel				
II/NJG 5				
I, II/NJG 102				

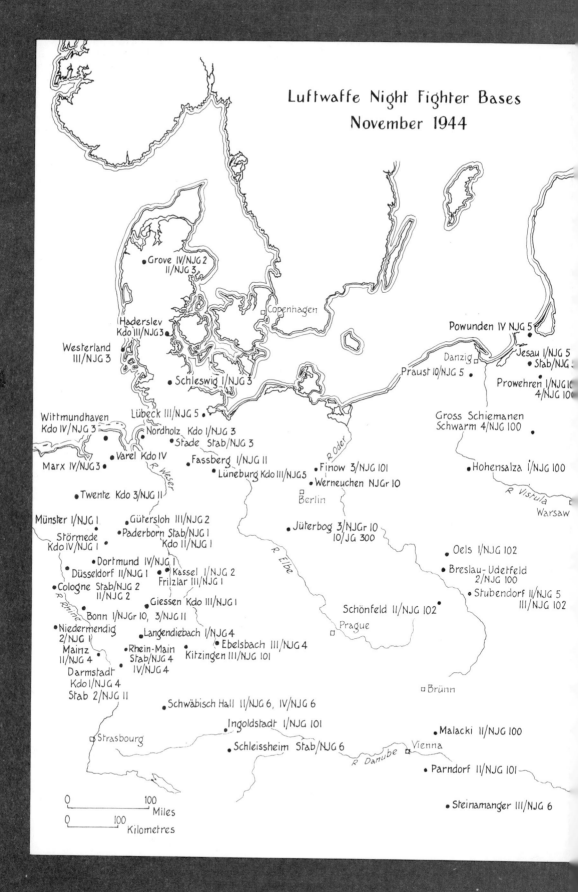

Luftwaffe Night Fighter Bases
November 1944

Grove IV/NJG 2
II/NJG 3
Haderslev Kdo III/NJG 3
Westerland III/NJG 3
Schleswig I/NJG 3
Copenhagen
Powunden IV NJG 5
Danzig
Jesau I/NJG 5
Stab/NJG 5
Praust 10/NJG 5
Prowehren I/NJG 10
4/NJG 100
Gross Schiemanen Schwarm 4/NJG 100
Lübeck III/NJG 5
Wittmundhaven Kdo IV/NJG 3
Nordholz Kdo I/NJG 3
Stade Stab/NJG 3
Marx IV/NJG 3
Värel Kdo IV
Fassberg I/NJG II
Lüneburg Kdo III/NJG 5
Finow 3/NJG 101
Werneuchen NJGr 10
Hohensalza I/NJG 100
R. Oder
R. Weser
Twente Kdo 3/NJG II
Berlin
Warsaw
R. Vistula
Münster I/NJG I
Gütersloh III/NJG 2
Paderborn Stab/NJG I
Kdo II/NJG I
Jüterbog 3/NJGr 10
10/JG 300
Störmede Kdo IV/NJG I
Dortmund IV/NJG I
Düsseldorf II/NJG I
Kassel I/NJG 2
Frilzlar III/NJG I
Cologne Stab/NJG 2
II/NJG 2
Giessen Kdo III/NJG I
R. Rhine
R. Elbe
Oels I/NJG 102
Breslau-Udetfeld 2/NJG 100
Stubendorf II/NJG 5
III/NJG 102
Schönfeld II/NJG 102
Bonn I/NJGr 10, 3/NJG II
Niedermendig 2/NJG I
Langendiebach I/NJG 4
Ebelsbach III/NJG 4
Prague
Mainz II/NJG 4
Rhein-Main Stab/NJG 4
Kitzingen III/NJG 101
Darmstadt Kdo I/NJG 4
IV/NJG 4
Stab 2/NJG II
Brünn
Schwäbisch Hall II/NJG 6, IV/NJG 6
Ingoldstadt I/NJG 101
Malacki II/NJG 100
Strasbourg
Schleissheim Stab/NJG 6
R. Danube
Vienna
Parndorf II/NJG 101
Steinamanger III/NJG 6

0   100
          Miles
0   100
        Kilometres

(1.6.43–20.2.44) and M Drewes (1.3.44–5.45).

IV Gruppe

Formed 1.10.42 from II/NJG 2. The Gruppe was commanded by the following:
H Lent (1.10.42–1.8.43), H J Jabs (1.8.43–1.3.44), H W Schnaufer (1.3.44–26.10.44) and H Greiner (1.11.44–5.45).

Aircraft Used

Do17Z-7 Kauz I (I & II/NJG 1), Do17Z-10 Kauz II (II/NJG 1), Do215B-5 Kauz 3 (I & IV/NJG 1), Do217J-1 (II/NJG 1) [J-2, N-1 & N-1/U1 and N-2], Fw190A (III/NJG 1), He219A-0 Uhu (I & II/NJG 1) [A-2 (I & II/NJG 1), A-5 (I/NJG 1), A-6 (I/NJG 1), A-7 (I/NJG 1. One machine only) and B-2 (I/NJG 1. One machine only)], Ju88A-4 (III/NJG 1. Probably Winter 1943–July 1944) [C-6 (IV/NJG 1), R-2, G-1 (III/NJG 1), G-6a, b and G-6c], Bf109E-3 (10/NJG 1. Late 1940–February 1943), Bf110C-1 [C-2, C-4, C-6, D-0, D-1, D-3, E-1, E-2, E-4, F-2, F-4, G-2 and G-4], Me210 (I/NJG 1. Used purely as a day reconnaissance plane) and Me410 (III/NJG 1. Not fitted with radar).

Known Bases

Arnhem-Deelen (Stab & II – 6.44), Athies – Laon (III – 3.44), Bönninghardt (Stab – 3.44. Kdo. IV – 2.45), Dortmund (IV – 11.44. Stab & IV – 2.45), Düsseldorf (II – 11.44 & 2.45), Fritzlar (III – 11.44), Giessen (Kdo. III – 11.44), Krefeld (Kdo. III – 2.45), Leeuwarden (IV – 3.44. III – 6.44), Münster (I – 11.44), Münster – Handorf (I – 2.45), Niedermendig (2 – 11.44), Paderborn (Stab & Kdo. II – 11.44), Quakenbruck (10 – 3.44), Störmede (Kdo. IV – 11.44. III – 2.45), St. Trond (II – 3.44. IV – 6.44), Venlo (I – 3.44. I – 6.44) and Werl (Kdo. II – 2.45).

Nachtjagdgeschwader 2 (Coded R4)

NJG 2 was formed in September 1940 and by May 1945 had claimed 800 victories by night and day. The Geschwader was commanded by the following:
? Hülshoff (1.11.41–31.12.43) [Prior to November 1941, the established elements of NJG 2 were under the control of NJG 1], Prinz Sayn-Wittgenstein (1.1–21.1.44), G Radusch (4.2.44–11.11.44), P Semrau (12.11.44–8.2.45) and ? Thimmig (8.2.45–5.45).

I Gruppe

Formed 1.9.40 from II/NJG 1 and 1/ZG 1. The Gruppe was commanded by the following:
? Heyse (1.9.40–23.11.40), ? Hülshoff (24.11.40–31.10.41), ? Jung (1.11.41–12.43), ? Buschmann (12.43–1.44), ? Zechlin (20.2.44–12.5.44) and ? Rath (12.5.44–5.45).

II Gruppe

In November 1940, 4/NJG 2 was formed from 1/ZG 2. On 1.11.41, 4/NJG 2, 4 and 6/NJG 1 were combined to form II/NJG 2. On 1.10.42, the Gruppe was redesignated IV/NJG 1. A new second Gruppe was formed from III/NJG 2. The Gruppe was commanded by the following:
H Lent (1.11.41–1.10.42. Became Kommandeur IV/NJG 1), ? Bönsch (2.10.42–12.43. Previously Kommandeur III/NJG 2), H Patuschka (3.12.42–6.3.43), ? Sewing (7.3.43–12.43), Prinz Sayn-Wittgenstein (12.43–1.1.44), P Semrau (1.1.44–1.11.44), H H Hissbach (1.11.44–14.4.45) and ? Brinkhaus (15.4.45–5.45).

III Gruppe

Formed March 1942. On 1.10.42, the Gruppe was redesignated II/NJG 2. Part of the ex-III/NJG 2 seems to have been used as a basis for the formation of IV/NJG 3. In July 1943, a new III/NJG 2 was formed by redesignating V/NJG 6. 9/NJG 2 was formed in September 1944 from LBeo Staffel 3. On 30.10.44, III/NJG 2 was redesignated IV/NJG 3. The existing IV/NJG 3 was redesignated III/NJG 2. The Gruppe was commanded by the following:
? Bönsch (3.4.42–1.10.42. Became Kommandeur II/NJG 2), P Semrau (7.43–1.1.44. Previously Kommandeur V/NJG 6), ? Ney (1.1.44–11.44. Became Kommandeur IV/NJG 3), ? Ferger (11.44–10.4.45. Previously Kommandeur IV/NJG 3) and H H Merker (11.4.45–5.45).

IV Gruppe

Formed 30.10.44 from I/NJG 7. Redesignated NSGr 30 on 23.2.45. During its brief career, IV/NJG 2's Kommandeur was ? Bengsch who went on to command NSGr 30. [NSGr 30 was formed from both IV/NJG 2 and II/NJG 3 and had a nominal strength of 42 Ju88 aircraft. The unit never saw operational service in the night ground attack role before the war's end.]

V Gruppe

Forming from III/KG 2 during November 1944 but never became operational.

Aircraft Used

Do17Z-10 Kauz II, Do215B-5 Kauz 3 (II/NJG 2), Do217J-1 (II & III/NJG 2 [J-2, N-1 & N-1/U1 and N-2], Ju88C-0 (1940–1) [C-1 (1940–1), C-2 (Up to 1942), C-4 (1941–9.44), C-5 (Up to 1944), C-6, R-2, G-1 and G-6a & b] and Bf110D-1 [D-3, E-1, E-2, E-4, F-2, F-4 and G-4].

Known Bases

Coulommiers (II – 6.44), Deelen (Stab & II – 3.44), Eelde (II – 2.45), Grove (IV – 11.44), Gütersloh (III – 11.44), Kassel (I – 3. & 11.44), Köln/Cologne (Stab & II – 11.44), Langendiebach (III – 6.44) Marx (III – 2.45), Twente (III – 3.44), Twenthe (Stab & I – 2.44) and Vechta (Kdo. II – 2.45).

Nachtjagdgeschwader 3 (Coded D5. During its service in North Africa, 1/NJG 3 carried the code L1.)

NJG 3 was formed in October 1940 and by May 1945 had claimed 820 victories by night and day. The Geschwader was commanded by the following:
J Schalk (29.3.41–1.8.41) [Prior to March 1941, the formed elements of NJG 3 were under the tactical control of NJG 1], H Lent (1.8.43–7.10.44) and G Radusch (12.11.44–5.45).

I Gruppe

Formed 1.10.40 from V/(Z)LG 1. The Gruppe was commanded by the following:
G Radusch (7.10.40–2.10.41), ? Knoetzen (3.10.41–30.9.42), Prinz Lippe-Weissenfeld (1.10.42–31.5.43), ? Peters (1.6.43–14.5.43), ? Mylius (15.8.43–13.12.43), P. Szameitat (14.12.43–2.1.44) and W. Husemann (4.1.44–5.45).

II Gruppe

Formed 1.9.41 from II/ZG 2 and Z. Erg. Gruppe. The Gruppe was commanded by the following:
G Radusch (3.10.41–1.8.43), Prinz Sayn-Wittgenstein

(18.8.43–11.43), P. Szameitat (12.43–14.12.43), ? Havenstein (15.12.43–9.43) and ? Hüschens (9.44–5.45).

III Gruppe
Formed 1.11.41 from elements of II/ZG 76 and 4/NJG 1. The Gruppe was commanded by the following: H Nacke (1.11.41–21.4.43), ? Mylius (22.4.43–14.8.43), ? Sigmund (31.8.43–3.10.43) and ? Barthe (15.10.43–5.45)

IV Gruppe
Formed in November 1942 from elements of III/NJG 2. On 30.10.44, III/NJG 2 and IV/NJG 3 swopped designations. The Gruppe was commanded by the following:
? Simon (1.11.42–7.10.43), ? Schulz (8.10.43–1.44), ? Buschmann (January–July 1944), ? Ferger (July–November 1944. Became Kommandeur III/NJG 2), ? Ney (November 1944–4.3.45. Previously Kommandeur III/NJG 2) and ? Tober (5.3.45–5.45).

Aircraft Used
Do217J-1 (I, II and IV/NJG 3) [J-2, N-1 & N-1/U1 and N-2], Do335A-6 (I/NJG 3. One machine only, the V-10), Fw190A (IV/NJG 3), Ta154A-1 (Stab/NJG 3), Ju88C-6 (II, III and IV/NJG 3) [R-2, G-1, G-6a & b and G-6c] and Bf110C-1 [C-2, C-4, C-6, D-1, D-3, E-1, E-2, E-4, F-4, G-2 and G-4].

Known Bases
Aalborg [Westerland] (IV – 3.44), Köln/Ostheim (IV – 6.44), Grove (10 – 3.44. II – 11.44), Haderslev (Kdo. III – 11.44), Jever (IV – 2.45), Lüneburg (8 – 3.44), Marx (IV – 11.44), Nordholz (7 – 3.44. Kdo. I – 11.44), Plantluenne (II – 6.44), Schleswig (II – 3.44. I – 11.44), Stade (Stab & III – 3. & 6.44 and 2.45. Stab – 11.44), St. Trond (I – 6.44), Varel (Kdo. IV – 11.44), Vechta (I – 3.44), Werneuchen (6 – 3.44), Westerland (III – 11.44) and Wittmundhafen (2 – 3.44. Kdo. IV – 11.44).

Nachtjagdgeschwader 4 (Coded 3C)
NJG 4 was formed in the Spring of 1941 and by May 1945 had claimed 579 victories by night and day. The Geschwader was commanded by the following:
? Stoltenhoff (18.4.41–20.10.43), ? Thimmig (20.10.43–14.11.44) and H W Schnaufer (14.11.44–5.45)

I Gruppe
Formed in the Spring of 1941 from I/ZG 26. In December 1941, the Gruppe was remustered as I/ZG 26 and transferred to the Eastern Front. I/NJG 4 was reformed in September 1942 from elements of I/NJG 3 and III/NJG 4. The Gruppe was commanded by the following:
W Herget (1.9.42–12.44) and H. Krause (12.44–5.45).

II Gruppe
Formed in the Spring of 1941 from II/ZG 26. In December 1941, the Gruppe was remustered as II/ZG 26 with the exception of 5/NJG 4. In April 1942, a new second Gruppe was formed with the 5th Staffel as a nucleus. The Gruppe's Kommandeure are unknown.

III Gruppe
Formed in May 1942 from 1, 4 and 8/NJG 1. The Gruppe was commanded by the following:
? Holler (1.5.42–22.6.43), ? Kamp (23.6.43–6.12.44) and L Meister (6.12.44–5.45).

IV Gruppe
Formed 1.1.43, being redesignated I/NJG 6 on 1.8.43. The Gruppe was commanded by the following:
H Wohlers (1.1.43 to 9.2.44. Became Kommandeur I/NJG 6 1.8.43).

Aircraft Used
Do217J-1 (1/NJG 4) [J-2, N-1 & N-1/U1 and N-2], Ju88C-6 (I/NJG 4) [R-2, G-1 and G-6a, b & c], Bf109G-6 (III/NJG 4) and Bf110C-1 [C-2, C-4, C-6, E-1, E-2, E-4, F-2, F-4, G-2 and G-4].

Known Bases
Athies-Laon (2.3.44), Chenay (Stab – 6.44), Coulommiers (II – 6.44), Darmstadt (Kdo. I – 11.44), Dijon (5 – 3.44), Ebelsbach (III – 11.44), Florennes (Stab – 3.44. I – 3. and 6.44), Gutersloh (III – 2.45), Merzebrock (Stab – 2.45), Juvincourt (III – 3.44), Langendiebach (I – 11.44), Lippspringe (Kdo. II – 2.45), Mainz (II – 11.44), Paderborn (III – 2.45), St. Dizier (II – 3.44), Rheims (III – 6.44), Rhein-Main (Stab – 11.44), Tavaux (6 – 3.44) and Vechta (I – 2.45)

Nachtjagdgeschwader 5 (Coded C9. This code was also used by 10 and 12/ZG 1 immediately following their remustering as II/NJG 100. NJG 5 also used the code 3C between 1.1.43 and 3.7.43):
NJG 5 was formed in September 1942 and by May 1945 had claimed 850 victories by night and day. The Geschwader was commanded by the following:
? Schaffer (30.9.42–1.8.43), G Radusch (2.8.43–3.2.44), Prinz Lippe-Weissenfeld (20.2.44–12.3.44), W Borchers (15.3.44–5.3.45) and R Schönert (6.3.45–5.45).

I Gruppe
Formed in September 1942 from II/ZG 2. The Gruppe was commanded by the following:
? Wandam (End 9.42–4.7.43), W Hoffmann (4.7.43–end 4.45) and ? Lang (4.–5.45).

II Gruppe
Formed in December 1942. On 10.5.44, the Gruppe was redesignated III/NJG 6. On the same date, a new II/NJG 5 was formed by the redesignation of V/NJG 5. The Gruppe was commanded by the following:
R Schönert (1.12.42–5.8.43), M Meurer (5.8.43–27.9.43), ? Bar (28.9.43–27.1.44), L Fellerer (2.44–10.5.44. Became Kommandeur III/NJG 6), ? Leickhardt (3.5.44–6.3.45. Previously Kommandeur V/NJG 5), ? Tham (10.3.45–4/5.45) and ? Rapp (5.4.45–5.45). Note: Tham and Rapp may have held command simultaneously in May 1945.

III Gruppe
Formed in April 1943. The Gruppe was commanded by the following:
W Borchers (4.43–15.3.44), ? Zorner (16.3.44–21.10.44), ? v. Mein (22.10.44–6.2.45), W Engel (6.2.45–4.45) and ? Piuk (4.–5.45).

IV Gruppe
Formed in December 1942. The Gruppe was redesignated I/NJG 100 on 1.8.43. A new fourth Gruppe was formed in September 1943. The Gruppe was commanded by the following:
Prinz Sayn-Wittgenstein (12.42–5.8.43. Became Kommandeur I/NJG 100), ? v. Niebelshütz (1.9.43–2.1.44), ? Altendorf (3.1.44–9.44), ? Höfele

(10.44–20.4.45) and ? Bussmann (21.4.45–5.45).

V Gruppe
Formed 11.8.43. On 10.5.44, the Gruppe was redesignated II/NJG 5. The Gruppe was commanded by the following:
? Peters (15.8.43–3.5.44) and ? Leickhardt (4.5.44–10.5.44. Became Kommandeur II/NJG 5).
Aircraft Used
Do217J-1 (II and IV/NJG 5) [J-2, N-1 & N-1/U1 and N-2], Fw189A-1 (IV/NJG 5. From May 1944. Fitted with wide-angle FuG 212), Ju88G-1 [G-6a & b], Bf110D-1 [D-3, E-1, E-2, F-2, F-4, G-2 and G-4] and Me410 (I/NJG 5. Not fitted with radar).
Known Bases
Athies-Laon (II – 6.44), Brandis (9 – 3.44), Döberitz (Stab – 3.44), Erfurt (IV –3.44), Erfurt-Bindesleben (IV – 6.44), Griefswald (IV – 2.45. At least part of II/NJG 100 was based at this airfield during February under the control of IV/NJG 5), Gütersloh (III – 6.44), Insterburg (V – 3.44), Jesau (Stab + I – 11.44), Königsberg-Neumark (III – 3.44), Lübeck (III – 11.44. III – 2.45), Lüneberg (Kdo. III – 11.44), Parchim (II – 3.44), Powden (IV – 11.44), Praust (10 – 11.44), Powunden (14 & 15–3.44), St. Dizier (I – 6.44), Stendal (I – 3.44) and Stubendorf (II – 11.44).

Nachtjagdgeschwader 6 (Coded 2Z)
NJG 6 was formed in August 1943 and by May 1945 had claimed 400 victories by night and day. The Geschwader was commanded by the following:
? Schaffer (10.8.43–8.2.44), H Wohlers (9.2.44–15.3.44), ? v. Reeken (16.3.44–14.4.44), ? Griese (15.4.44–12.9.44) and H Lütje (13.9.44–5.45).
I Gruppe
Formed 1.8.43 by the redesignation of IV/NJG 4. The Gruppe was commanded by the following:
H Wohlers (1.8.43–9.2.44), ? Reschke (19.2.44–24.4.44), H M Hadeball (26.4.44–3.7.44), G Friedrich (12.7.44–16.3.45) and ? Spoden (19.3.45–5.45).
II Gruppe
Formed 15.9.43. The Gruppe was commanded by the following:
? Leuchs (15.9.43–14.7.44) and H Schulte (23.7.44–5.45)
III Gruppe
Formed 10.5.44 by the redesignation of II/NJG 5. The Gruppe was commanded by the following:
L Fellerer (10.5.44–2.45. Previously Kommandeur II/NJG 5), W Johnen (2.45–31.3.45) and ? Floitgraf (1.4.45–5.45).
IV Gruppe
Formed in May 1943. The Gruppe was commanded by the following:
H Lütje (6.43–26.10.44) and M Becker (20.10.44–5.45).
V Gruppe
Formed in June 1943. On 15:8.43, the Gruppe was redesignated III/NJG 2. The Gruppe was commanded by the following:
P Semrau (6.–7.43. Became Kommandeur III/NJG 2).
Aircraft Used
Ju88C-6 (IV/NJG 6) [G-1 and G-6a & b] and Bf110D-1 [D-3, F-2, F-4, G-2 and G-4].

Known Bases
Arnhem-Deelen (I – 6.44), Gross Sachsenheim (I – 11.44 and 2.45), Hailtingen (Kdo. I – 2.45), Mainz-Finthen (I – 3.44), Neubiberg (IV – 2.45) and Schleissheim (Stab – 3., 6. and 11.44. II – 3.44).

Nachtjagdgeschwader 7 (Coded D9. This code was also carried by the aircraft of I/(Bel)KG 7.):
NJG 7 was formed in June 1944. As the 'Geschwader only ever had one Gruppe', there was no Kommodore appointed during its existence.

I Gruppe
Formed in January 1944 as I/(Beo)KG 7 from III/(Beo)KG 4. In June 1944 the Gruppe was redesignated I/NJG 7. The Gruppe was once more redesignated, as IV/NJG 2, on 30.10.44. The Gruppe was commanded by ? Bengsch (1.44?–30.10.44. Became Kommandeur IV/NJG 2).
Note: There is evidence that the code D9 continued to be used when I/NJG 7 became IV/NJG 2.
4/(Erg)NJG 7
Formed in June 1944 from 12/KG 51. In November 1944, the Staffel was absorbed into Stab/NJG 3.
Aircraft Used
Ju88A-4 (I/(Bel)KG 7) [G-1 and G-6a & b].
Known Bases (As I/(Bel)KG 7):
Hopsten (3 – 3.44) and Münster-Handorf (1 and 2 – 3.44).
Known Bases
Hopsten (3 – 3.44) and Münster-Handorf (I – 3.44).

Nachtjagdgeschwader 11 (No code)
NJG 11 was formed in August 1944. It was the Luftwaffe's only Nachtjagdgeschwader to exclusively fly single-engine, single-seat aircraft in the *Wilde Sau* role (with the exception of the 10th Staffel). During its existence, the Geschwader's Gruppen operated independently and there was never a Geschwader Stab.
I Gruppe
Formed in August 1944 and was commanded by K F Müller (26.8.44–5.45). The Gruppe comprised:
1/NJG 11
Formed 28.8.44 from elements of 6/JG 300. In January 1945, it was redesignated 7/NJG 11.
2/NJG 11
Formed 28.8.44 from part of 1/NJGr 10. In January 1945, the Staffel was redesignated 1/NJG 11.
3/NJG 11
Formed November 1944 from the residue of 1/NJGr 10. In January 1945, it was redesignated 8/NJG 11.
II Gruppe
Formed November 1944 around a nucleus of 10/JG 300. The Gruppe comprised three Staffeln (4, 5 and 6/NJG 11) and in March 1945, was redesignated 5/NJG 11. The Gruppe's Kommandeure are unknown with the possible exception of ? Finkeldey.
III Gruppe
Formed in January 1945 from 1 and 3/NJG 11 and new personnel. In March 1945, it was redesignated 2/NJG 11. The Gruppe was commanded by F. Krause (12.1.45–?).
10/NJG 11
Formed 28.1.45 from EKdo 262 (Welter) with K Welter as Staffel Kapitan. This was the only Staffel

within the Geschwader to fly multi-engined and -
seated aircraft.
Aircraft Used
Fw190A, Bf109G-6 [G-6/N, G-10, G-14 and K-4] and
Me262B-1a/U1 (10/NJG 11) [B-1a and B-2 (One
machine only)].
Known Bases
Bonn (3 – 11.44), Bonn-Hangelar (I – 2.45), Burg (10 –
1.45), Darmstadt (Stab I and 2 – 11.44), Fassberg (1 –
11.44), Juterborg (II – 2.45) and Twente (Kdo. 3 –
11.44).
Nachtjagdgeschwader 100 (Coded W7)
NJG 100 was formed in August 1943. The Gruppen
belonging to the Geschwader operated independently
so there was no Geschwader Stab.
I Gruppe
Formed 1.8.43 from IV/NJG 5. The Gruppe was com-
manded by the following:
Prinz Sayn-Wittgenstein (1.8.43–5.8.43. Previously
Kommandeur IV/NJG 5), R. Schönert
(5.8.43–31.12.43), A. Lechner (1.1.44–23.2.44), ?
Bonow (23.2.44–5.44), ? Bellinghausen (5.44–8.7.44)
and ? Fischer (8.7.44–5.45).
II Gruppe
Probably formed in June/July 1944. The Gruppe was
commanded by the following:
? v. Mein (2.7.44–21.10.44) and ? Zorner
(20.7.44–5.45).
Aircraft Used
Do217J-1 [J-2, N-1 & N-1/U1 and N-2], Fw58C-1 and
2 (I/NJG 100. Used from January 1945 and fitted with
wide-angle FuG 212), Fw189A-1 (I and II/NJG 100.
Used from May 1944 and fitted with wide-angle FuG
212), Ju87D-5 (I/NJG 100. One machine only,
August–December 1943), Ju88C-6 [G-1 and G-6a &
b] and Bf110G-2.
Known Bases
Breslau-Udetfeld (2 – 11.44), Hohensalza (1 – 11.44),
Laksberg (Estland) (4 – 3.44), Prowehren (I and 4 –
11.44), Malacki (II – 11.44) and Staaken (I – 5.45).

Apart from the nine units already described, the
Luftwaffe raised a number of other night fighter units
which did not fit into the normal Geschwader pattern.
These were as follows:

Trials Units (Eprobungskommando):
From time to time during the 1939–45 war, the
Luftwaffe raised specialised units to evaluate new air-
craft types under service conditions. Five of these
Eprobungskommando undertook trials with potential
night fighters as follows:

Eprobungskommando 154 (Code unknown, if any)
A trials unit formed to evaluate the Ta154 in December
1943. The Ta154V-3 was operated until it was passed
to NJGr 10.

Eprobungskommando 234/Kommando Bisp-
ing/(No code)
Formed on 11.12.44, EKdo 234 was commanded by J.
Bisping and was to evaluate the Ar234 as a night
fighter. The unit operated a single Ar234B-2 (W.Nr.
140 146) which was extensively modified for its new
role (see page 270). On 13.2.45, Bisping was killed and
his place taken by ? Bonow (from EKdo 338). EKdo
234 was stationed near Berlin and it is not known

whether it claimed any victories during its operational
sorties. One other Ar234 night fighter, an Ar234C-3/N
Nachtigall, saw service, this machine being operated
by E-Stella Oranienburg.

Eprobungskommando 262/Kommando Welter/
(No code)
Formed on 11.12.44, EKdo 262 was commanded by K
Welter and was to evaluate the Me262 as a night
fighter. The unit initially operated a modified
Me262A-1a (W.Nr. 130 056) (see page 000), which,
flown by Welter, was responsible for the destruction of
two heavy bombers and three Mosquitos in little over
a month! On 28.1.45, EKdo 262 was redesignated
10/NJG 11 and was based at Burg. The unit now
operated a mix of Me262B-1a and B-1a/U1 aircraft
and a single Me262B-2 and has been credited with the
destruction of 13 Mosquito aircraft between January
and March 1945.

Eprobungskommando 338 (Code unknown, if any)
Formed in January 1945 at Rechlin to carry out trials
with the Ju388J *Störtebeker* night fighter. The unit
was commanded by ? Bonow (previously Kommandeur I/NJG 100) and operated the Ju338V-2.
Bonow took command of EKdo 234 in February 1945.

Eprobungskommando 410 (Code unknown, if any)
A trials unit formed to evaluate the Me410 as a
specialised anti-Mosquito night fighter. The unit
operated from Venlo during March 1944 and was
possibly under the control of Nachtjagdgeschwader 1.

Nachtjagdgeschwader 101 and 102 (Coded 9W and
7J respectively):
These two units acted as the training schools for the
Luftwaffe's night fighter arm. NJG 101 was formed in
July 1941, as Nachtjagdschule 1) and eventually
reached a strength of three Gruppen. NJG 102 appears
to have been formed late in 1943 and reached a
strength of two Gruppen. At various times during the
war, elements of these two units became operational.
Nachtjagdgruppe 10 (No code):
Formed on 1.1.44 as a night fighter trials unit (roughly
equivalent to the RAF's Fighter Interception Unit). In
co-operation with the E-Stellen Werneuchen (radar
etc), Rechlin (aircraft) and Tarnewitz (armament),
the Gruppe evaluated new night fighting aircraft,
radar and radio aids, weapons and techniques under
service conditions. NJGr 10 was disbanded in April
1945 and was commanded by the following:
R Schönert (1.1.44–6.3.45) and ? Lüdtke
(6.3.45–4.45). The Gruppe comprised three Staffeln as
follows:
1/NJGr 10
Formed in March 1944 from personnel drawn from
I/JG 300. Under the command of K F Müller, the
Staffel flew Bf109 and Fw190 aircraft. On 27.4.44,
1/NJGr 10 was redesignated 3/NJG 11.
2/NJGr 10
The date of this Staffel's formation is unknown, but it
was certainly after the creation of 1 and 3/NJGr 10.
Led by ? Lüdkte, 2/NJGr 10 flew He219 and Ta154
aircraft crewed by personnel drawn from the Gruppe's
third Staffel.
3/NJGr 10
Formed in March 1944, 3/NJGr 10 was led by ? Tham

and flew Bf110 and Ju88 aircraft.

Aircraft Used
Fw190A (1/NJGr 10. Fitted with FuG 216, 217 or 218 radar), Ta154V-3 and A-1 (2/NJGr 10), He111H-20 (Fitted with FuG 220/350. Used as a training, reconnaissance and illuminator aircraft), He219A-0 [A-2 and A-5 (all used by 2/NJGr 10)], Ju88C-6 [G-1, G-6a & b and P-2 (all used by 3/NJGr 10. The P-2 was fitted with FuG 202 or 212 and was in service late in 1943)], Bf109G-6 [G-6/N (fitted with FuG 350. Used in limited numbers), G-10 and G-14 (all used by 1/NJGr 10. Some Bf109 aircraft may have been fitted with FuG 217 radar)] and Bf110G-4 (3/NJGr 10. All such aircraft fitted with *Schräge Musik*).

Known Bases
Bonn (1 – 11.44), Jüterborg (3 – 11.44) and Werneuchen (1, 2 and 3 – 3.44 and 2.45. 2 – 11.44).

Nachtjagdstaffel Finnland/Norwegen (Coded B4)
A night fighter Staffel was formed in July 1944 for the defence of Finnish air space. This unit, designated NJSt Finnland, came under the direct control of Luftflotte 5 and was equipped with Bf110G-4, He219A-0 and Ju88G-1 aircraft. In November 1944, the Staffel was moved to Norway and on the 27th of that month was redesignated NJSt Norwegen. In March 1945, the unit was incorporated into NJG 3 as that Geschwader's fourth Staffel, remaining in Norway until May 1945. By this time, it had supplemented its existing equipment with the Ju88G-6c. Even though the Staffel became part of NJG 3, there is photographic evidence that the code B4 continued to be used right up to the war's end.

Nachtjagdstaffeln Nantes, Brest and Nachtjagdstaffel/KG 40:
By the Spring of 1943, RAF Coastal Command was all but denying enemy shipping passage along the Western seaboard of Europe. Especially worrying for the Germans was the increase in night attacks; the hours of darkness having previously provided cover for the Kriegsmarine's submarines enroute to the Atlantic hunting grounds and for the running of coastal convoys. In order to provide support for these operations, the three named units were created.

Nachtjagdstaffel Nantes (Code unknown, if any)
Alternatively known as Kommando Kunkel after its commanding officer, this unit flew Ju88 aircraft, of the H-2 variant as far as possible (fitted with FuG 200 ASV used as AI?), for hunting Sunderland flying boats over the Bay of Biscay. In April 1944, the unit was redesignated 9/ZG 1 and now operated from Lorient.

Nachtjagdstaffel Brest (Code unknown, if any)
Nothing is known about this unit other than that it existed.

Nachtjagdstaffel/KG 40 (Code C9?)
This unit operated Ju88C-6 aircraft flown by crews on detachment from IV/NJG 5. The Staffel probably came under the control of V/KG 40.

Wilde Sau **Units**

30th Jagddivision
This formation comprised JG 300, 301, 302 and an illuminator Gruppe, III/KG 3 and was under the command of H Hermann. The Division was probably formed in August 1943 and was disbanded at the end of March 1944, its fighter elements becoming 'all-weather' units. However, the dissolution of the Division did not mean the end of the specialised night fighter role performed by its constituent Geschwader; 6 and 10/JG 300 continued to operate as anti-Mosquito Nachtjagdstaffeln until at least November 1944 (during this period, 6/JG 300 was alternatively known as Kommando Plöger and flew Fw190A-8 and A-9 aircraft fitted with *Neptun* radar), a Kommando from I/JG 302 operated in the night defence of Helsinki from March 1944 and 4 and 6/JG 301 flew as night-fighters in Rumania in June 1944.

JG 300 (No code)
Note: Details relate to the period August 1943–March 1944 only for JG 300, 301 and 302.
Formed 27.6.43. The Geschwader was commanded by the following:
H Hermann (27.6.43–8.43? Became CO 30th Jagddivision) and K Kettner (8.43?–?).
Aircraft Used
Predominantly Bf109Gs with a few Fw190s.
Known Bases
Bonn-Hangelar (I – 3.44), Krefeld (Stab – 3.44), Rheine (II – 3.44) and Wiesbaden (III – 3.44).

JG 301 (No code)
Formed in July 1943 under the command of H Weinreich.
Aircraft Used
Bf109G and Fw190A.
Known Bases
Leipheim (2 – 3.44), Neubiberg (1 – 3.44), Schleissheim (Stab – 3.44) and Zerbst (3 and III – 3.44).

JG 302 (No code)
Probably formed in July 1943 under the command of M Mossinger.
Aircraft Used
Bf109G and Fw190A.
Known Bases
Brandis [and Jüterborg] (I – 3.44), Döberitz (Stab – 3.44) Ludwigslust (II – 3.44) and Oldenburg (III – 3.44).

Note: Only one Gruppe in each of JG 300, 301 and 302 owned its own aircraft (until March 1944). The other Gruppen shared the aircraft of day fighter units based on the same airfields, ie II/JG 300 with III/JG 11 and I/JG 302 with II/JG 27.

I and II/Kampfgeschwader 51 (Coded 9K)
On 6.12.43, I/KG 51 moved into Evreux to undertake night bombing raids against targets in England. Equipped with the Me410, the Gruppe undertook *Wilde Sau* sorties as well as its normal duties during the early months of 1944. These night fighter activities were further expanded when a Fernnachtjagd Staffel was raised within the Gruppe. This unit undertook intruder missions against RAF bomber bases and was commanded by D Puttfarken until his death on 22.4.44. (There is some evidence to suggest that this Staffel was raised to counter 100 Group's long range fighter element.) On 3.6.44, I/KG 51 was stood down for retraining on the Me262 and its night fighter opera-

tions ceased.

II/KG 51, operating from Chartres and Gilz-Rijen, France and Holland respectively, also undertook night fighter operations with the Me410 during 1944. These operations continued until a dispute between the Director of Bombers and that of Night Fighters over who should control the Gruppe's operations, caused the unit to revert to the bombing role. In October 1944, the Gruppe, like I/KG 51, was stood down for retraining on the Me262.

Nachtjagdkommando 190 (No code)
Formed from 10/JG 11, this unit flew Fw190 aircraft against BOAC's Mosquito flights in and out of Sweden from Aalborg in Denmark during 1943.

I/Schnellkampfgeschwader 10 (No Code)
During the early months of 1944, I/SKG 10 combined its night hit and run raids on England with *Wilde Sau* sorties over France. Based at Dreux and flying Fw190A-4 and A-5 aircraft, the Gruppe continued these operations until its redesignation as III/KG 51 in June 1944.

Illuminator (Beleuchter) and Reconnaissance (Beobachtungs) Units
The introduction of the *Wilde-* and *Zahme Sau* techniques of night fighting by the Luftwaffe led to a requirement for the two types of named unit. As aircraft operating in the *Wilde Sau* role made their interceptions visually, illuminator units were formed to drop lanes of flares in the vicinity of the bomber streams so that the fighters could home in on their prey. The less rigid ground control exercised in both the new systems made it imperative to have as earlier a warning as possible of the raiding force's composition and direction of flight. To this end, specialised reconnaissance units were formed to shadow the bomber streams and report their whereabouts to the various control centres. The details of these units, were known, are as follows:

Beleuchter Units

III/KG 3 (Coded 5K)
In August 1943, this Gruppe was redesignated III/(Bel)KG 3 and came under the control of the 30th Jagddivision. In January 1944, III/(Bel) KG 3 was redesignated I/(Bel)KG 7 (Coded 'D9') and now came under the control of the 3rd Jagddivision. In June 1944, the Gruppe was again redesignated, this time becoming I/NJG 7 (see page 225). In March 1944, the Gruppe was based at Münster-Handorf (1st and 2nd Staffeln) and Hopsten (3rd Staffeln).

Behelfs Beleuchter Staffel 1 (Code unknown, if any)
Under the control of the 1st Jagddivision and based at Celle during March 1944.

Behelfs Beleuchter Staffel 2 (Code unknown, if any);
Under the control of the 'Führer Mittelrhein' and based at Rhein-Main during March 1944.

Behelfs Beleuchter Staffel 3 (Code unknown, if any)
Under the control of the 3rd Jagddivision and based at Münster-Handorf during 1944. Probably replaced I/(Bel)KG 7 when this unit was redesignated I/NJG 7.

Beobachtungs Units

Luftbeobachtungsstaffel 1 (Code unknown, if any)
Under the control of the 1st Jagddivision and based at Neurrupin during March 1944.

Luftbeobachtungsstaffel 2 (Code unknown, if any)
Under the control of the 2nd Jagddivision and based at Stade during March 1944.

Luftbeobachtungsstaffel 3 (Code unknown, if any)
Under the control of the 3rd Jagddivision and based at Deelen or Venlo during March 1944.

Luftbeobachtungsstaffel 7 (Code unknown, if any)
Under the control of the 7th Jagddivision and based at Stuttgart-Echterdingen during March 1944.

Aircraft Used
He111H-20 (Behelfs Beleuchter Staffeln), Ju88A-4 (I/(Bel)KG 7 and Behelfs Beleuchter Staffeln) [C-6 (Luftbeobachtungsstaffeln) and G-6c (Luftbeobachtungsstaffeln)], Bf110G-4 (Luftbeobachtungsstaffeln), Me210 (Luftbeobachtungsstaffel 1) and Me410 (Luftbeobachtungsstaffeln 1–7).

Appendix 4

Operations in support of Allied bomber forces other than RAF Bomber Command in England

This appendix is included to give an insight into those Allied bomber support operations which were not connected with the RAF's night offensive against Germany.

By late 1944, the RAF was operating six heavy bomber squadrons (Nos 37, 70, 40, 104, 178 and 614) in the Mediterranean. These squadrons formed 205 Group and were used in night raids against targets in Austria, Greece, Hungary, Italy and Yugoslavia. Although the Axis defences in this area were nowhere near as strong as those in Western Europe, radar cover was adequate and a strong response was encountered from predicted Flak.

It was therefore proposed to equip this force with *Moonshine, Bagful, Boozer* and *Carpet II*. Difficulties were encountered in that the effectiveness of *Boozer* was debatable and *Carpet II* was in extremely short supply due to the demands of UK-based formations. In fact, the European war ended before any of these measures could become operational in the Mediterranean.

At about the same time, five heavy bomber squadrons (Nos 99, 159, 215, 355 and 356) were pursuing a day and night offensive against the Japanese in Burma and Indo-China. The Japanese were extremely ill-equipped with radar and as most of the raids were carried out by day with fighter escort, there was little need for active electronic counter measures. However, the theatre did produce an ELINT unit, Number 160 Special Flight, to monitor enemy W/T and R/T transmissions and plot his radar stations.

The origins of 160 Flight are obscure, but on 21 July 1944 it came under the control of 159 Squadron (as 159 Special Flight) and its operational history becomes much clearer. At this time the Flight consisted of two Liberator V aircraft (BZ 938, coded 'W' and flown by F/Lt P O'Reilly and BZ 939, coded 'Y' and flown by P/O Seabrook) and began operations under its new designation in September, when five surveillance flights were made.

In the following month, the flight completed six ELINT sorties and one ASR search. An additional pilot, F/O Underhill, joined the unit, only to be classified as Missing in action when BZ 939 failed to return from a sortie on the 11 November. A replacement aircraft and pilot, KH170 (US serial 44-10735), a Liberator VI (B-24J-80-CF) and F/Lt Bradley respectively, were received in December 1944 and became operational on the 16th. Between 1 November and this date, the unit completed another 11 sorties.

Operations continued apace during January and February 1945, 18 sorties being completed during this period. At the beginning of January, O'Reilly was taken off operations along with his aircraft. Bradley and Seabrook followed him at the end of the month the three of them being replaced by F/Lt Markland who made his first sortie in KH 170 on the 27th.

During January 1945, the flight began to drop leaflets during its sorties and by the end of March had dropped 321,500 in Japanese and 67,500 in Burmese. The Flight's total number of sorties to date was 49.

In April 1945, the flight, now also known as 'C' Flight was detached to Ceylon for three weeks and accumulated 35 hours flying during the month. May saw no respite and another 36 hours of flying were accomplished. As well as recording all radar, W/T and R/T transmissions, the flight plotted searchlight positions and weather reports were brought back from all sorties.

At the end of May, 159 Squadron ceased to control the flight and its further history has defied attemtps to uncover it.

Both the American strategic bombing offensives against Germany and Japan were heavily supported by electronic counter measures.

In Europe the 8th and 15th Air Forces initially had little use for such measures in that daylight operations could not be effectively cloaked by blinding the enemy's radar. However the decline of the Luftwaffe's day fighter arm and Germany's increasing reliance on radar-predicted Flak during 1944 led to a renewal of interest in active counter measures.

In January 1944, the 803rd Bombardment Squadron (P) was formed within the 8th Air Force for *Mandrel* and *Carpet* jamming duties. (Details of this unit's operations will be found in Chapter Four). In addition to this specialised unit, the 8th and the 15th Air Forces installed and used the following devices at a general squadron level:

Chaff: The American equivalent of *Window* which was used by both Air Forces from late 1943. A dispenser unit, the A-1 was a standard fitment in late production B-17s and B-24s delivered to Europe.

AN/APQ-9: *Carpet III* was fitted to selected squadron aircraft of the two Air Forces from the autumn of 1943. By the end of the European war, 75% of all B-17s and B-24s used in the theatre were fitted with the device.

AN/APT-2 and AN/APT-5: These two devices were used for spot-jamming German ground radars and were closely related to *Dina II/Piperack*. Both were fitted extensively to 8th and 15th Air Force aircraft during 1944–45.

The American interest in electronic counter measures was extensive and it is known that a specialised jamming version of the B-24 was produced, the San Diego production facility producing 172 such aircraft. These aircraft were similar to those used by the 803rd/36th (see page 000) and were used exclusively in the Pacific.

Electronic counter measures in the Pacific Theatre reached their peak with the 20th Air Force, who liberally supplied its B-29 aircraft with jamming equipment during the devastating raids on the Japanese homeland during 1945. Each aircraft carried one or two jammers to counter the enemy's EW and GL radars and some 500 lb (227 kg) of *Chaff*. In addition, modified B-29s known as Porcupines, (a recognition of the vast numbers of aerials with which these aircraft were festooned) provided general jamming cover for the bomber formations. A Porcupine carried anything up to 14 jamming transmitters and a ton (1.1 tonnes) of *Chaff*.

The 20th Air Force also operated an ELINT force of nine Ferret B-24s and 26 F-7s (a photo-reconnaissance derivative of the B-24) whose task was to map the enemy's radar on the Nanpo Shoto chain of islands which stretched from Iwo Jima to Tokyo Bay. This operation began in May 1944 and had been completed by August 1945.

Appendix 5

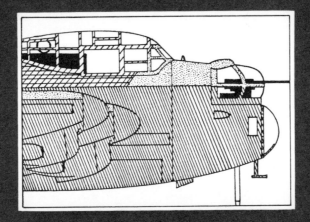

The Aircraft

NOTE: The reader should note that in the case of the RAF aircraft described, the 'specifications' refer to the standard aircraft unmodified for bomber support duties. In all cases, the figures quoted should be treated with caution as performance varied enormously due to the age of the airframe and a great number of other factors. Such figures are included in order to allow the reader to compare one type with another.

AVRO LANCASTER

Role:	Jamming aircraft.
User units:	101(B) Squadron: Lancaster BI and III – October 1943 to May 1945.
Variants:	Lancaster BI: Merlin 20, 22 or 24 engines. Lancaster BIII: Packard Merlin 28, 38 or 224 engines.
Special equipment:	Aircraft of the unit were equipped with *Airborne Cigar* jammers. Three transmission aerials were used with the device, two being mounted above the fuselage between the rear of the cockpit and the dorsal turret and the third being carried below the nose. The special operator's position was

situated on top of the bomb bay behind the main spar on the port side.

Remarks: 101's Lancasters carried a crew of eight comprising a pilot, flight engineer, navigator, wireless operator, bomb aimer (who also operated the front turret), two gunners (dorsal and tail turrets) and a special operator. A number of the squadron's aircraft were fitted with a Rose-Rice tail turret carrying two .5 in Browning machine guns in place of the normal four-gun unit. As well as the jamming gear, the unit's aircraft carried a full bomb load.

Specifications:

Lancaster BI/III: (BIII in brackets)

Power-plant:	Four Merlin 20, 22 or 24 liquid cooled engines (BIII: Merlin 28, 38 or 224).
Maximum speed:	245 mph (394 km/hr) at S/L
Range:	2,530 mls (4,070 km)
Service ceiling:	22,000 ft (6,706 m)
Empty weight:	37,000 lbs (16,780 kg)

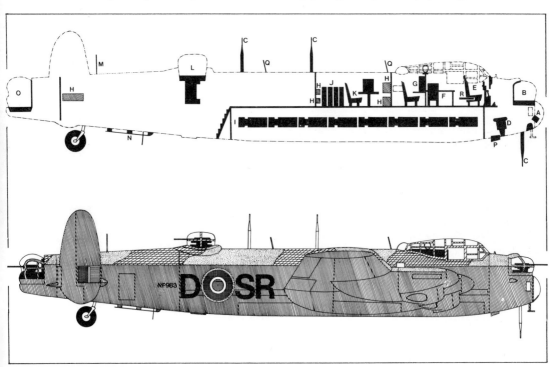

Lancaster Interior Key: *A – Bomb aimer's position, B – Nose turret, C – ABC transmission masts, D – Strike camera, E – Pilot's position, F – Navigator's position, G – Radio operator's position, H – Wing and tail spars, I – Bomb bay (normal bomb load carried), J – ABC transmitters and receiver (mounted on the port side of the fuselage), K – SO's position, L – Dorsal turret, M – ABC reception aerial, N – Beam approach aerial, O – Rose Rice tail turret, P – Window chute, Q – Standard radio fit aerials and R – Flight engineer's position.*

Lancaster BI NF983, SR – D of 101 Squadron, Ludford Magna: *Uppersurfaces in a disruptive pattern of Dark Earth (dot hatching) and Dark Green (cross hatching). Undersurfaces, fuselage sides and fins in Smooth Night (diagonal hatching). Type C1 roundels on the fuselage, Type B on the uppersurfaces of the wings. 1942-type fin flashes. ABC aerials in natural metal. Codes and serials in Dull Red. 'SR' ahead of the roundel on the port side of the fuselage.*

Normal loaded
weight: 65,000 lbs (29,480 kg)
Wing span: 102 ft (31.1 m)
Length: 69 ft 11 in (21.2 m)
Height: 20 ft 6 in (6.15 m)
Wing area: 1,297 sq ft (120.49 m²)
Defensive   Eight .303 in Browning machine
armament: guns (two each in the nose and dorsal
             turrets and four in the tail turret).
Bomb load: 18,000 lbs (8,165 kg)

BOEING B-17 FORTRESS

Role: Jamming, ELINT and training
             aircraft.
User units: 214(SD) Squadron: Fortress I, BII
             and III – January 1944 to July 1945.
             223(SD) Squadron: Fortress BII and
             III – April to July 1945.
             1669 Flight: Fortress BII and III –
             June 1944 to ?
             803rd/36th Bomb Squadron: B-17F
             and G (January to September 1944).

Variants:
Fortress I: British designation for the B-17C. One aircraft of this type (AN520 [possibly 40-2051]) was supplied to 214(SD) Squadron in February 1944 for training purposes. This machine had previously served with 90 and 220 Squadrons and was scrapped on 1 September 1944.

Fortress BII: British designation for the B-17F. In the spring of 1944, the RAF received 14 B-17s from the 1st Air Division of the 8th Air Force. These aircraft, serial numbers SR-376 to SR-389, were all employed by 214(SD) Squadron for training (four machines) and jamming (ten machines) duties. As Fortress BIII aircraft became available to the former unit, a number of its BIIs were passed to 223(SD) Squadron.

Fortress BIII: British designation for the B-17G.* Initial deliveries to 214(SD) Squadron were in the HB 761 to HB 805 serial range (Boeing and Vega-built aircraft) while from October 1944, this unit and 223(SD) Squadron received machines in the KH998 to KL837 range. (All Vega-built aircraft.) Some of the aircraft in the KJ100 to KL837 range were fitted with the 'Cheyenne' tail turret. This installation used hand operated guns which gave a greater arc of fire than the previous unit, gave the gunner more room and better visibility, had a reflector gun sight and reduced overall length by 5 in (12.5 cm).

Special equipment:
214(SD) SQUADRON:
April 1944–
ABC fitted to the unit's aircraft. An installation com-

---

*Known RAF–USAAF serial tie-ups as follows:
214(SD) Squadron – HB788; a B-17G-50-BO (42-102439), HB800; a B-17G-40-VE (42-98030), KJ101; a B-17G-55-VE (44-8243). 'Cheyenne' tail turret and KJ110; a B-17G-60-VE (44-8343). 'Cheyenne' tail turret.
223(SD) Squadron – KH998; a B-17G-55-VE (44-8240), KJ109; a B-17G-60-VE (44-8342), KJ118; a B-17G-75-VE (44-8621), KJ121; B-17G-75-VE (44-8624) and KL836; a B-17G-90-VE (44-8969). All these aircraft were fitted with the 'Cheyenne' tail turret.
1699 Flight – HB793; a B-17G-40-VE (42-98023).

prised six T.1624A/Type 20G receiver/indicator units and an unknown number of T.1260B transmitters.
May 1944–
Monica III tail warning device fitted to the unit's aircraft. The *Monica* aerial was fitted to the extreme rear fuselage below the tail guns.
June 1944–
The unit began to receive aircraft fitted with *Jostle* and *Airborne Grocer* (four to an aircraft). *Jostle* was installed in the bomb bay with its transmitting aerial mounted on top of the fuselage directly above the ventral turret wall. The four Yagi aerials for *Grocer* were mounted either side of the tail turret. *Airborne Grocer* was removed from the unit's aircraft at the end of June.
June–August 1944–
H2S navigation radar was fitted to the unit's aircraft. The device was mounted in a radome beneath the

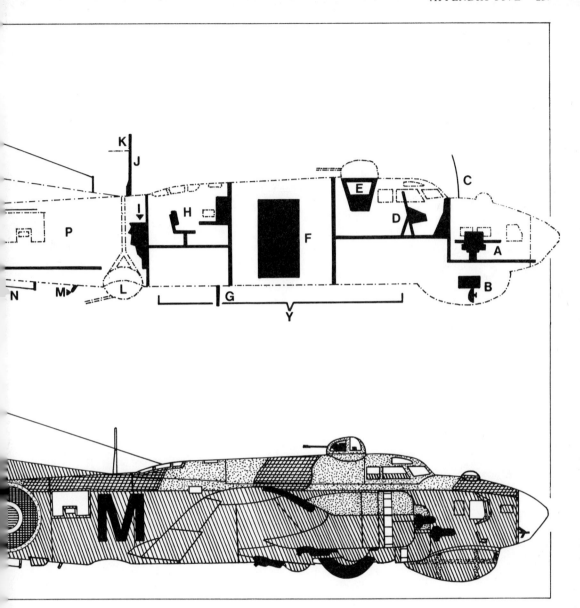

Fortress Interior Key: *A – Navigator's position*, *B – H2S scanner*, *C – Whip aerial seen only on* ABC *equipped aircraft, most probably the receiver aerial for this device*, *D – Pilot/Flight engineer's position*, *E – Dorsal turret*, *F – Jostle* IV *transmitter*, *G – Unidentified aerial seen on* Jostle *aircraft, possibly associated with the* Carpet *device*, *H – Wireless operator/SO's position*, *I – Probable location of electronic gear when the ventral turret was removed*, *J – Jostle* IV *transmission mast*, *K – ABC transmission mast*, *L – Ventral turret*, *M – Trailing aerial*, *N – Beam approach aerial*, *O – Window chute (one each side of the fuselage)*, *P – Beam gunners' position*, *Q – Jostle* IV *wire transmission aerial (see page 159)*, *R – Standard radio aerial*, *S – Location of electronic equipment*, *T – Unidentified aerials seen on* ABC *equipped aircraft (see page 39)*, *U – Unidentified aerial seen on* Jostle IV *equipped aircraft*, *V – Rear gunner's position*, *W – Airborne Grocer/Dina aerials (see page 000)*, *X – Monica and Y – Most probable location of* Mandrel *aerials when fitted (see page 61)*.

(1) Fortress BIII KJ103, BU – M of 214(SD) Squadron, Oulton: *Uppersurfaces in a disruptive pattern of Dark Earth (dot hatching) and Dark Green (cross hatching). Undersurfaces, fuselage sides and fin in Smooth Night (diagonal hatching). Type C1 roundels on the fuselage, Type B on the uppersurfaces of the wings. 1942-type fin flashes.* Jostle, Dina *and* Monica *aerials and engine cooling flaps in natural metal. Black de-icing boots and spinners. Codes and serials in Dull Red. Note the band of Smooth Night painted over the side cockpit windows, the painted out nose windows and the prominent areas of filler (dark grey) on the H2S radome.*

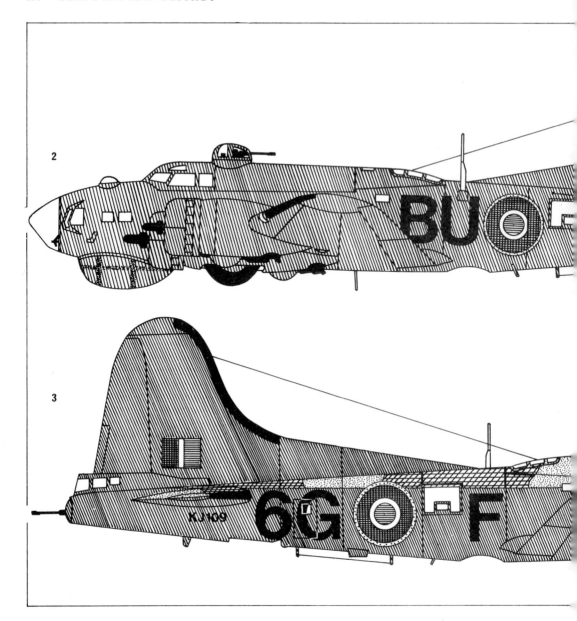

(2) Fortress BIII KJ110, BU – H of 214(SD) Squadron,
Oulton: *Smooth Night overall. Type C1 roundels on the
fuselage, Type B on the uppersurfaces of the wings. 1942-type
fin flashes.* Jostle *and* Monica *aerials in natural metal. Black
de-icing boots and spinners. Codes and serials in Dull Red. Note
the prominent areas of filler on the H2S radome.*

(3) Fortress BIII KJ109, 6G – F of 223(SD) Squadron,
Oulton: *Uppersurfaces in a disruptive pattern of Dark Earth
and Dark Green. Undersurfaces, fuselage sides and fin in
Smooth Night. Type C1 roundels on the fuselage, Type B on the
uppersurfaces of the wings. 1942-type fin flashes.* Jostle *aerial
in natural metal. Black de-icing boots and spinners. Codes and
serials in Dull Red. Note the prominent areas of filler on the
H2S radome and the* Cheyenne *tail turret.*

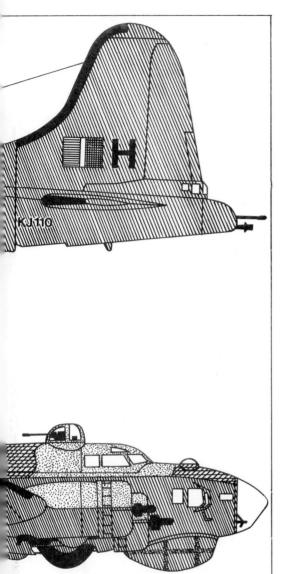

KJ110

wing-mounted whip aerials. The date for the installation of *Piperack* is uncertain.

223(SD) SQUADRON: This unit's aircraft were fitted
with *Carpet*, *DinaII/Piperack*, *H2S*, *Jostle* and *Window*
facilities, the installations being as those in the
B-17s of 214 (SD) Squadron.

803rd/36th BOMB SQUADRON: See Chapter Four.

Remarks:	In 100(SD) Group service, a B-17 had a crew of ten comprising a pilot, flight engineer, navigator, bomb-aimer (acting as air gunner) [nose armament when fitted] and second navigator), four gunners (dorsal, tail and beam positions, the ventral turret being un-manned or removed) and a special operator for the jamming equipment. In addition to the equipment already mentioned, each Fortress was also fitted with *Gee* or *Loran*, a dead reckoning compass, flame damping for the engines, MF and HF communications gear and HF and VHF R/T gear. The conversion work was carried out by Scottish Aviation at Prestwick. As the 803rd aircraft were modified by the RAF in England, it is probable that their B-17s were similar to their RAF counterparts. One of 214's aircraft was fitted with a pilot's indicator for a *Monica IIIC* whilst another was fitted with *5 Group Monica IIIC* by the BSDU.

Specifications:

B-17F/Fortress BII:

Power Plant:	Four 1,200 hp Wright R-1820-97 air-cooled radial engines.
Maximum speed:	325 mph (523 km/hr) at 25,000 ft 7,620 m)
Cruising speed:	160 mph (275 km/hr)
Maximum range:	4,420 mls (7,112 km)
Empty weight:	35,728 lbs (1,620 kg)
Maximum weight:	72,000 lbs (32,660 kg)
Wing span:	103 ft 9$\frac{3}{8}$ in (31.63 m)
Length:	74 ft 9 in (22.78 m)
Height:	19 ft 2$\frac{1}{2}$ in (5.85 m)
Wing area:	1,420 sq ft (131.92 m²)
Defensive armament:	One 0.3 in Browning machine gun in the nose position. Eight 0.5 in Brownings (two each in ventral, dorsal, and tail turrets. One each in the beam positions).
Bomb load:	17,600 lbs (7,983 kg)

B-17G/Fortress BIII:

Power plant:	Four 1,200 hp Wright R-1820-97 air-cooled radial engines.
Maximum speed:	302 mph (486 km/hr) at 25,000 ft (7,620 m)
Cruising speed:	160 mph (257 km/hr)
Maximum range:	3,400 mls (5,470 km)

fuselage nose (replacing the chin-turret on the B-17G).
By 16 August, ten aircraft had had the device installed.

July 1944–
Some of the unit's aircraft were modified to carry
Window. Chutes for dispensing the foil were probably
mounted on the fuselage sides below the beam gun
positions. At the end of the month, six aircraft were
fitted with *Mandrel III*, six sets per aircraft. Six
Type 90 IFF aerials were used.

September 1944–
The *Jostle* devices in six of the units aircraft were
modified to the *Big Ben* configuration. *Carpet III* was
also installed during the month. The four AS-69/APT
aerials associated with this device were probably
installed along the bottom of the rear fuselage.

October 1944–
Dina II installed in the units aircraft. This device used

Climb: 37 mins to 20,000 ft (6096 m)
Service ceiling: 35,600 ft (10,850 m)
Empty
weight: 36,135 lbs (16,391 kg)
Maximum
weight: 72,000 lbs (32,660 kg)
Wing span: 103 ft 9¼ in (31.62 m)
Length: 74 ft 9 in (22.78 m)
Height: 19 ft 1 in (5.82 m)
Wing area: 1,420 sq ft (131.92 m²)
Defensive   Twelve 0.5 in Browning machine
armament: guns. (Two each in chin, dorsal,
                        ventral and tail turrets. One each in
                        the cheek and beam positions.)
Bomb load: 17,600 lbs (7,983 kg)

Boulton Paul Defiant

Role: Jamming and training aircraft.
User units: Defiant Flight: Defiant II – April to
                        October 1942.
                        515 (SD) Squadron: Defiant II –
                        October 1942 to December 1943.
                        1692 Flight: Defiant ? – June 1943 to
                        ?

Special equipment:
DEFIANT FLIGHT: Aircraft of the unit were
equipped with *Moonshine* and, later, Mandrel. Exactly
how this equipment was installed in the Defiant and
whether armament was carried in jamming aircraft is
not known.
515(SD) SQUADRON: Aircraft of the unit were
equipped with *Mandrel*. Again, the exact nature of the
electronic installation in the squadron's aircraft is
unknown.
1692 FLIGHT: Aircraft of the unit were equipped
with a transmitter producing signals in the 420 and 490
MHz band to provide a 'target' for trainee *Serrate*
operators.

Specifications:
Defiant II:
Power plant: One 1,260 hp Merlin XX liquid-
                        cooled engine.
Maximum   315 mph (504 km/hr) at 16,500 ft
speed: (5,077 m)
Range: 465 mls (748 km)
Service ceiling: 30,500 ft (9,250 m)
Empty weight: 6,078 lbs (2,757 kg)
Loaded weight: 8,600 lbs (3,900 kg)
Wing span: 39 ft 4 in (11.99 m)
Length: 35 ft 4 in (10.77 m)
Height: 12 ft 2 in (3.71 m)
Wing area: 250 sq ft (23.23 m²)
Offensive   Four .303 in Browning machine guns
armament: mounted in a Boulton Paul power-
                        operated turret.
Crew: Pilot and gunner.

Bristol Beaufighter

Role: Fighter, jamming and training
                        aircraft.

User units: 141(F/SD) Squadron: Beaufighter
                        VIf – June 1943 to January 1944.
                        515(SD) Squadron: Beaufighter II –
                        June 1943 to January 1944.
                        1692 Flight: Beaufighter ? – June
                        1943 to ? (See page   .)
Variants: Beaufighter II: 1,280 hp Merlin XX
                        liquid-cooled engines.
                        Beaufighter VIf: 1,670 hp Hercules VI
                        or XVI air-cooled radial engines.

Special equipment:
141(F/SD) SQUADRON: Aircraft of the unit were
equipped with AI Mk IV radar and the *Serrate* homing
device.
515(SD) SQUADRON: Aircraft of the unit were
equipped with *Carpet*, *Mandrel* and *Moonshine* jammers.
The exact nature of the installations is unknown.
1692 FLIGHT: Aircraft of the unit were equipped
with 1.5 cm and, from November 1943, 3.6 cm
transmitters to act as 'targets' for trainee *Serrate*
operators.

Remarks: 515's Beaufighters were only
                        operational with *Mandrel*. In July
                        1943, work was begun on installing
                        Carpet and *Moonshine* but had not
                        been completed by the time the
                        squadron abandoned its jamming role
                        on joining 100(SD) Group.
Specifications:
Beaufighter II:
Power plant: Two 1,280 hp Merlin XX liquid-
                        cooled engines.
Maximum   301 mph (481.6 km/hr) at 20,200 ft
speed: (6,215 m)
Range: 1,040 mls (1,664 km)
Service ceiling: 26,500 ft (8,154 m)
Empty weight: 13,800 lbs (6,273 kg)
Loaded weight: 21,000 lbs (9,546 kg)
Wing span: 57 ft 10 in (17.84 m)
Length: 42 ft 9 in (13.23 m)
Height: 15 ft 10 in (4.92 m)
Wing area: 503 sq ft (51.5 m²)
Offensive   Four 20 mm Hispano cannon
armament: (fuselage nose) and six .303 in
                        Browning machine guns (wings)
Crew: Two.
Beaufighter VIf:
Power plant: Two 1,670 hp Hercules VI or XVI
                        air-cooled radial engines.
Maximum   333 mph (532.8 km/hr) at 15,600 ft
speed: (4,800 m)
Range: 1,480 mls (2,368 km)
Service ceiling: 26,500 ft (8,154 m)
Empty weight: 14,600 lbs (6,636 kg)
Loaded weight: 21,600 lbs (9,818 kg)
Wing span: 57 ft 10 in (17.84 m)
Length: 41 ft 8 in (12.92 m)
Height: 15 ft 10 in (4.92 m)
Wing area: 503 sq ft (51.5 m²)
Offensive
armament: As for the Beaufighter II.
Crew: Two.

Consolidated B-24 Liberator:

Role: Jamming, ELINT, spoofing and training aircraft.

User units: 223(SD) Squadron: Liberator BVI – August 1944 to July 1945.
1669 Flight: Liberator BVI – September 1944 to ?
803rd/36th Bomb Squadron: B-24H and J – June 1944 to May 1945.
857th Bomb Squadron ⎱ B-24H
858th Bomb Squadron ⎰ and J

Variants:

Liberator BVI: British designation for the B-24H and J. In the summer of 1944 a batch of 21 nose-turreted Liberators were transferred from the 8th Air Force to the RAF. Approximately nine of this number, in the serial range TS519 to TS539, were supplied to 223(SD) Squadron. Nine additional B-24s were transferred to the RAF at a later date, 223 also receiving aircraft from this batch. The 30 aircraft supplied were of no less than 14 different sub-variants! The particular squadron is believed to have operated predominantly B-24H aircraft built by Ford with a levening of B-24Js built by Consolidated. These two sub-variants differed mainly in that the 'H' was fitted with an Emerson A-15 nose-turret and enclosed K-6 type beam positions while the 'J' had a Consolidated A-6 nose-turret and open beam positions. (For details of Liberator jamming and ELINT aircraft outside the European theatre, see Appendix Four.)

Special equipment
223(SD) SQUADRON:
August–September 1944:
The *Jostle* jamming gear fitted in the unit's aircraft was modified to the *Big Ben* configuration. This equipment was most probably installed in the forward bomb bay with a transmitting mast on the top of the fuselage aft of the dorsal turret.
September 1944:
The unit's aircraft had their rear bomb bays modified for *Window* carriage. Chutes for dropping the foil were probably fitted to the bomb-bay doors.
October–November 1944:
Big Ben modifications to the unit's *Jostles* were removed. *Carpet* and *Dina II* installed.
1669 FLIGHT: Most probably used unmodified BVI bombers and at least one CVI, the transport derivative with the nose-turret faired over (TS538).
803rd/36th BOMB SQUADRON: See Chapter Four
857th AND 858th BOMB SQUADRONS: These units operated B-24H and J bomber aircraft which carried no special equipment other than navigational aids and engine flame dampers. In many cases, the front turret was faired over.

Remarks: In 100(SD) Group, a B-24 had a crew of ten comprising a pilot, flight engineer, navigator, wireless operator, four gunners (most probably nose, dorsal, ventral and tail turrets; the beam guns do not seem to have been fitted) and two special operators for the jamming gear. In September 1944, 223 dispensed with the nose gunner to give the navigator more room to work. There is evidence to indicate that some of the squadron's aircraft had the guns removed from the nose turret and the turret itself over-painted. The unit's aircraft were fitted with similar navigational and communications gear as 214s B-17s (see page 239) and with exhaust flame dampers.

223 was never happy with the Liberator as their second hand aircraft proved to be extremely difficult to keep serviceable and to have insufficient speed for the operations required of them. Because of this and to provide commolaty with the other *Jostle* squadron 214, 223 began to re-equip with the B-17 in April 1945. The only known RAF–USAAF serial tie-up for 223(SD) Squadron is TT336; a B-24J-65-CF (44-10597). During November 1944, one of 100(SD) Group's Liberator aircraft was fitted with a prototype *ABC* installation.

Specifications:
B-24J/Liberator BVI:

Power plant: Four 1,200 hp Pratt and Whitney R-1830-65 air cooled radial engines.
Maximum speed: 300 mph (483 km/hr) at 28,000 ft (8,534 m)
Range: 2,100 mls (3,380 km)
Climb: 25 mins to 20,000 ft (6096 m)
Service ceiling: 30,000 ft (9,144 m)
Empty weight: 36,500 lbs (16,556 kg)
Normal loaded weight: 56,000 lbs (25,400 kg)
Wing span: 110 ft (33.53 m)
Length: 67 ft 2 in (20.47 m)
Height: 18 ft (5.49 m)
Wing area: 1,048 sq ft (97.36 m²)
Defensive armament: Ten 0.5 in (1.25 cm) Browning machine guns (two each in nose, dorsal, ventral and tail turrets. One each in the beam position).
Offensive armament: 8,800 lbs (3,992 kg) of bombs.

Liberator Interior Key: *A – Emerson or Consolidated nose turret, B – Glazed nose seen on B-24s of the 36th and 857/858th Bombardment squadrons, C – Navigator's position, D – Nose wheel housing, E – Pilot/Flight Engineer's position, F – Dorsal turret, G – Wireless Operator's position. In 223 Squadron's aircraft, two SO's were carried. It may be that they were situated near the Wireless Operator (one possibly doubling in this role) or in the area between the ventral turret well and the rear wing spar (marked Cc), H – Liaison radio gear installed in 36th Squadron aircraft, I –* Carpet III *aerial (223(SD) Squadron), J –* Jostle IV *transmitter (223(SD)Squadron, K –* Mandrel *aerials (36th Squadron – three per wing), L – Wing spars, M –* Piperack *whip aerial (223(SD)Squadron – mounted on each wing tip), N – standard radio array (857/858th Squadrons), O – DF loop housing, P –* Jostle IV *transmission mast (223(SD)Squadron, Q – Ventral turret, R –* Window *dispenser (223(SD)Squadron). The associated chutes were probably mounted either side of the aft bomb bay. Before this area was modified for* Window *carriage, the bundles were most likely manually dispensed from the waist positions, S – SO's position (36th Squadron), T – Beam approach aerial, U –* Carpet II *aerial (36th Squadron), V –* Carpet III *aerial (36th Squadron), W – Beam Gunners' position, X –* Mandrel *aerials (36th Squadron – one under each tail plane), Y –* Jackal *aerials (36th Squadron), Z – Tail turret, Aa –* Monica *aerial (223(SD)Squadron and Bb –* Jostle IV *wire transmission aerial (223(SD)Squadron).*

(1) Liberator BVI TS520, 6G – J of 223(SD) Squadron, Oulton: *Uppersurfaces in a disruptive pattern of Dark Earth (dot hatching) and Dark Green (cross hatching). Undersurfaces, fuselage sides and fins in Smooth Night (diagonal hatching). Type C1 roundels on the fuselage, Type B on the uppersurfaces of the wings. 1942-type fin flashes.* Jostle *and* Monica *aerials in natural metal. Black de-icing boots and spinners. Codes and serials in Dull Red. Eight operations marked up on the port side of the nose in the form of Dull Red lightning flashes. Note the over-painted and unarmed nose turret. The external finish of this aircraft was very worn.*

(2) Liberator BVI serial unknown, 6G – M of 223(SD) Squadron, Oulton: *Smooth Night overall. Type C1 roundels on the fuselage, Type B on the uppersurfaces of the wings. 1942-type fin flashes.* Jostle *and* Monica *aerials in natural metal. Black de-icing boots and spinners. Codes in Dull Red. Note the over-painted and unarmed front turret. The external finish of this aircraft was very worn.*

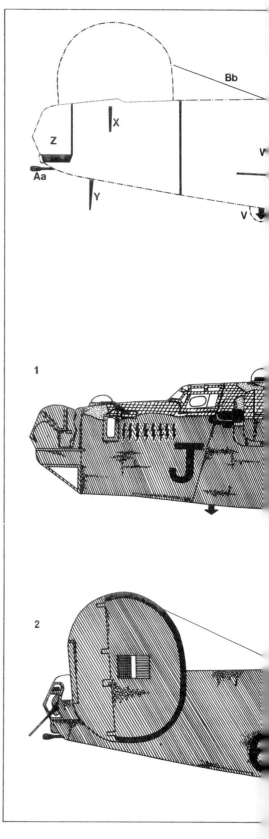

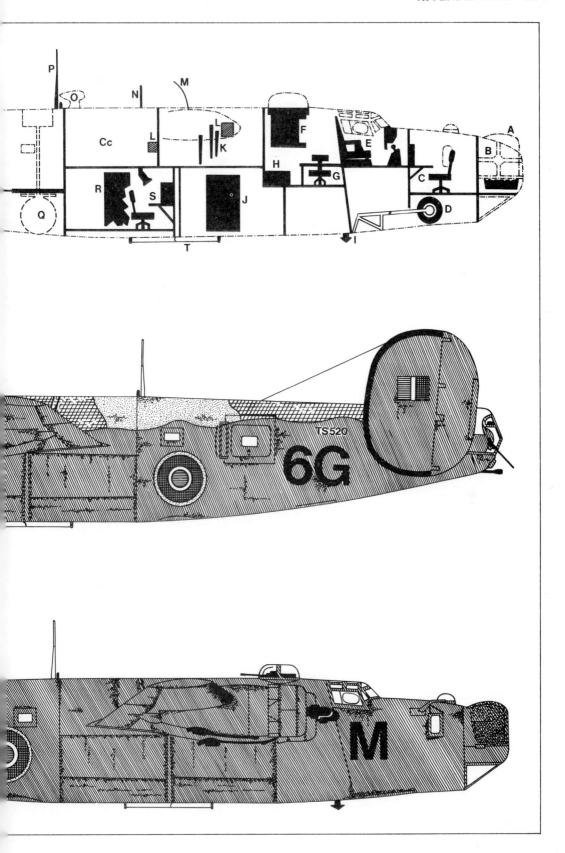

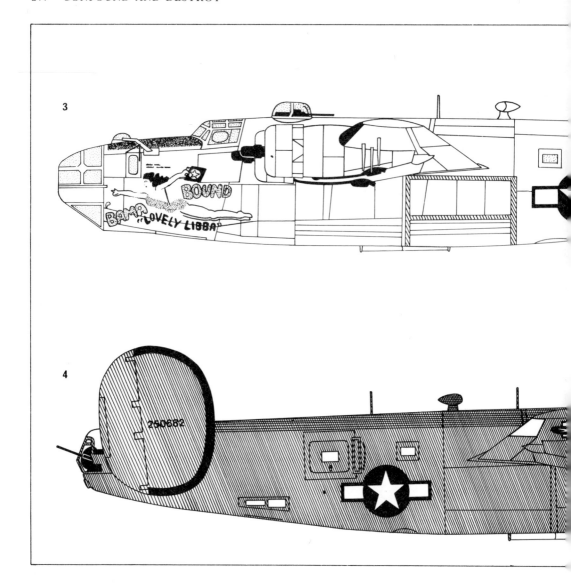

(3) B-24J-1-FO 42-50622, R 4 – N of the 36th Bombardment Squadron (H), Cheddington: *Natural metal overall. Olive Drab anti-glare panel forward of the cockpit. 1943-type national insignia on the fuselage sides, above the port wing and below the starboard. Codes and serials in black. Joints on the aft bomb-bay sealed with off-white filler. Black de-icing boots and spinners. Personal insignia on the port fuselage nose only. Hair – black, flesh areas – natural metal with black detail, flag – blue with blue outline star, swim suit – red, 'Bama Bound' – red with blue outline and 'Lovely Libba' – black.*

(4) B-24J-1-FO 42-50682, P of the 857th Bombardment Squadron (H), Harrington: *Fuselage spine in Olive Drab (cross hatching). All other surfaces in Jet 622 Black (diagonal hatching). 1943-type national insignia on the fuselage sides, above the port wing and below the starboard. Codes, serials and mission markings in red. Black de-icing boots and spinners. Ailerons and central engine cooling flaps in natural metal. Note the over-painted nose windows and the fact that Jet 622 was a gloss finish.*

DE HAVILLAND MOSQUITO

Role: Fighter, ELINT, jamming and training aircraft.

User units: 23(SD) Squadron: Mosquito FBVI – May 1943 to September 1945.
25(F) Squadron: Mosquito NFII and FBVI – October 1942 to February 1945.
85(SD) Squadron: Mosquito NFXII, XVII and 30 – March 1943 to 1947.
141(SD) Squadron: Mosquito NFII and 30 and FBVI – November 1943 to September 1945.
151(F) Squadron: Mosquito NF30 and FBVI – ? to October 1946.
157(SD) Squadron: Mosquito NFXIX and 30 – May 1944 to August 1945.
169(SD) Squadron: Mosquito NFII

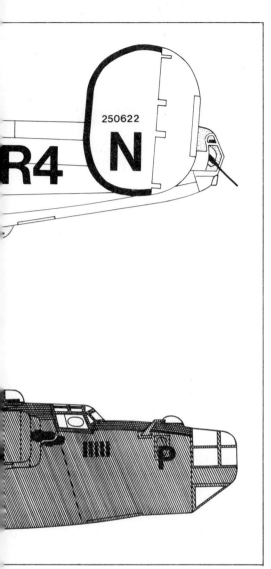

250622

R4 N

P

and XIX and FBVI – October 1943 to August 1945.

192(SD) Squadron: Mosquito BIV and XVI, NFII and PRI – November 1943 to ?

239(SD) Squadron: Mosquito NFII and 30 and FBVI – December 1943 to July 1945.

264(F) Squadron: Mosquito NFXII and FBVI – August 1943 to August 1945.

307(F) Squadron: Mosquito NF30 – July 1944 to 1945.

406(F) Squadron: Mosquito NF30 – July 1944 to September 1945.

410(F) Squadron: Mosquito NFII and FBVI – October 1942 to September 1943.

456(F) Squadron: Mosquito NF30 –

December 1944 to June 1945.

515(SD) Squadron: Mosquito NFII and FBVI – February 1944 to June 1945.

605(F) Squadron: Mosquito NFII and FBVI – February 1943 to November 1944.

1692 Flight: Mosquito NFXIX, FBVI and TIII – ?

BSDU: Mosquito ? – ?

Variants:

Mosquito BIV: Day and night bomber powered by Merlin 21 or 23 engines. 2,000 lb (909 kg) bomb load. Wing mounted drop tanks could be carried.

Mosquito BXVI: Bomber powered by Merlin 72/73 or 76/77 (handed) engines. Pressure cabin. 4,000 lb (1,818 kg) bomb load. Wing mounted drop tanks could be carried.

Mosquito FBVI: Fighter bomber powered by Merlin 21, 22, 23, or 25 engines. Four by .303 machine guns and four by 20 mm cannon. 1,500 lb (682 kg) bomb load. Wing mounted drop tanks could be carried.

Mosquito NFII: Night fighter powered by Merlin 21, 22 or 23 engines. Four by .303 machine guns and four by 20 mm cannon. AI Mk IV radar.

Mosquito NFXII: Night fighter. Conversion of NFII air frames to carry AI Mk VIII radar. Armament reduced to four 20 mm cannon. Wing mounted drop tanks could be carried.

Mosquito NFXVII: Night fighter powered by Merlin 21 or 23 engines. AI Mk 10 radar. Four by 20 mm cannon. Wing mounted drop tanks could be carried.

Mosquito NFXIX: Night fighter powered by Merlin 25 engines. AI Mk VIII or Mk 10 radar. Four by 20 mm cannon. Wing mounted drop tanks could be carried.

Mosquito NF 30:   Night fighter powered by Merlin 72 or 76 engines. AI Mk X radar. Four by 20 mm cannon. 500 lb (227 kg) bomb load. Wing mounted drop tanks could be carried.

Mosquito PRI: Photo reconnaissance aircraft powered by Merlin 21 engines.

Mosquito TIII: Dual control trainer powered by Merlin 21, 23 or 25 engines. Unarmed. Wing mounted drop tanks could be carried.

Special equipment:

23(SD) SQUADRON: Towards the end of the war, the squadron's aircraft were fitted with AI Mk XV radar. All aircraft fitted with *Gee*.

25(F) SQUADRON: This squadron operated 25 NFIIs especially converted for the intruder role. The radar was removed and additional fuel tanks were fitted.

85(SD) SQUADRON: In addition to the AI Mk X, 85's aircraft were variously fitted with *Gee, Monica III, IV* and *VIII, Perfectos,* Type F or Z infra-red IFF gear and SCR 274 long range MF radio receivers.

141(SD) SQUADRON: Aircraft of the unit were fitted with AI Mk IV (NF II and FB VI), AI Mk X (NF 30) and AI Mk XV (FB VI). Its NF IIs and FB VIs were

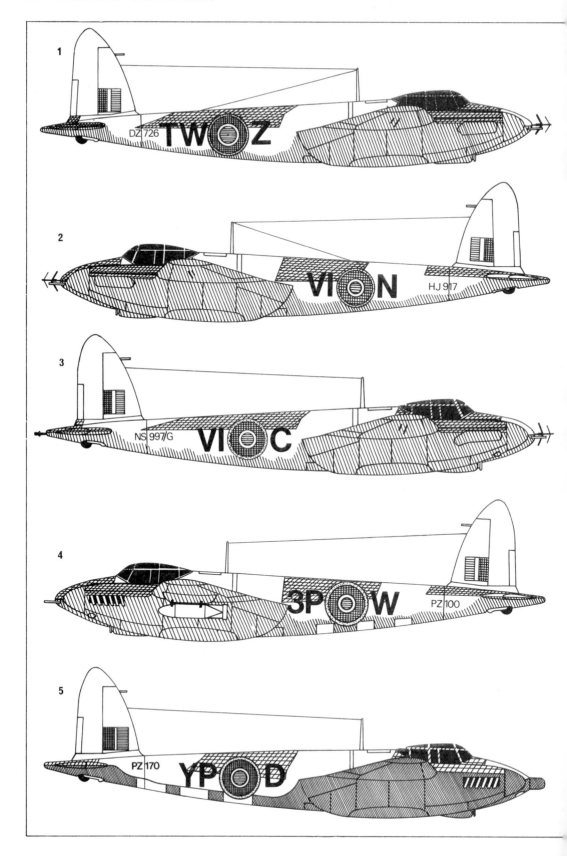

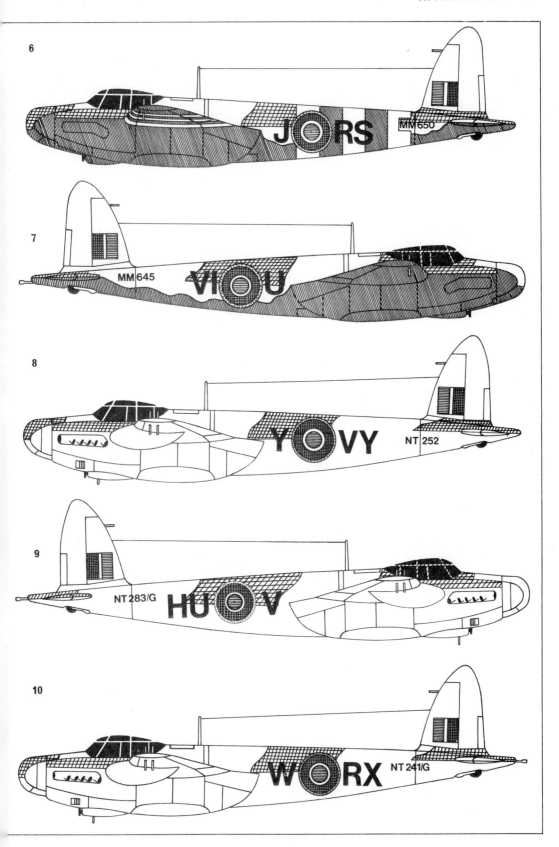

(1) Mosquito NFII DZ726, TW-Z of 141(SD) Squadron, West Raynham: *Uppersurfaces in Medium Sea Grey (white areas) with a disruptive pattern of Dark Green (cross hatching). Undersurfaces in Smooth Night (diagonal hatching). Type C1 roundels on the fuselage, Type B on the uppersurfaces of the wings. 1942-type fin flashes. Dull Red codes, black serials. Supports for the AI Mk IV aerials black, dipoles in natural metal.*

(2) Mosquito NFII HJ917, VI-N of 169(SD) Squadron, Little Snoring: *Uppersurfaces in Medium Sea Grey with a disruptive pattern of Dark Green. Undersurfaces in Smooth Night. Type C1 roundels on the fuselage, Type B on the uppersurfaces of the wings. 1942-type fin flashes. Dull Red codes, black serials. AI Mk IV aerials as for 1.*

(3) Mosquito FBVI NS997/G, VI-C of 169(SD) Squadron, Great Massingham: *Uppersurfaces in Medium Sea Grey with a disruptive pattern of Dark Green. Undersurfaces in Smooth Night. Type C1 roundels on the fuselage, Type B on the uppersurfaces of the wings. 1942-type fin flashes. Dull Red codes, black serials. AI Mk IV aerials as for 1. Monica aerial in natural metal. This aircraft was unusual in that it was fitted with exhaust shrouds.*

(4) Mosquito FBVI PZ100, 3P-W of 515(SD) Squadron, Little Snoring: *Uppersurfaces in Medium Sea Grey with a disruptive pattern of Dark Green. Undersurfaces in Smooth Night with 'invasion stripes' applied to the lower fuselage. Type C1 roundels on the fuselage, Type B on the uppersurfaces of the wings. 1942-type fin flashes. Dull Red codes, black serials.*

(5) Mosquito FBVI PZ170, YP-D of 23(SD) Squadron, Little Snoring: *Uppersurfaces in Medium Sea Grey with a disruptive pattern of Dark Green. Undersurfaces in Smooth Night with 'invasion stripes' applied to the lower fuselage. Note the different widths and position of the stripes compared to 4. Type C1 roudels on the fuselage, Type B on the uppersurfaces of the wings. 1942-type fin flashes. Dull Red codes, black serials. Aircraft letter 'P' repeated on a white circle under the nose. This aircraft was equipped with AI Mk XV radar.*

(6) Mosquito NFXIX MM650, RS-J of 157 (SD) Squadron, Swannington: *Uppersurfaces in Medium Sea Grey with a disruptive pattern of Dark Green. Undersurfaces in Smooth Night. Full 'invasion stripes' on the wings and fuselage. Type C1 roundels on the fuselage, Type B on the uppersurfaces of the wings. 1942-type fin flashes. Dull Red codes, black serials. Wing aerials in natural metal.*

(7) Mosquito NFXIX MM645, VI-U of 169(SD) Squadron, Great Massingham: *Uppersurfaces in Medium Sea Grey with a disruptive pattern of Dark Green. Undersurfaces in Smooth Night. Type C1 roundels on the fuselage, Type B on the uppersurfaces on the wings. 1942-type fin flashes. Dull Red codes, black serials. Wing aerials as for 6.*

(8) Mosquito NF 30 NT252, VY-Y of 85(SD) Squadron, Swannington: *Medium Sea Grey overall with a disruptive pattern of Dark Green on the uppersurfaces. Type C1 roundels on the fuselage, Type B on the uppersurfaces of the wings. 1942-type fin flashes. Dull Red codes, black serials. Wing and fuselage aerials in natural metal. This aircraft probably carried a Monica aerial (natural metal).*

(9) Mosquito NF30 NT283/G, HU-V of 406 Squadron, Manston: *Medium Sea Grey overall with a disruptive pattern of Dark Green on the uppersurfaces. Type C1 roundels on the fuselage, Type B on the uppersurfaces of the wings. 1942-type fin flashes. Dull Red codes, black serials. Wing, fuselage and Monica aerials as for 8.*

(10) Mosquito NF30 NT241/G, RX-W of 456 Squadron, Bradwell Bay: *Medium Sea Grey overall with a disruptive pattern of Dark Green on the uppersurfaces. Type C1 roundels on the fuselage, Type B on the uppersurfaces of the wings. 1942-type fin flashes. Dull Red codes, black serials. Wing, fuselage and Monica aerials as for 8.*

fitted with *Serrate* and all aircraft were equipped wit *Gee.*

151(F) SQUADRON: Aircraft of the unit were fitte with *Monica.*

157(SD) SQUADRON: Aircraft of the unit were fitte with *Gee* and *Monica.*

169(SD) SQUADRON   Aircraft of the unit were fitte with AI Mk IV (NF II and FB VI) and AI Mk X (N XIX). Its NF IIs and FB VIs were fitted with *Serrat* and from November 1944, *Perfectos* was installed i the FB VIs and presumably the XIXs. All aircraft wer equipped with *Gee.*

192(SD) SQUADRON: The unit's aircraft were fitte with various receivers (see Handley Page Halifax page 249, for details of the associated aerials), *Bagf* and *Blonde* recorders, *Gee* and *Piperack* jammers.

239(SD) SQUADRON: Aircraft of the unit were fitte with AI Mk IV (NF II and FB VI) and AI Mk X (N 30). Its NF IIs and FB VIs were fitted with *Serrat* and all aircraft were equipped with *Gee.*

264(F) SQUADRON: Aircraft of the unit (FB IV were possibly fitted with AI Mk IV.

406(F) SQUADRON: Aircraft of the unit were fitte with *Monica.*

515(SD) SQUADRON: Towards the end of the wa the squadron's aircraft were fitted with AI Mk X radar. All aircraft fitted with *Gee.*

BSDU: The unit's Mosquito flight was variousl equipped with *Monica IIIE, Serrate IV, Perfectos* and AI Mk XV.

Remarks: In the case of those squadrons belonging to 100(SD) Group, the foregoing must be regarded as general, as the installation of equipment was an ongoing process within the particular organisation. All AI Mk X and Mk XV equipped aircraft of the Group involved in high level patrols would in all probability be equipped with *Monica.*

Specifications:

Mosquito BXVI:

Power plant:	Two 1,680 hp Merlin 72/73 liquid cooled engines.
Maximum speed:	408 mph (656 km/hr) at 26,000 ft (7,925 m)
Cruising speed:	245 mph (394 km/hr)
Range:	1,485 mls (2,389 km)
Service ceiling:	37,000 ft (11,278 m)
Empty weight:	14,635 lb (6,638 kg)
Loaded weight:	23,000 lb (10,433 kg)
Wing span:	54 ft 2 in (16.51 m)
Length:	44 ft 6 in (13.56 m)
Height:	12 ft 6 in (3.81 m)
Wing area:	452 sq ft (42.18 m²)
Offensive armament:	Up to 4,000 lb (1,814 kg) of bombs (carried as a single store).
Crew:	Pilot and navigator/bomb-aimer.

Mosquito FBVI:

Power plant:	Two 1,460 hp Merlin 21 or 23 liquid cooled engines.
Maximum speed:	380 mph (611 km/hr) at 13,000 ft (3,962 m)

Cruising
speed: 255 mph (410 km/hr)
Range: 1,885 mls (2,985 m)
Service ceiling: 33,000 ft (10,085 m)
Empty weight: 14,344 lb (6,506 kg)
Loaded weight: 22,258 lb (10,096 kg)
Wing span: 54 ft 2 in (16.51 m)
Length: 40 ft 6 in (12.34 m)
Height: 12 ft 6 in (3.81 m)
Wing area: 452 sq ft (42.18 m²)
Offensive   Four .303 in Browning machine guns
armament: and four 20 mm Hispano cannons.
                Four 250 lb (113 kg) or 500 lb
                (227 kg) bombs.
Crew: Pilot and navigator.

Mosquito NF XIX:

Power plant: Two 1,635 hp Merlin 25 liquid
                cooled engines.
Maximum   378 mph (608 km/hr) at 13,200 ft
speed: (4,023 m)
Cruising
speed: 295 mph (476 km/hr)
Service ceiling: 28,000 ft (8,534 m)
Empty weight: 15,550 lb (7,052 kg)
Maximum
weight: 21,750 lb (9,866 kg)
Wing span: 54 ft 2 in (16.51 m)
Length: 41 ft 2 in (12.55 m)
Height: 15 ft 3 in (4.65 m)
Wing area: 454 sq ft (42.18 m²)
Offensive
armament: Four 20 mm Hispano cannon.
Crew: Pilot and radar operator.

HANDLEY PAGE HALIFAX

Role: Jamming and ELINT aircraft.
User units: 171(SD) Squadron: Halifax BIII –
                October 1944 to July 1945.
                192(SD) Squadron: Halifax BII, III
                and V – January 1943 to August 1945.
                199(SD) Squadron: Halifax BIII –
                February to July 1945.
                462(SD) Squadron: Halifax BIII –
                March to September 1945.

Variants:

Halifax BII:
Series I: Four by 1,390 hp Merlin XXS or XXII
liquid-cooled engines. Nose, dorsal, and tail turrets.
Series I (Special): Nose and dorsal turrets removed.
Nose faired over. Exhaust flame dampers removed.
Series IA: Merlin XII engines. Perspex clear nose
cone. Boulton Paul four-gun dorsal turret. Late
production IAs had rectangular tail fins.
Halifax BIII: Four by 1,615 hp Hercules XVI air-
cooled radial engines. Perspex clear nose cone four-
gun dorsal and tail turrets. Late production BIIIs had
a wing span of 104 ft 2 in (34.72 m).
Halifax BV: As the BII but fitted with a Dowty
undercarriage in place of the Messier units.
Special equipment:
171(SD) SQUADRON: Aircraft of the unit were
equipped with *Mandrel* jammers and *Window*
dispensers. There is some evidence to indicate that
six *Mandrels* were fitted per aircraft with the

associated transmitting aerials mounted below the
fuselage aft of the bomb bay. A *Window* chute was
also mounted below the rear fuselage. No *H2S*
radome.
192(SD) SQUADRON: Aircraft of the unit were fitted
with a variety of receivers, and *Bagful* and *Blonde*
recording devices. The following types of aerials were
associated with the reception equipment:
¼ wave vertically polarised general search dipole.
½ wave horizontally polarised general search dipole.
½ wave vertically and horizontally polarised general
search dipoles mounted on the port and starboard
sides of the airframe respectively ¼ wave wide band
cone covering the 1,000 to 5,000 MHz band for general
search purposes.
A wide band capped cone covering the 200 to 1,000
MHz band.
199(SD) SQUADRON: Aircraft of the unit were
equipped with *Mandrel* jammers and *Window*
dispensers. The disposition of the *Mandrel* equipment was similar to that of the squadron's Stirling
(see page 253).
462(SD) SQUADRON: Aircraft of the unit were fitted
with *Airborne Cigar*. The three transmission aerials
associated with the device were mounted above the
fuselage (two) and below the nose cone.

Remarks: The Halifax normally carried a crew
                of seven comprising a pilot, navigator,
                wireless operator, flight engineer,
                bomb aimer and two gunners (tail
                and dorsal turrets). In 100(SD)
                Group, this number would be
                augmented by a special operator for
                the jamming gear. In addition to the
                equipment already detailed, jamming
                Halifax's were fitted with *Gee*,
                Monica and, where possible, *H2S*.
                Latterly, 171 and 199 carried bomb
                loads in addition to the jamming
                gear, while 462 did so throughout its
                bomber support service. Because of
                its capacious fuselage and ready
                availability, 100(SD) Group planned
                to standardise on the Halifax as
                equipment for its jamming squadrons.
                The end of the European war came
                before this could be done. The BSDU
                completed a prototype jamming
                Halifax in November 1944. This
                aircraft was fitted with three
                Airborne Cigars, three *Carpet IIs*,
                three *Carpet IIIs*, one ARP-4, one
                TR1143A and one *Monica IIIc*.
                During the following month, a trial
                installation of 'Loran' was made in a
                Halifax at Foulsham. In April 1945,
                a *Grocer* Halifax was completed
                which carried four *Airborne Grocers*,
                three *Carpet IIs*, two *Carpet IIIs*,
                one *Carpet IV*, one ARP-4 and
                one TR1143A.

Specifications:
Halifax BIII:
Power plant: Four by 1,615 hp Bristol Hercules
                XVI air-cooled radial engines.

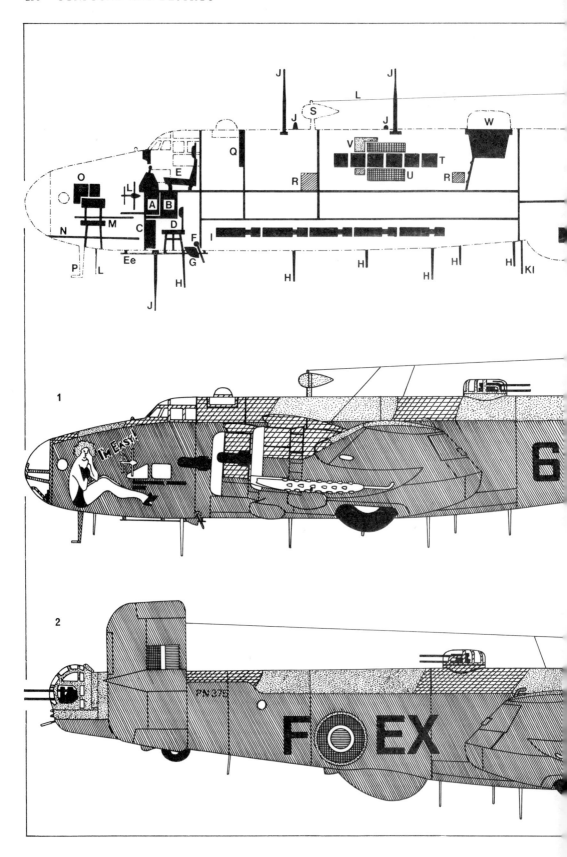

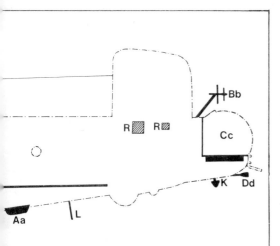

Halifax Interior Key: *A – H/F radio fit, B – L/F radio fit, C – Radio equipment, D – Radio operator's position, E – Pilot's (port) and Flight engineer's (starboard) positions, F – Trailing aerial, G – Forward* Window *chute (171(SD)/199(SD) Squadrons), H –* Mandrel *aerials (171(SD)/199(SD) Squadrons), I – Bomb bay (bomb loads carried by 171(SD)/199(SD)/462(SD) Squadrons), J –* ABC *transmission aerials (462(SD) Squadron), K – Capped cone receiving aerial (192(SD) Squadron), K1 – Receiving aerial (192(SD) Squadron), L – Standard radio fit aerials, M – Navigator's position, N – Bomb aimer's position, O – Possible location of H2S and* Gee *indicators, P – Pitot tube, Q – Flight engineer's panel, R – Wing and tail spars, U –* ABC *equipment, T –* Mandrel *equipment, V – ELINT equipment (U, T and V all racked along the port side of the fuselage. SOs stationed alongside their respective equipment.), W – Dorsal turret, X – H2S scanner, Y – Possible* Window *dispenser location (171(SD)/199(SD) Squadrons), Z – Aft* Window *chute (171(SD)/199(SD) Squadrons), Aa –* Window *chute (192(SD) Squadron), Bb –* Boozer *aerial, Cc –* Tail turret, *Dd –* Monica *aerial and Ee – Beam approach aerial.*

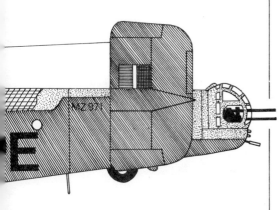

(1) Halifax BIII MZ971, 6Y – E of 171(SD) Squadron, North Creake: *Uppersurfaces in a disruptive pattern of Dark Earth (dot hatching) and Dark Green (cross hatching). Undersurfaces, fuselage sides and fins in Smooth Night (diagonal hatching). Type C1 roundels on the fuselage, Type B on the uppersurfaces of the wings. 1942-fin flashes.* Mandrel *aerials in natural metal. Bronze collector rings and exhausts. Black spinners. Codes and serials in Dull Red. Personal insignia on the port side of the nose only. Swim suit – green, face/arms/legs – flesh with black detail, hair – yellow ochre, shoes – white and 'I'm Easy' – white.*

(2) Halifax BIII PN375, EX – F of 199(SD) Squadron, North Creake: *Uppersurfaces in a disruptive pattern of Dark Earth and Dark green. Undersurfaces, fuselage sides and fins in Smooth Night. Type C1 roundels on the fuselage, Type B on the uppersurfaces of the wings. 1942-type fin flashes.* Mandrel *aerials in natural metal. Bronze collector rings and exhausts. Black spinners. Codes and serials in Dull Red.*

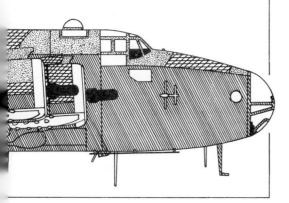

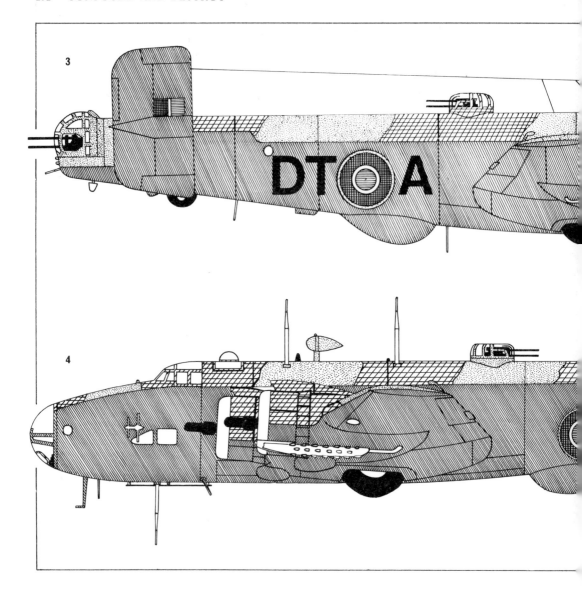

(3) Halifax BIII serial unknown, DT – A of 192(SD)
Squadron, Foulsham: *Uppersurfaces in a disruptive pattern
of Dark Earth and Dark Green. Undersurfaces, fuselage sides
and fins in Smooth Night. Type C1 roundels on the fuselage,
Type B on the uppersurfaces of the wings. 1942 – type fin flashes.
Bronze collector rings and exhausts. Black spinners. Codes and
serials in Dull Red. This aircraft carried an unidentifiable
personal insignia on the port side of the fuselage nose.*

*process of having its squadron markings applied. Almost
without exception, the squadron's aircraft photographed post-
war in various 'graveyards' carry the tail stripes.*

(4) Halifax BIII PN451/G of 462(SD) Squadron,
Foulsham: *Uppersurfaces in a disruptive pattern of Dark
Earth and Dark Green. Undersurfaces, fuselage sides and fins in
Smooth Night. Type C1 roundels on the fuselage, Type B on the
uppersurfaces of the wings. 1942 – type fin flashes. ABC aerials
in natural metal. Bronze collector rings and exhausts. Black
Spinners. Serials in Dull Red. Yellow stripes on the fins. There
is evidence that 462 Squadron retained its 4 Group tail markings
when it joined 100 Group. PN451/G was a new aircraft when it
was photographed (see page 105) and was obviously in the*

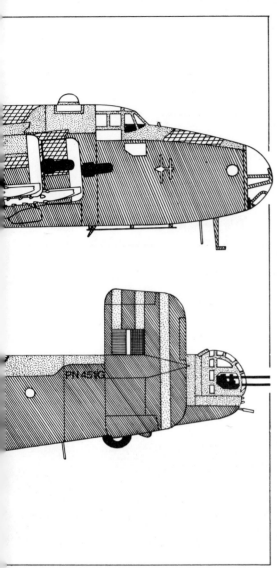

Short Stirling

Role: Jamming aircraft.
User units: 171(SD) Squadron: Stirling BIII –
                September to November 1944.
                199(SD) Squadron: Stirling BIII –
                May 1944 to March 1945.
Special equipment:
171(SD) SQUADRON: Aircraft of the unit were equipped with *Mandrel* jammers. The installation was the same as that used by 199.
199(SD) SQUADRON: Aircraft of the unit were equipped with *Mandrel* jammers. Each Stirling was fitted with three *Mandrel Is*, one *American Mandrel* and four *Mandrel IIIs*. The allocation of pre-set frequencies for *Mandrel I* and *American Mandrel* was such that two aircraft could cover the 68 to 148 MHz band without a gap in coverage. This was accomplished by staggering the frequencies allocated to each pair of aircraft constituting a jamming centre (see page 54). The actual allocation of transmitters was as follows:

Each 'A' Flight aircraft – One T1661P (68 to 75 MHz), one T1408A (88 to 98 MHz), one T1408C (108 to 118 MHz), one T1408E (128 to 138 MHz) and four TR1657Gs [?] (148 to 203 MHz).
Each 'B' Flight aircraft – One T1661P (78 to 88 MHz), one T1408B (98 to 108 MHz), one T1408D (118 to 128 MHz), one T1408F (138 to 142 MHz) and four TR1657Gs [?] (148 to 208 MHz). [Obviously, a jamming centre comprised one 'A' and 'B' Flight aircraft].
Each aircraft had three Type 90 aerials (*Mandrel III*) and five VHF (matched to the individual frequency of the particular *Mandrel I* or *American Mandrel*) mounted along the bottom of the fuselage. A U-type alternator on each outboard motor provided the power for the jammers. The eight sets were racked along the starboard side of the fuselage approximately amidships. A table and seat were provided for the special operator.

In January 1945 a TR1657A (29 to 39.5 MHz) was added to the installation. In service, the TR1657 proved to have difficulty discriminating between German and British signals. This was overcome by applying the output from the unit to the *Gee* indicator so that the navigator could identify which was which. He would then pass this information to the special operator. In practice, this proved difficult and so, from September 1944, the special operator was provided with his own *Gee* indicator mounted with the *Mandrel* units.

Remarks: In 100(SD) Group service, the
                Stirling carried a crew of eight
                comprising a pilot, flight engineer,
                wireless operator, navigator, three
                gunners (nose, dorsal and tail
                turrets) and a special operator. The
                Gee navigational aid was of vital
                importance as precise station keeping
                was the corner-stone of *Mandrel*
                operations.

Specifications:
Stirling BIII:
Power plant: Four by 1,650 hp Bristol Hercules
                XVI air-cooled radial engines.

Maximum
speed: 282 mph (454 km/hr) at 13,500 ft
                (4,115 m)
Cruising
speed: 215 mph (346 km/hr)
Range: 1,985 mls (3,194 km)
Climb: 37.5 mins to 20,000 ft (6,096 m)
Service ceiling: 24,000 ft (7,315 m)
Empty weight: 38,240 lbs (17,346 kg)
Maximum
weight: 65,000 lbs (29,484 kg)
Wing span: 98 ft 10 in (30.12 m)
Length: 71 ft 7 in (21.82 m)
Height: 20 ft 9 in (6.32 m)
Wing area: 1,250 sq ft (116.13 m²)
Defensive
armament: Nine by .303 in Browning machine
                guns. (One in the nose and four each
                in the dorsal and tail turrets.)
Offensive
armament: 13,000 lbs (5,897 kg) of bombs.

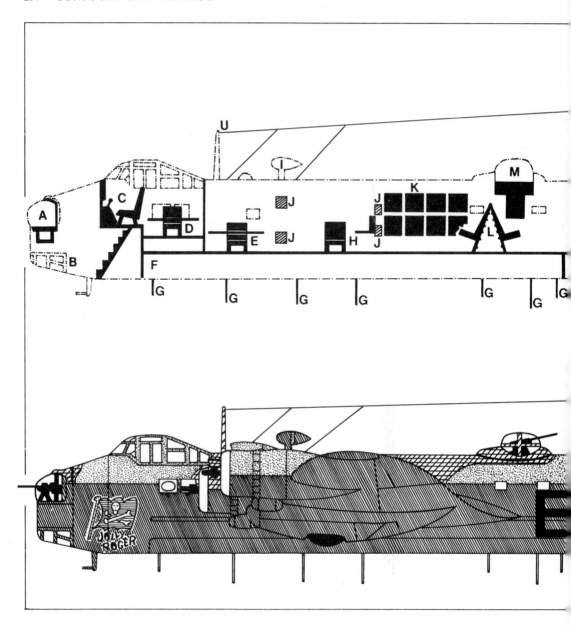

Stirling Interior Key: *A – Nose turret, B – Bomb aimer's position, C – Pilot's position, D – Navigator's position, E – Radio operator's position, F – Bomb bay, G –* Mandrel *aerials, H – Flight engineer's position, I – DF loop housing, J – Wing spars, K –* Mandrel *transmitters etc (racked along the port side of the fuselage) and SO's position, L – Rest seats mounted on the dorsal turret access ladder, M – Dorsal turret, N –* Window *chute, P – Beam approach aerial, Q – Flare chute, R – Standard radio fit aerial (as with U), S – twin tail wheels and T – Tail turret.*

uppersurfaces of the wings. 1942 – type fin flashes. Mandrel *aerials in natural metal. Bronze collector rings and exhausts. Black spinners. Codes and serials in Dull Red, the individual aircraft letter being repeated on the nose in the same colour. Personal insignia on the port side of the nose only. Flag pole – yellow, flag – red, skull and cross bones – white with black detail and '*Jolly Roger*' – yellow.*

Stirling BIII LJ525, EX – R of 199(SD) Squadron, North Creake: *Uppersurfaces in a disruptive pattern of Dark Earth (dot hatching) and Dark Green (cross hatching). Undersurfaces, fuselage sides and fin in Smooth Night (diagonal hatching). Type C1 roundels on the fuselage, Type B on the*

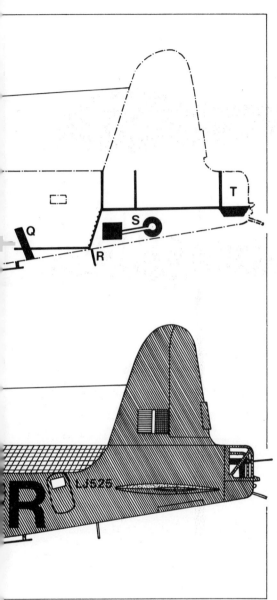

Maximum
speed: 270 mph (434 km/hr) at 14,500 ft
                 4,420 m)
Range: 2,010 mls (3,240 km)
Service ceiling: 17,000 ft (5,181 m)
Empty
weight: 46,900 lbs (21,200 kg)
Maximum
weight: 70,000 lbs (31,790 kg)
Wing span: 99 ft 1 in (30.2 m)
Length: 87 ft 3 in (26.5 m)
Height: 22 ft 9 in (6.93 m)
Wing area: 1,460 sq ft (135.6 m²)
Defensive   Eight .303 in Browning machine
armament: guns (two each in the nose and dorsal
                 turrets and four in the tail turret).
Offensive
armament: 14,000 lbs (6,350 kg) of bombs.

VICKERS WELLINGTON
Role: ELINT and training aircraft.
User units: 192(SD) Squadron: Wellington BX –
                 November 1943 to late 1944.
                 1692 Flight: Wellington TXVIII – ?
Variants:
Wellington BX: Two 1,675 hp Hercules VI or
XVI engines. Strengthened structure for high
operating weights.
Wellington TXVIII: Flying classroom AI trainer.
Special equipment:
192(SD) SQUADRON: Wellingtons of the unit were
fitted out for ELINT duties in a similar manner to the
Halifax aircraft described on page 249.
1692 FLIGHT: Wellingtons of the unit carried AI
Mk X and possibly AI Mk XV radar for training
purposes.
Specifications:
Wellington BX:
Power Plant: Two 1,675 hp Hercules VI or XVI air-
               cooled radial engines.
Maximum   235 mph (378 km/hr) at 15,500 ft
speed: (4,724 m).
Range: 2,550 mls (4,104 km)
Service ceiling: 18,000 ft (5,486 m)
Empty weight: 21,118 lbs (9,579 kg)
Loaded weight: 30,000 lbs (13,080 kg)
Wing span: 86 ft 2 in (26.26 m)
Length: 64 ft 7 in (19.68 m)
Height: 17 ft 5 in (5.31 m)
Wing area: 840 sq ft (78.04 m²)
Defensive   Eight .303 in machine guns (two
armament: in the nose turret, four in the tail
               turret and one each in the beam
               positions).
Offensive
armament: 4,500 lbs (2,041 kg) of bombs.
Crew: Pilot, navigator, wireless operator
               and three gunners.

DORNIER DO17, 215 and 217
Role: Night fighter and training aircraft.
User units: See pages 221 to 228.

Variants
Do17Z-7 *Kauz I* (Screech Owl I): Three-seat
fighter based on the Z-3 bomber airframe and powered
by Bramo 323P engines. Used the nose cone and

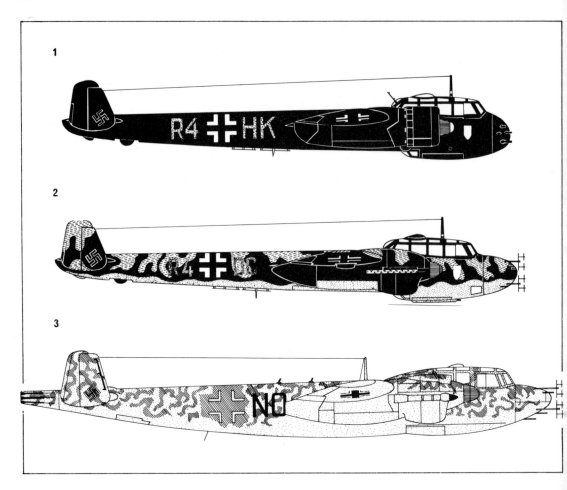

(1) Dornier Do17Z-7 Kauz I R 4-HK of 2/NJG 2: *Black 22 overall. All national markings of the white outline type. Light Grey 77 codes. Spinner in Black Green 70 with white caps. Propellor blacks in Black Green 70.* England Blitz *badge on both sides of the nose. (Black shield outlined in white carrying a white and black diving eagle with a red lightning flash in its claws. The tip of the flash is striking a black map of England set in a blue and black hemisphere of Europe.)*

FuG 202/212 dipoles in blued metal. The code 'NO' was part of the factory registration and not the operational identification markings. This aircraft is particularly interesting in that it was fitted with the rarely seen braking parachute installation.

These three profiles show well the development of Luftwaffe night fighter camouflage from the solid black of 1940/41 to the lighter multi grey scheme of the mid war years.

(2) Dornier Do215B-5 Kauz 3 R4-DC of Stab II/NJG 2: *Black 22 uppersurfaces over-sprayed with a mottle of Light Grey 76 (broken line hatching). Fuselage undersurface and main wheel doors in Light Blue 65 (dot hatching). All national markings of the white outline type. Light Grey 77 codes. Spinners and propellor blades in Black Green 70.* England Blitz *badge on both sides of the nose. Oxidised flame dampers. FuG 202 dipoles in blued metal. This aircraft was flown by Helmut Lent and carried an MG FF cannon in a mounting under the port fuselage nose.*

(3) Donier Do217N-2/R22 of an unidentified unit in the Balkans: *Light Grey 76 overall (dot hatching) with a Mid Grey 75 (diagonal hatching) 'wave mirror' pattern on the upper surfaces. White outline crossed above the wings and on the fuselage (backed by large patches of Mid Grey 75), black/white crosses below the wings and black/white swastikas. Codes in Black 22. Spinners and propellor blades in Black Green 70.*

forward firing armament from the Ju88C-2 (see page 000). One 7.9 mm MG 15 machine gun mounted in the cockpit for rear defence.

Do17Z-10 *Kauz II* (Screech Owl II): Three-seat fighter similar to the Z-7 but with a redesigned nose containing a forward firing armament of four 7.9 mm MG 17 machine guns and two 20 mm MG FF cannon. Defensive armament as before.

Do215B-5 *Kauz 3* (Screech Owl 3): Three-seat night fighter based on B-0, -1 and -4 airframes and powered by DB601A engines. Forward firing and defensive armaments as for the Do17Z-10.

Do217J-1: Four-seat night fighter based on the E-2 airframe and powered by BMW801L engines. Forward firing armament of four MG 17 machine guns and four MG FF cannon. One 13 mm MG 131 in a dorsal turret for rear defence. Provision for an additional fuel tank to be carried in the forward bomb bay.

Do217J-2: As the J-1 with the rear bomb bay blanked off.

Do217N-1: Four-seat night fighter based on the M-1 airframe and powered by DB603A engines. In all other respects similar to the J-2.

Do217N-2: Refined version of the N-1 with the dorsal turret removed and an aerodynamic fairing over the ventral gun position 'step'. MG FF cannon in the forward firing armament replaced by 20 mm MG 151/20 weapons.

Rustsätze:*

Applicable to the Do217N-2:	R 22 Four MG 151/20 cannon in a dorsal *Schräge Musik* installation.

Umrüst:†

Applicable to the Do217N-1:	U1 Removal of the dorsal turret and the application of the aerodynamic fairing to bring the airframe up to N-2 standards. Substitution of MG 151/20's for the MG FF cannon.
	U3 Combination of U1 modification with the MG 151/20 *Schräge Musik* installation to bring the airframe up to N-2/R22 standards.
Period of service:	Z-7: Summer to the winter of 1940.
	Z-10: 1940 to 1943.
	B-5: January 1941 to May 1944.
	J-1: ?
	J-2: ?
	N-1: January 1943 to September 1944.
	N-2: From May 1943.
Radar equipment:	FuG 202: Fitted to the B-5, J-2, N-1, and N-2. Entered service during 1942/43.
	FuG 212: Fitted to the J-2, N-1 and N-2 from the summer of 1943.

---

* Rustsätze		Field conversion set – packs of parts installed by Luftwaffe maintenance units to modify a basic airframe.
† Umrüst (Bausätz).		Factory conversion set – as above but installed on the production line.

	FuG 212C-1: Possibly fitted in combination with SN-2b to the N-2.
	FuG 220SN-2b and c: Possibly fitted to the N-2 from September 1943.
Other equipment:	*Spanner*: Fitted to the Z-10 and B-5.
	FuG 227: Possibly fitted to the N-2. Wing mounted aerials.
	FuG 350: Possibly fitted to the N-2.

Specifications:

Dornier Do217N-2:

Power plant:	Two 1,850 hp DB603A liquid-cooled engines.
Maximum speed:	320 mph (515 km/hr) at 19,685 ft (6,000 m).
Cruising speed:	264 mph (425 km/hr)
Range:	1,088 mls (1,750 km)
Empty weight:	22,665 lb (10,280 kg)
Loaded weight:	29,101 lb (13,200 kg)
Wing span:	62 ft 4 in (19 m)
Length:	62 ft (18.9 m)
Height:	16 ft 4¾ in (5 m)
Wing area:	613.54 sq ft (57 m²)
Offensive armament:	Four 20 mm MG 151/20 cannon and four 7.9 mm MG 17 machine guns mounted in the nose firing forwards.
Crew:	Pilot, observer, navigator and wireless/radar operator.

FOCKE WULF FW190 AND MESSERSCHMITT Bf109:

Role:	Night fighter.
User units:	See pages 221 to 228.

Variants:

Fw190A-5: Single-seat fighter powered by a BMW801D-2 engine. Forward firing armament of two 7.9 mm MG 17 machine guns, two 20 mm MG FF cannon and two 20 mm MG 151/20 cannon.

Fw190A-6: As the A-5 except for the replacement of the MG FF weapons by another pair of MG 151/20s.

Fw190A-8: Powered by a BMW801D-2 engine with MW 50 methanol-water injection. Forward firing armament of two 13 mm MG 131 machine guns and four MG 151/20 cannon.

Bf109E-3: Single-engined fighter powered by a DB601Aa engine. Forward firing armament of two MG 17 machine guns and three MG FF cannon.

Bf109G-5: Powered by a DB605A or AS engine with GM-1 nitrous oxide injection. Forward firing armament of two MG 131 machine guns and a single MG 151/20 cannon.

Bf109G-6: Powered by a DB605A, D or AS engine. Single MG 151/20 replaced by a 30 mm MK 108 cannon.

Bf109G-6/N: Night fighter derivative of the G-6/R6 equipped with the FuG 350 device mounted in a blister behind the cockpit.

Bf109G-10: Powered by a DB605D engine with a refined canopy and engine cowling. Armament as for the G-6. Tall wooden rudder as standard.

Bf109G-14: Powered by a DB605AM or AS engine. Refined canopy. Armament as for the G-6.

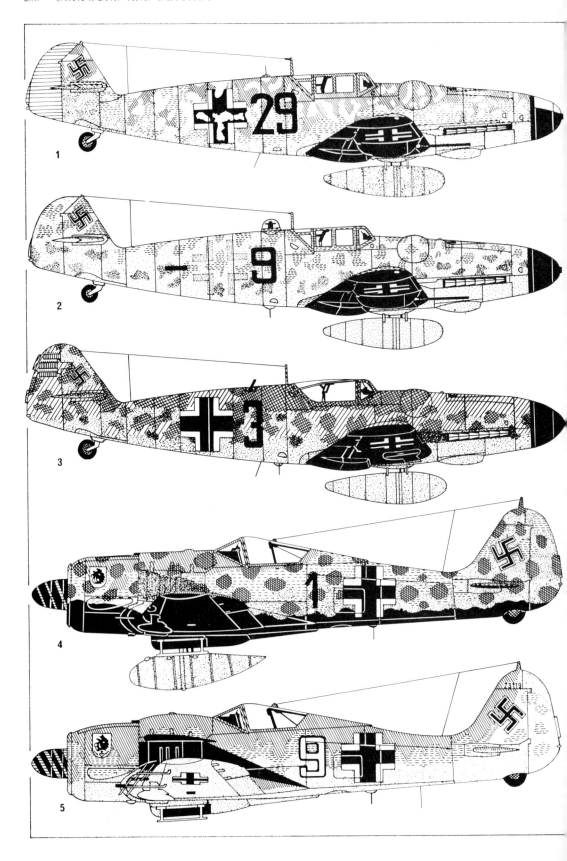

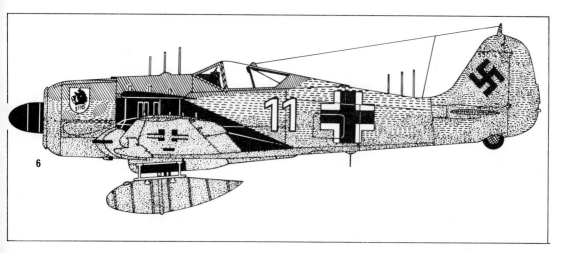

(1) Messerschmitt Bf109G-6/R6 'Red 29' of 2/JG 302: *Dark Grey 74 (diagonal hatching) and Mid Grey 75 (broken line hatching 'splinter' pattern on the fuselage spine and the wing/tailplane uppersurfaces. Fuselage sides and port lower wing in Light Grey 76 (dot hatching). Starboard lower wing and the cannon housing under the port wing in Black 22. Fuselage sides mottled in the two greys 74 and 75. All uppersurfaces over sprayed in a temporary White 21 winter scheme. Rudder in Yellow 04. Code number in Red 23 thinly outlined in Yellow 04. White outline crosses above both wings and below the port one, black/white crosses on the fuselage, black/white/black cross below the starboard wing and black/white swastikas. Spinner in Black Green 70 with a quarter of its area in White 21 (not including the back plate). Propellor blades in Black Green 70.*

(2) Messerschmitt Bf109G-6/N 'Yellow 9' most probably of 1/NJGr 10: *Mid Grey 75 and Light Grey 76 'splinter' pattern on the wing and tailplane uppersurfaces. Fuselage and starboard lower wing in Light Blue 65 (dotk hatching). Port lower wing in Black 22. Fuselage upper-surfaces mottled in the two greys 75 (heavy dot hatching) and 74 (broken line hatching). Codes in Yellow 04 thinly outlined in Black 22. Light Grey 77 outline crosses above the wings and on the fuselage, white outline cross below the port wing, black/white/black cross below the starboard wing and black/white swastikas. Black Green 70 spinner and propellor blades. This aircraft had almost certainly seen service with JG 300 previously.*

(3) Messerschmitt Bf109G-14/U2 'Green 3' of Stab I/NJG 11: *Dark Green 81 (diagonal hatching) and Dark Green 82 (cross hatching) 'splinter' pattern on the fuselage spine and the wing/tailplane uppersurfaces. Fuselage sides and lower starboard wing in Light Grey 76 (dot hatching). Port lower wing in Black 22. Fuselage sides mottled in the two greens 81 and 82 and RLM Grey 02 (heavy dot hatching). Code number in Light Green 25. White outline crosses above the wings and below the port one, black/white crosses on the fuselage, black/white/black cross below the starboard wing and black/white swastikas. Black 22 spinner with Black Green 70 propellor blades. Thirty victory markings carried on each side of the rudder comprising white rectangles cut by a diagonal black band surmounted by an RAF roundel. This aircraft was flown by Karl Friedrich Müller and was unusual in that it carried a MG 151/20 cannon in a fuselage Schräge Musik installation.*

(4) Focke Wulf Fw190A-6 'Black 1' of Stab/JG 300: *Mid Grey 75 and Dark Grey 74 'splinter' scheme on the wing and tailplane uppersurfaces. Fuselage spine in Dark Grey 74 (diagonal hatching) blending into Mid Grey 75 (broken line hatching) and then Light Grey 76 (dot hatching). Undersurfaces in Black 22. Fuselage upper surfaces oversprayed with a Dark Grey 66 (cross hatching) mottle. Code number in Black 22. White outline crosses above the wings, black/white crosses on the fuselage and black/white swastikas. Wilde Sau badge on both sides of the nose. (A yellow shield with a black boar's head with white detail. White tusksk and red mouth and tongue. White teeth and red nostrils.) Spinner in Red 23 with a Yellow 04 spiral. Black Green 70 propellor blades. Heavy staining around the engine exhausts. This aircraft was flown by Hajo Herrmann.*

(5) Focke Wulf Fw190A-8 'White 9' of 1/NJGr 10: *Mid Grey 75 and Dark Grey 74 'Splinter' scheme on the wing and tailplane uppersurfaces. Fuselage spine in Dark Grey 74 (Diagonal hatching) blending into Mid Grey 75 (broken line hatching) and then Light Grey 76 (dot hatching). Undersurfaces in Light Grey 76. Code number in White 21 thinly outline in Black 22. White outline crosses above the wings, black/white crosses below the wings and on the fuselage and black/white swastikas. Wilde Sau badge on both sides of the nose (as 4 except on a white ground). AI dipoles in blued metal. Spinner in Yellow 04 with a Black 22 spiral. Black Green 70 propellor blades. Black 22 angular exhaust masks.*

(6) Focke Wulf Fw190A-5 'White 11' of 1/NJGr 10: *Mid Grey 75 and Dark Grey 74 'splinter' scheme on the wing and tailplane uppersurfaces. Fuselage spine in Dark Grey 74 (diagonal hatching) blending into Mid Grey 75 (broken line hatching) and then Light Grey 76 (dot hatching). Undersurfaces in Light Grey 76. Code number in White 21 thinly outlined in Black 22. White outline crosses above the wings, black/white crosses below the wings and on the fuselage and soild black swastikas. Wilde Sau badge on both sides of the nost (As 5 with the nickname Illo in Blue 24 script below the boar's head). AI dipoles in blued metal. Spinner in Black 22 with Black Green Propellor blades. Werke Nummer 550143 on the fin in small Black 22 characters. Black 22 angular exhaust masks.*

Bf109K-4: Powered by a DB605ASCM engine. Refined canopy and engine cowling, tall wooden rudder, enlarged main wheels and a retractable tail wheel. Armament as for the G-6.

Rüstsätze:	(Note – The Rustsätze applicable to these aircraft were legion. Only those applied to night fighters are described.)
Applicable to the Fw190 A-5, -6 and -8:	R11 FuG 216V, FuG 217J-2 or FuG 218J-3 radar and flame dampers.
Applicable to the Bf109G-6/N:	R6 Two MG 151/20 cannon in gondolas beneath the wings.
Period of service:	Bf109E-3: Late 1940 to August 1943.
	Bf109G-5: From August 1943.
	Bf109G-6: August 1943 to 1945.
	Bf109G-10: August 1944 to 1945.
	Bf109G-14: Late 1944 to 1945.
	Bf109K-4: Late 1944 to 1945.
Radar equipment:	FuG 216V: Fitted to the Fw190A-5, -6 and -8.
	FuG 217J-2: Fitted as above and to some Bf109Gs.
	FuG 218J-3: Fitted to the Fw190A-8 and at least one Bf109G-5.
Other equipment:	FuG 350: Fitted to the Bf109G-6/N.
	Flame dampers: Fitted to both types of aircraft.
	Schräge Musik: Fitted to at least one Bf109 G-14 (single MG 151/20 cannon).

Specifications:

Focke Wulf Fw190A-8:

Power plant:	One 1,700 hp BMW801D-2 radial engine (MW 50 boost).
Maximum speed:	382 mph (615 km/hr) at 19,685 ft (6,000 m)
Cruising speed:	278 mph (447 km/hr)
Range:	497 mls (800 km)
Service ceiling:	34,775 ft (10,600 m)
Empty weight:	7,652 lbs (3,478 kg)
Loaded weight:	10,800 lbs (4,909 kg)
Wing span:	34 ft $5\frac{1}{2}$ in (10.5 m)
Length:	29 ft $4\frac{3}{4}$ in (9.02 m)
Height:	12 ft $11\frac{1}{2}$ in (3.95 m)
Wing area:	196.98 sq ft (18.3 m²)
Offensive armament:	Two 13 mm MG 131 machine guns and four 20 mm MG 151/20 cannon.
Crew:	Pilot.

Messerschmitt Bf109K-4:

Power plant:	One 2,000 hp DB605ASCM liquid-cooled engine (MW 50 and GM-1 boost).
Maximum speed:	452 mph (727 km/hr) at 19,685 ft (6,000 m)
Range:	366 mls (590 km)
Service ceiling:	41,000 ft (12,500 m)
Empty weight:	4,886 lbs (2,380 kg)
Loaded weight:	7,937 lbs (3,600 kg)
Wing span:	32 ft $8\frac{1}{2}$ in (9.97 m)
Length:	29 ft $\frac{1}{2}$ in (8.85 m)
Height:	8 ft $2\frac{1}{2}$ in (2.5 m)
Wing area:	173.3 sq ft (16.1 m²)
Offensive armament:	One 30 mm MK 108 cannon and two 13 mm MG 131 machine guns.
Crew:	Pilot.

HEINKEL He219 *UHU* (OWL)

Role:	Night fighter.
User units:	See pages 221 to 228.

Variants:

He219A-0: Two-seat night fighter powered by DB603A engines. Forward firing armament of six 20 mm. MG 151/20 cannon, (two in the wing roots and four in a ventral tray).

He219A-2: Powered by DB603A engines. Forward firing armament of four cannon of various types and a twin 30 mm MK 108 cannon *Schräge Musik* installation.

He219A-5: Powered by DB603Aa, E or G engines. Forward firing armament of four cannon of various types and a twin MK 108 *Schräge Musik* installation.

He219A-6: Powered by DB603L engines with GM-1 nitrous oxide injection. Forward firing armament of four MG 151/20 cannon. A stripped variant for anti-Mosquito operations.

He219A-7: Powered by DB603G engines. Forward firing armament of six cannon of various types and a twin MK 108 *Schräge Musik* installation.

He219B-2: Powered by DB603Aa or L engines. Long span wings (72 ft $4\frac{1}{2}$ in [22.25 m]). Forward firing armament of two MG 151/20 cannon and a twin MK 108 *Schräge Musik* installation. A stripped variant based on the A-6 airframe for anti-Mosquito duties.

Rustsatze:	
Applicable to the A-0:	R1 Four 30 mm MK 103 cannon in the ventral tray.
	R2 Four MK 108 cannon in the ventral tray.
	R6 Forward firing armament of two MG 151/20 and two MK 108 canno and a twin MK 108 *Schräge Musik* installation.
Applicable to the A-2:	R1 Provision for a single 198 Imp gal (900.1 l) drop tank on a rack beneath the ventral tray. Two MG 151/20 cannon in the tray.
	R2 Two MK 103 cannon in the ventral tray. (Both R1 and R2 sub-variants carried two MG 151/20 cannon in the wing roots.)
Applicable to the A-5:	R1 Two MK 108 cannon in the ventral tray.
	R2 Two MG 151/20 cannon in the ventral tray.
	R3 Two MK 103 cannon in the ventral tray. (R1, R2 and R3 sub-variants carried two MG 151/20 cannon in the wing roots.)
	R4 Three-seat variant with a modified canopy carrying a 13 mm MG 131 machine gun for rear defence. A forward firing armament of four MG 151/20 cannon (two in

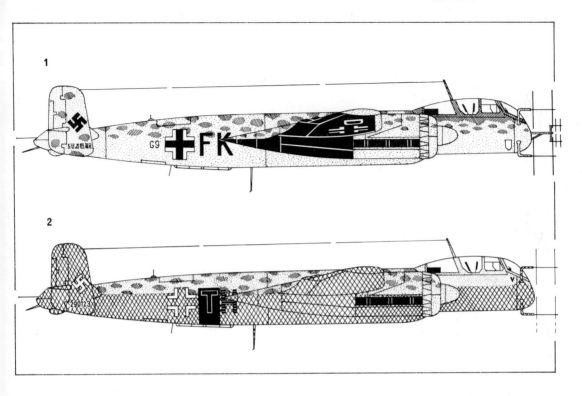

1

2

(1) Heinkel He219A-2 G9-FK of 2/NJG 1: *Light Grey 76 (dot hatching) overall with a Mid Grey 75 (diagonal hatching) mottle over the uppersurfaces. Canopy frames in solid Mid Grey 75. The lower starboard wing was partially oversprayed with Black 22 as shown (including the inboard section with the leading edge in Light Grey 76). This was to aid identification by friendly forces during* Wilde Sau *operations. The White 21 'D' outboard of the national marking on this surface probably served the same purpose. Black outline crosses above the wings, white outline cross below the starboard wing, black/white crosses on the fuselage and below the port wing and solid black swastikas. Codes in Black 22.* England Blitz *badge on both sides of the nose. Black Green 70 propellor blades. Werk Nummer in Black 22 on the fins. Dark exhaust flame dampers. FuG 212/220 dipoles in blued metal.*

(2) Heinkel He219A-2 G9-TH of 1/NJG 1: *Light Grey 76 (dot hatching) overall with a Mid Grey 76 (diagonal hatching) mottle over the uppersurfaces. Canopy frames in solid Light Grey 76. Undersurfaces, fuselage sides and fins (including the inner surfaces except for the rudders) oversprayed in either Dark Grey 74 or Dark Blue 24 (cross hatching). Black outline crosses above the wings, white outline crosses on the fuselage and solid white swastikas. Black 22 'T' thinly outlined in White 21 on a black panel (port and starboard). 'H' in a shade of grey. Werk Number 290123 in small White 21 characters on the fin. 'V' in small Black 22 characters below the windscreen on both sides. Black Green 70 propellor blades. Dark exhaust flame dampers. FuG 220 dipoles in blued metal.*

Applicable to the A-7:

the wing roots and two in the ventral tray).

R1   Two MK 108 cannon in the wing roots and two MK 103 and two MG 151/20 cannon in the ventral tray.

R2   Two MK 103 and two MK 108 cannon in the ventral tray. Wing root armament as above.

R3   Two MG 151/20 cannon in the wing roots and two MK 108 and two MG 151/20 cannon in the ventral tray.

R4   Two MG 151/20 cannon in the wing roots and two similar weapons in the ventral tray.

Radar equipment:

FuG 212C-1:   Fitted to the A-0, A-2 and A-5 in combination with SN-2b from the summer of 1943.
FuG 220 SN-2b, c and d: Fitted to the A-0 ('b'), A-2 ('b', 'c' and 'd'), A-5 ('b', 'c' and 'd') A-6 ('c' and 'd'), A-7 ('c' and 'd') and B-2 ('c' and 'd') from September 1943. When the set's tail warning capacity was used the associated aerial was mounted on the extreme rear of the fuselage.

Other equipment:

FuG 350:   Possibly carried by the A-2, A-5, A-6, A-7 and B-2 variants.

Remarks:

There is evidence to suggest that very few of the post-A-2 variants were produced and that A-2 airframes were progressively modified to later standards while retaining the 'A-2' designation. The *Uhu* was the first operational aircraft to be equipped with ejector seats. Tricycle undercarriage.

Specifications:

Heinkel He219A-5/R2:

Power plant:	Two 1,800 hp DB603Aa, E or G liquid-cooled engines.
Maximum speed:	391 mph (630 km/hr) at sea level.
Cruising speed:	310 mph (500 km/hr)
Range:	1,740 mls (2,800 km)
Service ceiling:	37,073 ft (11,300 m)
Empty weight:	21,826 lb (9,900 kg)
Loaded weight:	28,990 lb (13,150 kg)
Wing span:	60 ft 8$\frac{1}{4}$ in (18.5 m)
Length:	50 ft 11$\frac{3}{4}$ in (15.54 m)
Height:	13 ft 5$\frac{1}{2}$ in (4.10 m)
Wing area:	478.99 sq ft (44.5 m²)
Offensive armament:	Two 20 mm MG 151/20 cannon in the wing roots and two similar weapons in the ventral tray. Two 30 mm MK 108 cannon in a *Schräge Musik* installation.
Crew:	Pilot and wireless/radar operator.

JUNKERS Ju88

Role:	Night fighter and reconnaissance aircraft.
User units:	See pages 221 to 228.

Variants:

Ju88A-4: Four-seat bomber aircraft powered by Jumo 211J engines. 65 ft 7$\frac{1}{2}$ in (20.0 m) wing span. Defensive armament of three 7.9 mm MG 81 and two 13 mm MG 131 machine guns. 7,935 lb (3,600 kg) bomb load.

Ju88C-0: Three-seat heavy fighter based on A-1 airframes (60 ft 3$\frac{1}{4}$ in [18.54 m] wing span). A forward firing armament of three 7.9 mm MG 17 machine guns and one 20 mm MG FF cannon. A single 7.9 mm MG 17 machine gun for rear defence. Jumo 211B engines.

Ju88C-1: As the C-0 but powered by BMW801A engines.

Ju88C-2: Three-seat heavy fighter based on the A-1 airframe (60 ft 3$\frac{1}{4}$ in [18.54 m] wing span). Forward firing armament as for the C-0. Two MG 17 machine guns for rear defence. Jumo 211B engines.

Ju88C-4: Three-seat heavy fighter powered by Jumo 211F or J engines. (Note, all subsequent variants to the C-2 featured the long span wing.) Two additional forward firing MG FF cannon mounted in the ventral gondola.

Ju88C-5: Three-seat heavy fighter powered by BMW801D engines. Ventral gondola replaced by a *Waffentropfen* carrying two MG 17 machine guns. Forward firing MG FF cannon replaced by 20 mm MG 151/20.

Ju88C-6: Three-seat heavy/night fighter powered by Jumo 211J engines. Forward firing armament of three MG 17 machine guns and three MG FF/M cannon. Two MG 17s for rear defence (in late production C-6 aircraft the cockpit canopy was refined and the MG 17s replaced by a single MG 131). Ventral gondola reintroduced.

Ju88R-2: As the C-6 but powered by BMW801D engines.

Ju88G-1: Four-seat night fighter powered by BMW801D engines. Ventral gondola removed and replaced by a ventral tray carrying a forward firing armament of four MG 151/20 cannon. Refined canopy of the late production C-6 with a single MG 131 machine gun for rear defence. Ju188 vertical tail surfaces.

Ju88G-6a: Four-seat night fighter powered by BMW801G engines. Basically an improved G-1 with revised internal equipment.

Ju88G-6b: As the G-6a with some internal rearrangement to accommodate two MG 151/20 cannon in a *Schräge Musik* installation as standard. (Mid fuselage position).

Ju88G-6c: As the G-6c but powered by Jumo 213E engines. *Schräge Musik* installation moved to immediately behind the cockpit.

Period of service:	A-4:	Winter 1943 to July 1944.
	C-0:	1940/41.
	C-1:	1940/41.
	C-2:	1940/41 to 1942.
	C-4:	1941 to September 1944.
	C-5:	? to 1944.
	C-6:	Spring 1942 to 1945.
	R-2:	Spring 1942 to October 1944.
	G-1:	January 1944 to 1945.
	G-6a:	July 1944 to 1945.
	G-6b:	July 1944 to 1945.
	G-6c:	November 1944 to 1945.
Radar equipment:	FuG 202:	Fitted to the C-6 and R-2. Entered service during 1942/43.
	FuG 212:	Fitted to the C-6 and R-2 from the summer of 1943.
	FuG 212C-1:	Fitted in combination with SN-2b to the C-6 and R-2. (The aerials for the SN-2b were carried on the wings or the nose of the C-6.)
	FuG 218VR or GR:	Fitted to the G-6b and c. *Hirschgeweih* or covered or uncovered *Morgenstern* aerial array. When the set's tail warning capacity was used, the associated aerial was mounted above the tail fin.
	FuG 220 SN-2b, c and d:	Fitted to the C-6 ('b' and 'c'), R-2 ('b' and 'c'), G-1 ('c' and 'd') and G-6a ('d'). When the set's tail warning capacity was used, the associated aerial was mounted below the tail fin.
	FuG 240:	Fitted to a small number of G-6c aircraft at the war's end. Plywood nose radome.
Other equipment:	FuG 227:	Fitted to the C-6, R-2, G-1 and the G-6a. Wing mounted aerials.
	FuG 350:	Fitted to the C-6, R-2, G-1, G-6a, b and c. Aircraft with the

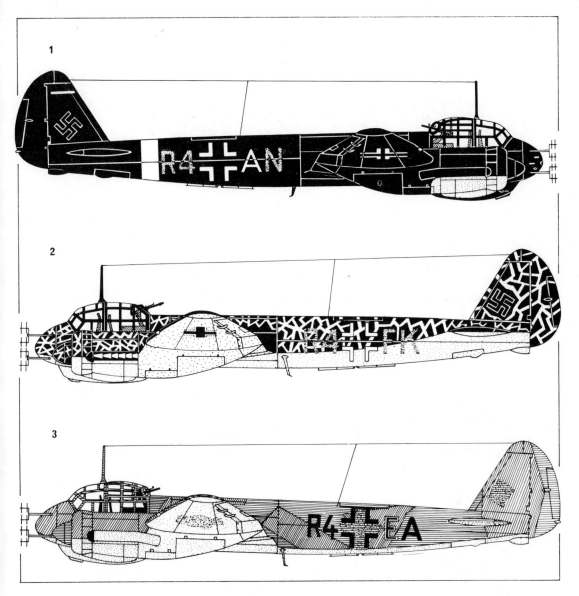

1

2

3

(1) Junkers ju88C-6 R4-AN of 5/NJG 2: *Black 22 overall with the exception of two areas of Light Blue 65 (dot hatching) under both engine cowlings. All national markings of the white outline type. Codes in Light Grey 77 with the individual aircraft letter presented in White 21. Fuselage band and Werk Nummer (presented in small characters on the fin) 360263 in White 21. Spinner in Black 22 with Black Green 70 propellor blades. England Blitz badge on both sides of the nose. FuG 212 dipoles in blued metal. This aircraft was destroyed during a bombing raid on Catania airfield, Sicily, in June 1943.*

(2) Junkers Ju88C-6 R4-FK of 2/NJG 2: *This aircraft presents an extremely interesting example of defennsive camouflage which was to become more and more common on the Luftwaffe's night fighters as the war progressed. Originally the aircraft was Black 22 overall but the increase in Allied air attacks on its base in Sicily led to the application of a 'crazy paving' pattern of Sand Yellow 79 over all the uppersurfaces. In addition, the introduction of lighter night camouflage led to the re-spraying of 'FK's' undersurfaces in Light Blue 65 (dot*

hatching). It is interesting to compare this scheme with that of the Do215B-5 shown on page 256. 'FK's' codes were in Light Grey 77 and she carried white outline crosses on the fuselage and above the wings, black/white crosses below the wings and white outline swastikas. Propellor blades in Black Green 70. FuG212 dipoles in blued metal. England Blitz badge on both sides of the nose. Note the later style of canopy carrying a single MG 131 rather than the standard 'bulged' type carrying twin MG 17s and the lack of flame dampers.

(3) Junkers Ju88C-6 R4-EA of Stab/NJG 2: *Dark Green 71 (Diagonal hatching) and Black Green 70(horizontal hatching) 'splinter' pattern over the uppersurfaces. light Blue 65 (dot hatching) on the undersurfaces. All national markings painted out (in the background colour of their location) and replaced with black outline crosses on the fuselage and above the wings only. Codes in Black 22 with the aircraft letter 'E' thinly outlined in Dark Blue 24. FuG 212 dipoles in blued metal. Spinner and propellor blades in Black Green 70. England Blitz badge probably carried on both sides of the nose.*

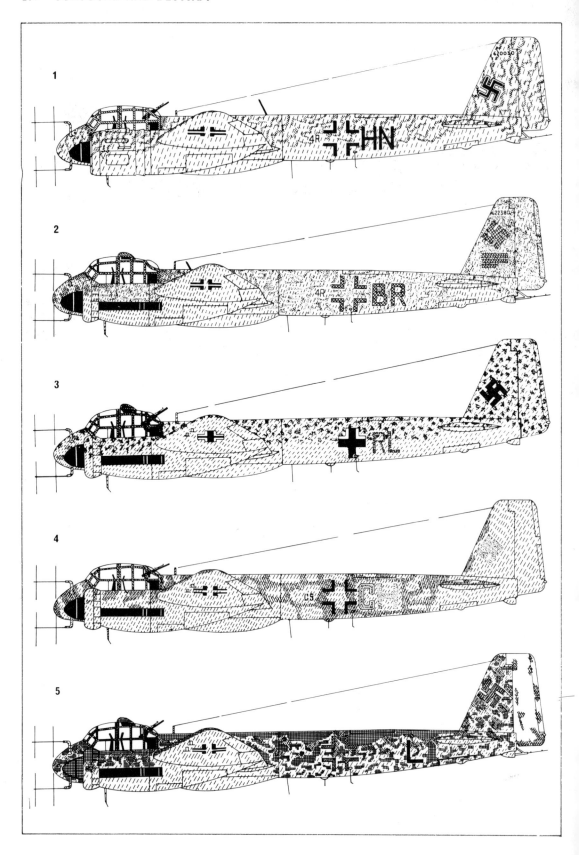

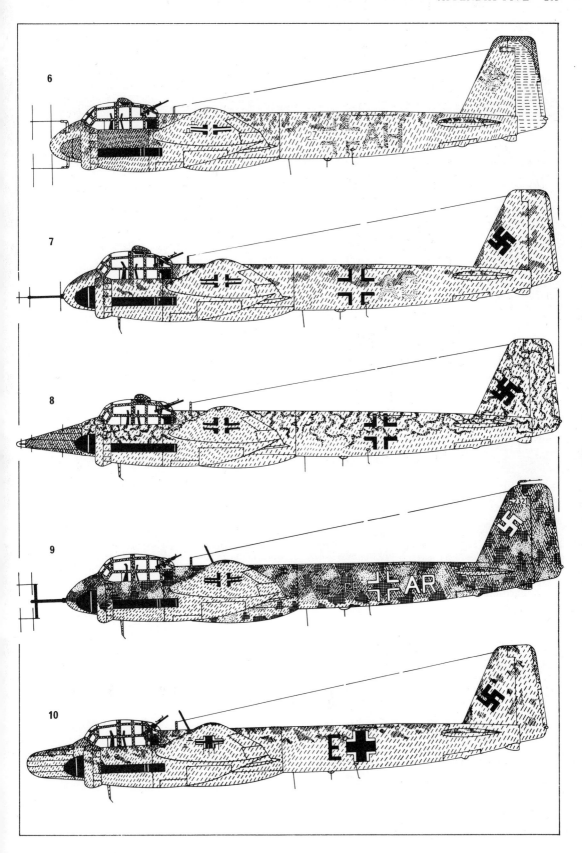

(1) Junkers Ju88G-6b 4R-HN of 5/NJG 2: *Light Grey 76 (broken line hatching) overall with a Mid Grey 75 (diagonal hatching) 'wave mirror' scheme over the upper-surfaces. Black outline crosses on the wings and fuselage and black/white swastikas. Werk Nummer 620030 in small Black 22 characters on the fin. Codes in Black 22. FuG 220 dipoles and* Schräge Musik *cannon in blued metal. Cockpit framing in solid Mid Grey 75. Black 22 spinners with Black Green 70 propellor blades.*

(2) Junkers Ju88G-6c 4R-BR of 7/NJG 2: *Light Grey 76 (broken line hatching) overall with a close mottle of RLM Grey 02 (dot hatching) on the uppersurfaces. Canopy frames and mottle on the nose, aft of the cockpit and on the engine cowlings in Mid Grey 75 (diagonal hatching). Mid Grey 75 outline crosses above the wings and on the fuselage, black outline below the wings and solid Mid Grey 75 swastikas. Twenty five victory markings on the fin comprising white rectangles cut by a diagonal black band surmounted by RAF roundels. 'LA' in small light coloured characters above on the fin. Codes in Mid Grey 75. FuG 220 dipoles and* Schräge Musik *cannon in blued metal. Black 22 spinners with Black Green 70 propellor blades. Dark exhaust flame dampers.*

(3) Junkers Ju88G-6c RL of 3rd Staffel of an unidentified Geschwader: *Light Grey 76 (broken line hatching) overall with an RLM Grey 02 (dot hatching) close mottle over the uppersurfaces. Canopy frames in Mid Grey 75 (diagonal hatching). White outline crosses above the wings, black/white crosses on the fuselage and below the wings (those on the fuselage having the lower white segments painted out) and solid black swastikas oversprayed to lessen their visibility. Codes in Mid Grey 75. FuG 220 dipoles in blued metal with white warning bands on the lower ones. Black 22 spinners with Black Green 70 propellor blades. Dark exhaust flame dampers.*

(4) Junkers Ju88G-6c C9-CH of 1/NJG 5: *Light Grey 76 (broken line hatching) overall with a 'snake skin' pattern of Mid Grey 75 (diagonal hatching) over the upper surfaces. White outline crosses above the wings, black outline below the wings and on the fuselage and solid black swastikas oversprayed to lessen their visibility. Codes in Mid Grey 75 with the letter 'C' thinly outlined in White 21. Canopy framing in solid Mid Grey 75. FuG 220 dipoles in blued metal. Black 22 spinners with Black Green 70 propellor blades. Dark exhaust flame dampers.*

(5) Junkers Ju88G-6c L of 1/NJG 6: *Light Grey 76 (broken line hatching) overall with a Mid Grey 75 (diagonal hatching) mottle over the uppersurfaces. These in turn were oversprayed with Dark Green 81 or 82 (cross hatching). This overspray was solid on the fuselage spine and the wing trailing edges. Rudder probably in natural metal with a sparse Dark Green 81 or 82 mottle. Canopy frames in solid Mid Grey 75. Black outline crosses below the wings, Mid Grey 75 outline fuselage crosses and solid swastikas. Code letter in Black 22. FuG 220 dipoles in blued metal. Spinners in Dark Green 81 or 82 with Black Green 70 propellor blades. Dark exhaust flame dampers.*

(6) Junkers Ju88G-6c 2Z-AH of 1/NJG 6: *Light Grey 76 (broken line hatching) overall with a Mid Grey 75 (diagonal hatching) mottle over the uppersurfaces. Solid Mid Grey 75*

canopy frames, engine access hatches and spinners. The top of the fin and rudder in Mid Grey 75 painted in such a way as to make the 'G' tail look like a 'C' one. Rudder in a grey (horizontal broken line hatching) darker than 76 with a false hinge projecting into the fin. White outline crosses above the wings, black outline below and Mid Grey 75 outline fuselage crosses and solid swastikas. Codes in Mid Grey 75. FuG 220 dipoles in blued metal. Propellor blades in Black Green 70. Dark exhaust flame dampers.

(7) Junkers Ju88G-6c AC of Stab II/NJG 5: *Light Grey 76 (broken line hatching) overall with a Mid Grey 75 (Diagonal hatching) mottle over the uppersurfaces. Solid Mid Grey canopy frames and upper nose. White outline crosses above the wings, black outline below and on the fuselage and solid black swastikas. Codes in Dark Blue 24? A six figure Werk Nummer in Black 22 on the fin. FuG 218 dipoles and support in blue metal. Black 22 spinners with Black Green 70 propellor blades. Dark exhaust flame dampers.*

(8) Junkers Ju88G-6c of an unidentified unit: *Light Grey 76 (broken line hatching) overall with a RLM Grey 02 (dot hatching) 'wave mirror' pattern over the uppersurfaces. Solid Mid Grey 75 (diagonal hatching) canopy frames and nose cone. White outline crosses above the wings, black outline below and on the fuselage and solid black swastikas. FuG 218 dipoles in blue dk metal. Black 22 spinners with Black Green 70 propellor blades. Dark exhaust flame dampers.*

(9) Junkers Ju88G-6c C9-AR of 7/NJG 5: *Uppersurfaces in a solid mottle of Mid Grey 75 (diagonal hatching), RLM Grey 02 (dot hatching) and Dark Green 81 or 82 (cross hatching). Undersurfaces in Light Grey 76 (broken line hatching) with the 75/02/81-82 mottle continued under the fuselage. Solid Mid Grey 75 canopy frames. Vee-shaped area of Light Grey 76 on the nose (broad end covering the area of the central windscreen and the tip at the extreme nose). White outline crosses above the wings and on the fuselage, black outline below the wings and solid white swastikas. Codes and Werk Nummer (623211) in White 21. FuG 218 dipoles and* Schräge Musik *cannon in blued metal. Dipole supports (nose and tail) in Light Grey 76. Black 22 spinners with Black Green 70 propellor blades. Dark exhaust flame dampers.*

(10) Junkers Ju88G-6c E of NJG 1: *Light Grey 76 (broken line hatching) overall with a Mid Grey 75 (diagonal hatching) mottle on the uppersurfaces. Solid Mid Grey 75 canopy frames and upper fuselage nose. Black/white crosses above and below the wings and on the fuselage and solid black swastikas. Code letter in Black 22. FuG 101 and 217 wing aerial dipoles in blued metal. Black 22 spinners with Black Green 70 propellor blades. Dark exhaust flame dampers.*

covered *Morgenstern* FuG 218 aerial and FuG 240 carried the device within the fairing. All other aircraft carried it in a blister above the cockpit.

FuG 351:   Fitted to an experimental batch of C-6 aircraft. Housed in a blister mounted above the middle fuselage.

Schräge Musik: Fitted as standard to the G-6b and c. Retrofitted to large numbers of C-6, R-2, G-1 and G-6a aircraft.

Remarks: At least one G-6 aircraft, ('C9-AA' flown by Rudolf Schönert), was equipped with a FuG 220 AI set with the aerials *vertically* disposed *above and below* the rear fuselage. An indication of the level of electronic sophistication reached in Germany's night fighters in 1945 can be gleaned from the following inventory of equipment carried by a late model Ju88G-6:

FuG 10 – HF R/T and W/T communications set.

FuG 16 – VHF R/T and W/T communications set with a D/F capacity.

EiV 10 – Crew intercommunication set.

Peilgerät 6 – Radio compass.

FuBl 2 – Blind approach receiver.

FuG 120 – Bearing and 'running commentary' teleprinter.

FuG 25a – IFF set.

FuG 101 – Radio altimeter.

FuG 213 – AI set with a tail warning capacity.

FuG 350 – Homing and tail warning receiver.

It is interesting to compare the above with the equipment carried by a Mosquito aircraft of 85(SD) Squadron detailed on page 245.

Specifications:

Junkers Ju88C-6:

Power plant:	Two 1,340 hp June 211J-1 or J-2 liquid-cooled engines.
Maximum speed:	303 mph (488 km/hr) at 19,685 ft (6,000 m)
Cruising speed:	263 mph (423 km/hr)
Range:	1,230 mls (1,980 km)
Service ceiling:	32,480 ft (9,900 m)
Empty weight:	19,973 lbs (9,060 kg)
Loaded weight:	27,225 lbs (12,350 kg)
Wing span:	65 ft 7½ in (20 m)
Length:	47 ft 1½ in (14.36 m)
Height:	16 ft 7½ in (5.06 m)
Wing area:	586.63 sq ft (54.5 m²)
Offensive armament:	Three 7.9 mm MG 17 machine guns and three 20 mm MG FF/M cannon.
Defensive	Two 7.9 mm MG 17 or one 13 mm

armament:	MG 131 machine gun mounted in the rear of the cockpit.
Crew:	Pilot, observer/gunner and wireless/radar operator.

Junkers Ju88G-6c:

Power plant:	Two 1,725 hp Jumo 213E liquid-cooled engines.
Maximum speed:	363 mph (585 km/hr) at 33,500 ft (10,200 m).
Range:	1,400 mls (2,250 km)
Service ceiling:	35,000 ft (10,769 m)
Loaded weight:	28,900 lbs (13,100 kg)
Wing span:	65 ft 7½ in (20 m)
Length:	47 ft 8½ in (22.77 m)
Height:	15 ft 11 in (4.85 m)
Wing area:	586.63 sq ft (54.5 m²)
Offensive armament:	Six 20 mm MG 151/20 cannon (two mounted in a *Schräge Musik* installation).
Defensive armament:	One 13 mm MG 131 machine gun mounted in the rear of the cockpit.
Crew:	Pilot, observer/navigator, wireless/radar operator and gunner/observer.

MESSERSCHMITT Bf110C-1

Role:	Night fighter and reconnaissance aircraft.
User units:	See pages 221 to 228.
Variants:	

Bf110C-1:   Two-seater with DB601A-1 engines. Four 7.9 mm MG 17 machine guns and two 20 mm MG FF cannon firing forwards. A single 7.9 mm MG 15 machine gun for rear defence.

Bf110C-2:   Improved electrical system and rear gun mounting.

Bf110C-4:   MG FF cannon replaced by MG 151/20s. Increased armour protection for the crew.

Bf110C-6:   MG 151/20s replaced a single 30 mm Mk 101 cannon.

Bf110D-0:   Two-seater with DB601A-1 engines. Ventral fairing housing 264 Imp gal (1,000 l) of fuel. Forward firing armament of four MG 17s.

Bf110D-1:   Ventral fairing deleted. MG 151/20 cannon reinstated. Two 198 imp gal (750 l) drop tanks could be carried.

Bf110D-3:   DB601N engines. Two 66 or 198 imp gal (250 or 750 l) drop tanks could be carried. Dinghy stowage in an extended tail section. External auxiliary oil tank carried beneath the fuselage.

Bf110E-1:   Two-seater with DB601A or DB601N engines. Gun armament as for the C-4. Four ETC 50 wing mounted bomb racks.

Bf110E-2:   DB601N engines. Gun armament and bomb racks as for the E-1. Dinghy stowage in an extended tail section.

Bf110E-4:   DB601A or DB601N engines.

Bf110F-2:   Two-seater with DB601F engines. Gun armament as for the C-4.

Bf110F-4:   Three-seat night fighter. Ventral tray carrying two 30 mm Mk 108 cannon. Enlarged and reprofiled vertical tail surfaces.

Bf110G-2:   Two-seater with DB605B engines. Forward firing armament as for the C-4. Vertical tail surfaces as for the F-4. Revised cockpit access. Two

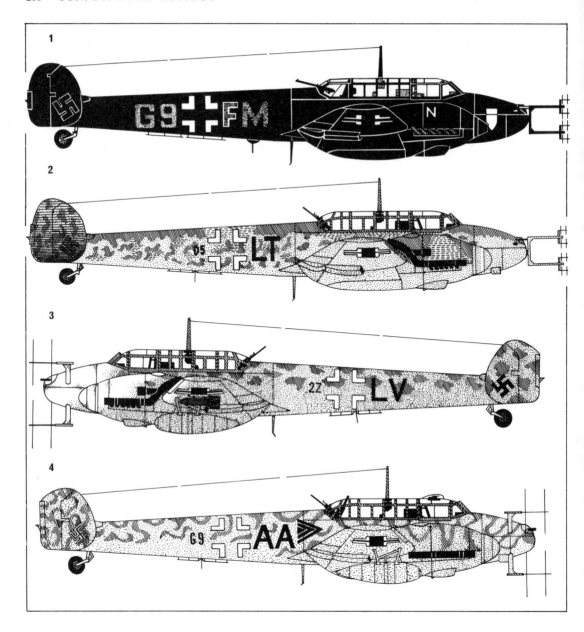

(1) Messerschmitt Bf110F-4a G9-FM of 4/NJG 1:
*Black 22 overall with white outline national insignia in all
positions. Codes in Light Grey 77 with the aircraft letter 'F'
presented in Red 23 thinly outlined in White 21. DB 601N
engine fuel type denoted by the small White 21 'N' on each
engine cowling.* England Blitz *badge on both sides of the nose.
FuG 202 dipoles in blued metal. Oxidised exhaust stubs. Black
Green 70 propellor blades.*

(2) Messerschmitt Bf110G-4 D5-LT of 9/NJG 3:
*Fuselage spine, wing uppersurfaces and engine cowlings in a
'splinter' pattern of Dark Grey 74 (diagonal hatching) and
Mid Grey 75 (broken line hatching). Canopy framing in solid
Mid Grey 75. Fuselage sides, fins and undersurfaces in Light
Grey 76 (dot hatching). Fins mottled in Mid Grey 75 and then
completely covered (including the swastikas) with a grey
overspray becoming progressively darker towards the bottoms.*

*Fuselage sides mottled in the two greys 74 and 75. White outline
crosses above the wings and on the fuselage, black/white crosses
below the wings and solid black swastikas. Cokes in Black 22.
Spinners in Light Grey (with a thin White 21 band) with Black
Green 70 propellor blades Dark exhaust flame dampers. FuG
212 dipoles in blued metal. This aircraft was unusual in that it
was fitted with F-series tail fins.*

(3) Messerschmitt Bf110G-4 2Z-LV of 11/NJG 6:
*Light Grey 76 (dot hatching) overall with a Mid Grey 75
(diagonal hatching) mottle on the uppersurfaces. Canopy
framing in solid Mid Grey 75. Nose, spinners, engine cowlings
and wing leading edges oversprayed with White 21 to further
break up the aircraft's outline for the night ground attack sorties
it was involved in. White outline crosses above the wings and on
the fuselage, black/white crosses below the wings and solid
black swastikas. Codes in BLack 22. Black Green 70 propellor*

blades. Dark exhaust flame dampers. FuG 220 dipoles in blued metal. This aircraft carried two 500kg and four 50kg bombs and was lost due to damage caused by the explosion of faulty ammunition for the nost mounted M M G 151/20 cannon.

(4) Messerschmitt Bf110G-4 G9-AA of Stab/NJG 1:
Light Grey 76 (dot hatching) overall with a Mid Grey 75 (diagonal hatching) 'wave mirror' pattern on the uppersurfaces. Canopy framing in solid Mid Grey 75. White outline crosses above the wings and on the fuselage, black/white crosses below the wings and black/white swastikas. Codes and staff chevrons (both sides) in Black 22. Black Green 70 propellor blades. Dark exhaust flame dampers. FuG 220 dipoles in blued metal. This aircraft was flown by Hans Joachim Jabs and was used by two of the Geschwader's personal to escape to Sweden in May 1945. Points of interest are the FuG 350 aerial above the cockpit, the Schräge Musik *installation and the late war 'straight through' exhausts.*

7.9 m MG 81 machine guns for rear defence.
Bf110G-4: Three-seat night fighter with DB605B engines. Other details as for the G-2.
Rüstsätze:

Applicable to the E series:	R2	ETC 1,000 bomb rack below the fuselage.
Applicable to the G series:	R1	37 mm Bk 3.7 (Flak 18) cannon in a ventral fairing interchangeable with an under fuselage ETC bomb rack.
	R2	GM-1 nitrous oxide injection system and the deletion of the forward firing machine guns.
	R3	Forward firing machine guns replaced by two 30 mm MK 108 cannon. ETC 5,000 bomb rack or twin 20 mm MG 151/20 tray carried beneath the fuselage.
	R4	As above but with the Bk 3.7 as an alternative ventral store. Also thought to apply to the replacement of the forward firing machine guns by two long barrelled MG 151/20 cannon.
	R5	Any combination of 1, 2, 3 and 4.
	R6	A combination of 2 and 3.
	R7	R3 with a 119 imp gal (540.9 l) fuel tank in the radio/radar operators position.

Umrüst:

Applicable to the D and E series:	U1	Nose mounted *Spanner* device.
Applicable to the F series:	U1	Twin MK 108 cannon in a *Schräge Musik* installation

Period of service:	C-1:	July 1940 to the summer of 1943.
	C-2:	July 1940 to the summer of 1943.
	C-4:	July 1940 to the summer of 1943.
	C-6:	July 1940 to the summer of 1943.
	D-0:	Summer 1940 to the summer of 1941.
	D-1:	Summer 1940 to April 1943.
	D-3:	Summer 1940 to April 1943.
	E-1:	1941 to the summer of 1943.
	E-2:	1941 to the summer of 1943.
	E-4:	1941 to the summer of 1943.
	F-2:	Summer 1942 to late 1943.
	F-4:	Summer 1942 to the spring of 1944.
	G-2:	From the summer of 1943.
	G-4:	From the summer of 1943.

Radar equipment:	FuG 202: Fitted to E-1 (for operational trials), F-4 (twin MK 108 tray omitted when carried) and G-4. Entered service during 1942/43.
	FuG 212: Fitted to F-4 and G-4. Entered service during the summer of 1943.
	FuG 212C-1: Fitted in combination with SN-2b to the G-4.
	FuG 218 VR or GR: Fitted to a small number of G-4 aircraft at the end of the war.
	FuG 220 SN-2b, c and d: Fitted to G-4 from September 1943. 'b', 'c' and 'd' variants of the radar all carried.
Other equipment:	FuG 227: Fitted to the G-4. Wing mounted aerials.
	FuG 350: Fitted to the G-4. Probably carried in a blister above the cockpit.
	Schräge Musik: Mostly fitted to G-4 aircraft.

Specifications:

Messerschmitt Bf110C-1:

Power plant:	Two 1,100 hp DB601A-1 liquid-cooled engines.
Maximum speed:	326 mph (525 km/hr) at 13,120 ft (4,000 m).
Cruising speed:	217 mph (350 km/hr)
Service ceiling:	32,810 ft (10,000 m)
Empty weight:	9,755 lb (4,425 kg)
Loaded weight:	14,880 lb (6,750 kg)
Wingspan:	53 ft 3¾ in (16.25 m)
Length:	39 ft 7¼ in (12.7 m)
Height:	13 ft 6½ in (4.13 m)
Wing area:	413.33 sq ft (38.4 m²)
Offensive armament:	Four 7.9 mm MG 17 machine-guns and two 20 mm MG FF cannon.
Defensive armament:	One 7.9 mm MG 15 machine gun mounted in the aft cockpit.
Crew:	Pilot and wireless operator/navigator/rear gunner.

Messerschmitt Bf110G-4:

Power plant:	Two 1,475 hp DB605B liquid-cooled engines.
Maximum speed:	342 mph (550 km/hr) at 22,950 ft (7,000 m).
Range:	1,305 mls (2,100 km)

Service
ceiling: 26,250 ft (8,000 m)
Empty weight: 12,346 lb (5,600 kg)
Loaded weight: 15,653 lb (7,000 kg)
Wing span: 53 ft 4¾ in (16.27 m)
Length: 41 ft 6¼ in (12.65 m)
Height: 13 ft 1¼ in (3.99 m)
Wing area: 413.33 sq ft (38.4 m²)
Offensive   Four 7.9 mm MG 17 machine guns
armament: and two 20 mm MG 151/20 cannon.
Defensive   Two 7.9 mm MG 81 machine guns
armament: mounted in the aft cockpit.
Crew: Pilot, wireless/radar operator and
                     observer/rear gunner.

MINOR TYPES
Arado Ar234B-2 *Blitz* (Lightning)
A single example (W.Nr. 140 146) of this, the world's
first jet bomber, was extensively converted for use as a
night fighter by Eprobungskommando 234 (see page
000). Powered by two Jumo 004B turbojets, this aircraft had a second seat for a radar operator installed,
FuG 218 radar and was armed with two 20 mm MG
151/20 cannon mounted in a WB 151 container
carried on the central hard point under the fuselage.

Dornier Do335A-6 *Pfeil* (Arrow)
Perhaps one of the most unconventional interceptors
produced by any of the combatants, the Do335 was
powered by two DB603 engines mounted along the aircraft's centre line in a tractor/pusher configuration.
Several night fighter variants were proposed of which
the A-6 was the first. The aerodynamic prototype for
this series, the V-10, saw service with NJG3. The V-10
was equipped with FuG 218 radar, the operator of
which was seated in a separate compartment above
and behind the pilot, and was armed with two 15 mm
MG 151 machine guns and a 30 mm MK 103 cannon.

Focke Wulf Ta154A-1
The Ta154, unofficially known as the Mosquito, was
an all-wooden specialised night fighter. The type failed
to see major service because of a lack of suitable wood
glues, the ones used resulting in the mid-air disintegra-
tion of one of the prototypes. The few aircraft completed saw some service under the designation 'A-1'.
Powered by two Jumo 213E engines, the Ta154 carried
a crew of two and was equipped with FuG 218 radar.
Forward firing armament comprised two MG 151/20
and two 30 mm MK 108 cannon. One of the
prototypes, the V-3, fitted with FuG 212 radar and full
armament, also saw service with Eprobungskommando 154 and NJGr10 (see page 226).

Junkers Ju388J-1 *Stortebeker*
The Ju388 was the final development in the line of
Junker's night fighters begun with the Ju88C-2. The
Stortebeker was basically the Ju88G series fuselage
married to the wings and vertical tail surfaces of the
Ju188 and a pressurised cockpit. A single prototype,
the V-2, was given service trials by Eprobungskommando 388 (see page 226). This aircraft carried a crew
of four, was powered by BMW 801TJ engines, carried
FuG 220SN-2c radar and was armed with two MG
151/20 and two MK 108 cannon mounted in a ventral

blister firing forwards.

Messerschmitt Me262
At the end of the war, a small number of this jet fighter
were used for nocturnal interception. A number of
variants were employed as follows:
Me262A-1a
A single example (W.Nr. 130 056) of this variant was
fitted with FuG 218 radar for trials with Eprobungskommando 262 (see page 226). This unit also used a
number of standard A-1a's for *Wilde Sau* operations.
The type was powered by two Jumo 004B turbojets
and carried a forward firing armament of four MK 108
cannon.
Me262B-1a
The B-1a was a two-seat training variant of the A-1.
The type was used by 10/NJG 11 for *Wilde Sau*
operations (see page 225). The normal forward firing
armament was retained.
Me262B-1a/U1
An interim night fighter based on the B-1a, the B-
1a/U1 was equipped with FuG 218 radar and the FuG
350 device. Forward firing armament was usually
restricted to two long barrelled MG 151/20 cannon.
Used operationally by 10/NJG 11.
Me262B-2a
The B-2a was a 'stretched' version of the B-1a which
supplemented the forward firing armament with a
twin-cannon *Schräge Musik* installation aft of the
cockpit. A single example, fitted with FuG 218, was
used by 10/NJG 11 in the spring of 1943.

SELECTIVE BIBLIOGRAPHY

Aders, G, *Geschichte der deutschen Nachtjagd*. Motorbuch Verlag, Stuttgart: 1977.

Air Ministry, *Pilot's Notes – Fortress GRIIA, GRII and III, BII and BIII*. Air Data Publications, St Anne's on Sea.

Air Ministry, *Pilot's Notes – Liberator III, V, VI and VIII*. Air Data Publications, St Anne's on Sea.

Air Ministry, *The Rise and Fall of the German Air Force 1933 to 1945*. HMSO, London: 1948.

Barker, R, *The Thousand Plan*. Chatto and Windus, London: 1965.

Bekker, C, *The Luftwaffe War Diaries*. Macdonald and Jane's, London: 1967.

Birdsall, S, *B-17 in Action*. Squadron Signal, Michigan: 1973.

Birdsall, S, *B-24 Liberator in Action*. Squadron Signal, Michigan: 1975.

Blue, A G, *The B-24 Liberator*. Ian Allan, Surrey: 1976.

Bowman, M, *Fields of Little America, An Illustrated History of the 8th Air Force 2nd Air Division 1942–45*. Wensum Books, Norwich: 1977.

Bowyer, C, *Mosquito at War*. Ian Allan, Surrey: 1973.

Bowyer, M J F, *Bombing Colours 1937–1973*. PSL, Cambridge: 1973.

Bowyer, M J F, *Fighting Colours, RAF Fighter Camouflage and Markings 1937–1975*. PSL, Cambridge: 1975.

Brandon, L, *Night Flyer*. William Kimber, London: 1961.

Bridgeman, L., *Jane's All The World's Aircraft 1945/6*. Sampson and Low, London: 1946.

Bushby, J, *Air Defence of Great Britain*. Ian Allan, Surrey: 1973.

Butler, P H, *Air Min, A Log of the 'Air Min' Numbered Aircraft*. Merseyside Aviation Society, Liverpool: 1977.

Chisholm, R, *Cover of Darkness*. Chatto and Windus, London: 1953.

Crowther, J G, and Whiddington, R., *Science at War*. HMSO, London: 1947.

Cynk, J B, *History of the Polish Air Force*, Osprey, Reading: 1972.

Dierich, W (Ed), *Die Verbande der Luftwaffe 1933–1945*. Motorbuch Verlag, Stuttgart: 1976.

Frankland, N, *Bomber Offensive, The Devastation of Europe*. Purnell, London: 1970.

Freeman, R A *American Bombers of World War Two (Volume I)*. Profile Publications, Windsor: 1973.

Freeman, R A, *B-17 Fortress at War*. Ian Allan, Surrey: 1977.

Freeman, R A, *The Mighty Eighth, A History of the US 8th Army Air Force*. Macdonald and Jane's, London: 1970.

Freeman, R A *The US Strategic Bomber*. Macdonald and Jane's, London: 1975.

Garbett, M, and Goulding, B, *Avro Lancaster in Unit Service*. Osprey, Canterbury: 1970.

Garbett, M, and Goulding, B, *The Lancaster at War*. Ian Allan, Surrey: 1971.

Girbig, W., *Im Anflug auf dem Reichshauptstadt*. Motorbuch Verlag, Stuttgart: 1970.

Girbig, J., *Six Months to Oblivion, The Eclipse of the Luftwaffe Fighter Force*. Ian Allan, Surrey: 1975.

Goulding, J, and Moyes, P, *RAF Bomber Command and its Aircraft 1936–1940*. Ian Allan, Surrey: 1975.

Green, W, *The Warplanes of the Third Reich*. Macdonald and Jane's, London: 1970.

Gunston, B, *Night Fighters, A Development and Combat History*. PSL, Cambridge: 1976.

Halley, J J, *Famous Fighter Squadrons of the RAF (Volume I)*. Profile Publications, Windsor: 1971.

Halley, J J, *Royal Air Force Unit Histories (Volumes I and II)*. Air Britain, Essex: 1973.

Handel, S, *A Dictionary of Electronics*. Penguin, Middlesex: 1971.

Hardy, M J, *The de Havilland Mosquito*. David and Charles, Devon: 1977.

Hill, R, *The Great Coup*, Arlington, London: 1977.

Hoffman, K O, *Geschichte der Luftnachrichten-truppe*. Vorwinckel Verlag, Neckargemund: 1968.

Howard-Williams, J, *Night Intruder, A Personal Account of the Radar War between the Luftwaffe and the RAF Night Fighter Forces*. David and Charles, Devon: 1976.

Irving, D, *The Mare's Nest*. William Kimber, London: 1964.

Irving, D, *The Rise and Fall of the Luftwaffe, the Life of Erhard Milch*. Weidenfeld and Nicolson, London: 1973.

Jackson, R, *Storm from the Skies, The Strategic Bombing Offensive 1943–1945*. Arthur Barker, London: 1974.

Johnen, W, *Duel under the Stars*. William Kimber, London: 1957.

Koch, H A, *Flak Die Geschichte der deutschen Flakartillerie und der Einsatz der Luftwaffenhelfer*. Bad Nauheim: 1954.

Mason, F K, *De Havilland Mosquito in RAF, FAA, RAAF, SAAF, RNZAF, USAAF, French and Foreign Service*. Osprey, Canterbury: 1972.

McDowell, E R, *Boeing B-17-B-H Flying Fortress in USAAF, USAF, USN, USMC, USCG, RAF, French, Danish, Portuguese, IDF/AF, Dominican and Brazilian AF Service*. Osprey, Canterbury: 1976.

McDowell, E R, *Consolidated B-24D-M Liberator in USAAF, RAF, RAAF, MLD, IAF, Czech AF and CNAF Service*. Osprey, Canterbury:

Middlebrook, M., *The Nuremburg Raid*. Allen Lane, London: 1973.

Millar, G, *The Bruneval Raid, Flashpoint of the Radar War*. Bodley Head, London: 1974.

Mohlenbeck, O, and Leihse, M, *Ferne Nachtjagd*. Motorbuch Verlag, Stuttgart: 1975.

Moyes, P J R, *Bomber Squadrons of the RAF and their Aircraft*. Macdonald and Jane's, London: 1976.

Musgrove, G, *Pathfinder Force, A History of 8 Group*. Macdonald and Jane's London: 1976.

Nielsen, A, *The German Air Force General Staff*. Arno, New York: 1968.

Philpott, B, *RAF Bomber units 1939–42*. Osprey, London: 1977.

Price, A, *Battle over the Reich*. Ian Allan, Surrey: 1973.

Price, A, *Instruments of Darkness, The History of Electronic Warfare*, Macdonald and Jane's, London: 1977.

Price, A, *Luftwaffe Handbook 1939–1945*. Ian Allan, Surrey: 1977.

Rawlings, J D R, *Fighter Squadrons of the RAF and their Aircraft*. Macdonald and Jane's, London: 1976.

Ries, K, *Luftwaffen – Story 1935–1939*. Verlag Dieter Hoffmann, Mainz: 1974.

Robertson, B, *British Military Aircraft Serials 1911–1971*. Ian Allan, Surrey: 1971.

Robertson, B, *Lancaster – The Story of a Famous Bomber*. Harleyford, Letchworth: 1964.

Saunders, H St, G and Richards, D, *Royal Air Force 1939–45 (Volumes 1 to 3)* HMSO, London: 1954.

Scroggie, M G, *Foundations of Wireless and Electronics.* Iliffe, London: 1971.

Sharp, C M, and Bowyer, J F, *Mosquito.* Faber and Faber, London: 1971.

Shores, C F, and Williams, C, *Aces High, The Fighter Aces of the British and Commonwealth Air Forces in World War II.* Neville Spearman, London: 1966.

Shores, C F, *The 2nd Tactical Air Force.* Osprey, Reading: 1970.

Smith, J R, and Kay, A L, *German Aircraft of the Second World War.* Putnam, London: 1972.

Suchenwirth, R, *Historical Turning Points in the German Air Force War Effort.* Arno, New York: 1968.

Tanner, J (Ed), *British Aviation Colours of World War Two.* Arms and Armour, London: 1976.

Tanner, J (Ed), *The Mosquito Manual, The Official Air Publication for the Mosquito F Mk II, NF Mk XII and NF Mk XVIII, 1941–1945.* Arms and Armour, London: 1977.

Thetford, O, *Aircraft of the Royal Air Force 1918–58.* Putnam, London: 1958.

Various, *Radiation Laboratory Series (Volumes 1 to 28).* McGraw–Hill, New York: 1947.

Verrier, A, *The Bomber Offensive.* Batsford, London: 1968.

Vincent, C, *Canada's Wings 2 – The Liberator and Fortress.* Canada's Wings, Ontario: 1975.

Weal, E C, and J A and Barker, R F, *Combat Aircraft of World War Two.* Arms and Armour, London: 1977.

Webster, G, and Frankland, N, *The Strategic Air Offensive against Germany 1939–45 (Volumes 1 to 4).* HMSO, London: 1961.

West, K S, *The Captive Luftwaffe.* Putnam, London: 1977.

Wood, D, *Attack Warning Red. The Royal Observer Corps and the Defence of Britain 1925 to 1975.* Macdonald and Jane's, London: 1976.

Other Publications

Camouflage and markings, RAF Northern Europe 1936–45: (Ducimus) Numbers 6, 8, 9 and 10.

Camouflage and Markings, USAAF: Numbers 13 and 17.

Aircraft Profiles: (Profile Publications) Numbers 11, 19, 52, 65, 77, 113, 117, 125, 130, 137, 142, 148, 161, 164, 202, 205, 207, 209, 219 and 235.

Periodicals

Articles in the following (covering the period 1945 to 1977):

The Aeroplane; The Aeroplane Spotter; Aeroplane Monthly; Aero Modeller; Aerosphere; Air Britain Digest; The Airfix Magazine; Air Force; Air Pictorial; Airpower; Aircraft Illustrated/Extra; Air International/Enthusiast/Enthusiast Quarterly; Aviation News; Flight International; Flug Reveu/Flugwelt; Flying Review/International; IPMS Magazine (Various countries); *Le fanatique de L'Aviation; Modell Fan; Scale Models; Wings.*

A NOTE ON SOURCE MATERIAL

Air Publications
A.P. 2019 (AI Mk VIII and AI Mk X) and S.D. 0165(1) (AI Mk IV).

American Documents
APO 557 (Mission record of the 803rd/36th Bombardment Squadron) and
CO-AN 08-20-4 (AN/APS 4).

Public Records Office
The following are a selection of the documents consulted; AIR 10/206
(Survey of RCM), AIR 10/2288 (Introductory survey of radar), AIR
10/4018 (AI Mk IV), AIR 10/4048 (AI Mk VIII), AIR 10/4165 (AI Mk X),
AIR 10/4701 (AN/APS 4), AIR 10/4942 (*Monica*), AIR 14/737 (B-17 as an
RCM aircraft), AIR 14/2911 (100 Group review of operations November
1943 to May 1945), AIR 20/1444 (*Tinsel*), AIR 20/1446 to 53 (*Window*), AIR
20/1454 to 59 (*Mandrel*), AIR 20/1461 and 2 (*Moonshine*), AIR 20/1492
(RCM 1939-45), AIR 20/1532 (TRE), AIR 20/1558 (*Grocer*), AIR 20/1559
(*Airborne Cigar*), AIR 20/1560 and 61 (VHF jamming January to November
1943), AIR 20/1563 (*Jostle IV*), AIR 20/1564 (*Corona*), AIR 20/1565 (515
Squadron operations with *Mandrel* and *Moonshine*), AIR 20/1566 *Serrate*
operations), AIR 20/1568 (100 Group progress reports), AIR 20/5800
(*Window*), AIR 20/5810 (RCM), AIR 20/5830 (Measures against enemy
defences), AIR 20/5843 (*Window* trials), AIR 25/777 (100 Group
operational record book 1943–45), AIR 25/778 (100 Group December
1943–April 1944), AIR 25/779 (Do. May to June 1944), AIR 25/780 (Do.
July 1944), AIR 25/781 (Do. August to September 1944), AIR 25/782 (Do.
October to November 1944), AIR 25/783 (Do. December 1944 to January
1945), AIR 25/784 (Do. February to March 1945), AIR 25/785 (Do. April to
May 1945), AIR 25/786 (Do. June to August 1945), AIR 25/787 (Do.
September to December 1945), AIR 25/788 (Do. January to April 1945),
AIR 27/287 to 88 (23 Squadron), AIR 27/705 and 6 (85 Squadron), AIR
27/970 and 1 (141 Squadron), AIR 27/1046 (157 Squadron), AIR
27/1061/2 and 1064 (159 Squadron SD Flight), AIR 27/1094 (169
Squadron), AIR 27/1456 (239 Squadron), AIR 27/1981 (515 Squadron),
AIR 27/1102 (171 Squadron), AIR 27/1156 (192 Squadron), AIR 27/1172
(199 Squadron), AIR 27/1323 and 24 (214 Squadron), AIR 27/1375 and 6
(223 Squadron), AIR 27/1917 (462 Squadron), AIR 40/111 (He219), AIR
40/184 (Ju88C, G and R) and AIR 40/879 (Heidelberg).

Others
Disarmament handbooks on Luftwaffe ground and airborne radio and radar
equipment.
RAF Weekly Intelligence Summaries/USSAF Air Intelligence Summaries,
1943–45.
Record of Scientific Work undertaken by W. A. S. Butement C.B.E.

INDEX